ROMAN JAKOBSON

MY FUTURIST YEARS

Compiled and edited by Bengt Jangfeldt and
Stephen Rudy

Translated and with an introduction
by Stephen Rudy

MARSILIO PUBLISHERS
NEW YORK

Original title: *Jakobson–Budetljanin*

Copyright © 1992
The Roman Jakobson and Krystyna
Pomorska Jakobson Foundation

Translation copyright © 1997 by Stephen Rudy
with the exception of "The Newest Russian Poetry" and
"On a Generation that Squandered Its Poets,"
from *Major Soviet Writers,* ed. E.J. Brown
© 1973 by Oxford University Press,
and reprinted with permission.

Of this edition copyright © 1997 by
Marsilio Publishers Corp.
853 Broadway
New York, NY 10003

ISBN 0-941419-79-7
LOC 92-62369

Distributed in the United States by
Consortium Book Sales and Distribution
1045 Westgate Drive
Saint Paul, MN 55114

CONTENTS

Introduction

I.

Roman Jakobson was one of the major scholars of this century. His publications encompassed over 650 books and articles on the subjects of linguistics, Slavic studies, poetics, and semiotics (see Rudy 1990),* and have been translated into fifteen languages. His *Collected Works* is currently up to its tenth volume and contains some seven thousand pages of his writings. During his lifetime he was a member of some thirty learned societies and received honorary degrees from over two dozen universities.

Roman Osipovich Jakobson was born in Moscow on October 10, 1896 and died in Cambridge, Massachusetts on July 18, 1982. In between he underwent a personal and intellectual odyssey that is remarkable by any standard. He grew up in the heyday of Russian culture that preceded the Revolution. An active member of the avant-garde, he was one of the founders of the Moscow Linguistic Circle and a leader of the

---

* All references in this book are given in the short form (Author Date, page); for full references see the List of Works Cited at the end of the volume.

literary-critical school known as Russian Formalism. In 1920 he went to Prague as a translator for a Soviet diplomatic mission and decided to continue his studies there. He soon became deeply involved in the cultural life of the Czech Republic, helping in 1926 to found the Prague Linguistic Circle. When the Nazis invaded Czechoslovakia on March 15, 1939, Jakobson, who was a virulent anti-fascist and well-known to the Gestapo, was alerted by friends to leave Brno, where he taught at the Masaryk University. After having reduced his archive to "nine pails of ashes," as he would later put it, he fled to Prague, where he hid in his father-in-law's wardrobe for a month while attempting to obtain visas to various countries. He finally succeeded in obtaining a visa to Denmark, and on April 22, 1939, travelled there by train via Berlin. (He spent time at the station during the change of trains writing to his friends, who were astonished when they received postcards from Jakobson posted in Berlin a couple of days after Hitler's fiftieth-birthday celebration.) His sojourn in Denmark, where he lectured at the University of Copenhagen, was brief: anticipating the coming invasion, he fled to Norway in September, which was in turn invaded by the Nazis on April 9, 1940, and barely escaped with his life. (It was a dramatic escape indeed: he was driven by a Norwegian Socialist from Oslo to the far Northern border with Sweden in a cart, lying in a coffin in the back, while his wife sat in front with the driver, playing the role of the grieving widow.) His brief time in Sweden, where he researched the topics of child language and aphasia, was one of the most productive in his life, and he always recalled it later with great affection. In May 1941 he was able to obtain a visa for America, and travelled on the same boat as the philosopher Ernst Cassirer which floated through the wreckage of the German battleship Bismarck, having narrowly missed the actual battle. In New York Jakobson was fortunate enough to find refuge at the Free

French and Belgian University attached to the New School for Social Research, one of the few American institutions hospitable to Jewish émigré scholars. He later obtained a professorship at Columbia, where he taught from 1943 until 1949, when he moved to Harvard, where he taught until 1967, holding a simultaneous apppointment as Institute Professor at the Massachusetts Institute of Technology from 1957 until 1967. He continued active research and lecturing until his death at the age of eighty-five.

Those who knew Jakobson personally were struck not only by his genius as a scholar, but by his charm and vitality as a human being. He was a brilliant raconteur with a fabulous memory, and dining at his table was both a convivial and educational experience. One of his favorite topics was his youthful friendship with the great poets and artists of the Russian avant-garde. He often spoke about the influence that experience had had on his later scientific views, in particular his intensive, decades-long work on the question of poetic language. The current volume opens with his most detailed discussion of his early formative years, a fascinating account of his life with and in the Russian avant-garde in the period from 1910 to 1920. Since it is based on taped interviews, it also gives one an impression of his oral style as a story-teller. The volume then proceeds—through Jakobson's essays, letters, and his own literary writings—to further document his role in the turbulent cultural life of that era. A few words about the literary and cultural background and some of the theoretical issues involved in approaching the "new art" of the period may be of help in orientating the reader before turning to Jakobson's own texts.

II.

There are few instances in the history of the arts of such an intense feed-back system as existed in the artistic and theoretical praxis of the Russian avant-garde in the period 1910-1920. As Hugh McLean writes: "More than a dozen major poets were at the height of their powers; the air was filled with their harmonies—and with the jangling discords of their theoretical wrangling. As if by a law of nature, the poets in their turn engendered a succession of brilliant young critics and theoreticians of verse to classify and interpret their work. One of the greatest of these, of course, was Roman Jakobson" (1987, 34). Indeed, Jakobson's early critical works must be regarded not just as an attempt to create a methodology for the literary-critical movement known as Russian Formalism, but to defend the "new art," in particular Russian Futurism in its most radical form.

One of the central tendencies of the Futurists, derived from a conscious parallel with the art of the Cubists in particular, was the liberation of poetic language from referentiality and an emphasis on the medium itself, its autonomous values and possibilities. Their emphasis on the materiality of poetic form led to works which fragmented and distorted language to the extreme, testing the relationship of sound and sense. In categorizing such works they coined phrases such as "transrational language" (*zaumnyj jazyk* or *zaum'*) and the "selfsome word" (*samovitoe slovo*). Jakobson himself experimented in this vein (see the poems on pp. 251-255 of the present volume) and was one of the first to examine its theoretical implications for linguistics. As he emphasized in *The Newest Russian Poetry*,

Futurist poetry was simply an extreme example of the difference between everyday speech and poetic language: "The mechanical association between sound and meaning by contiguity is realized all the more rapidly as it is made by habit. Hence the conservatism of practical speech. The form of the word quickly dies out." In poetic language, on the contrary, "the connection between the aspect of sound and that of meaning is tighter, more intimate, and language is accordingly more revolutionary, insofar as habitual associations by contiguity retreat into the background" (see p. 178 below). The type of revolutionary estrangement that occurs in transrational poetry is so severe that familiar words are wrenched from habitual meanings and aligned on the basis of similarity and parallelism with nonexistent words, fragments of words, or even sheer sounds. On this level, the meaning of a poem in transrational languages lies both in its disruptive gesture—its challenge to linguistic cerebration—and in its formal reorganization of language.

Another point is that—however disparaging the critics of transrational verse care to be in dismissing it as sheer nonsense—there can be no doubt that it is composed of "words" and pertains to the field of language. The Russian Formalists, who both championed and analyzed the sound poem, were the first theorists to attack the problematics of the so-called "empty word." The theme is so obsessive that one finds the identical example in Viktor Shklovskij's essay in the first OPOJAZ publication, "On Poetry and Trans-sense Language," 1916, and in Jakobson's article on Goldstein's book *Wortbegriff* [*The Word-Concept*], written almost half a century later, in 1959. The "empty word" in this example is *kuboa*, which appears in Knut Hamsun's novel *Hunger*. In a remarkable passage, Hamsun describes the effort of a speaker to figure out the meaning of a verbal sign that has emerged in his consciousness. In this case the speaker is not a sound poet or *zaumnik*; rather, the emergence of a "new word" is motivated by the hero's state of exhaustion and delirium:

> It is not in the language; I discovered it. "Kuboa." It has letters as a word has. . . . With the most significant jerks in my chain of ideas I seek to explain the meaning of my new word. There was no occasion for it to mean either God or the Tivoli; and who said that it was to signify cattle show? . . . No, on second thought, it was not absolutely necessary that it should mean padlock, or sunrise. . . . I had fully formed an opinion as to what it should not signify. . . . No! . . . it is impossible to let it signify emigration or tobacco factory. (Hamsun 1920, 87ff.)

In glossing this passage in 1959, Jakobson emphasized the fact that as soon as a sound sequence has been perceived as a signifier, it demands a signified, if only by negation and divergence: "as far as the 'new word' is believed to belong to the given language, its meaning with high probability is expected to be in some respect divergent from the meanings of the other words of the same language. Thus one has an opinion 'as to what it should not signify' without knowing 'what it should signify.'" Jakobson uses the technical linguistic concept of the "zero sign," as he had done some forty years earlier in his essay on Xlebnikov, to label *kuboa*, "or any word one knows to exist in a given language without remembering its meaning," as not a signifier without a signified but a signifier with a "zero signified."

The Dadaist Hugo Ball, who practised and promoted the new medium of the sound poem, labelled such words "grammologues" or "magical floating words." Today we might call them, after Lacan, "floating signifiers," or "occasional words" in the terminology of the Russian semiotician Jurij Lotman. Such

words are *nonce* words, rather than *nonsense* strictly speaking.
They depend upon the context of their situational utterance as
well as upon that of their compositional patterning and relation
to similar existing words, and there can be no doubt that they
exercise a spell on both poet and audience. As Hugo Ball
recounts in describing his first poetic efforts in this direction,
"such word images, when they are successful, are irresistibly and
hypnotically engraved on the memory, and they emerge again
from the memory with just as little resistance and friction. It
has frequently happened that people who visited our evening
performances without being prepared for them were so
impressed by a single word or phrase that it stayed with them
for weeks. Lazy or apathetic people, whose resistance is low, are
especially tormented in this way." (Ball 1974, 67; entry of June
15, 1916.) It is interesting to note that apart from the typolog-
ical similarities between *zaum´* and the experiments of the
Dadaists, there was a direct historical link; apparently
Kandinskij read Ball some of Xlebnikov's poems in Zurich in
1916 (see Watts 1988, 128).

For Jakobson the linguist it became apparent quite early that
any sound sequence within language, even if in a foreign or
unknown tongue, is categorically different from natural sounds
or music, and thus demands a meaning, even if purely differen-
tial or relational. This is one of the reasons, I believe, that
Jakobson's works on the relation between neurological disrup-
tions and language are of such importance for poetics, in particular his avid interest in research on the two hemispheres of
the brain. The "split brain" hpothesis provides, as it were, a bio-
logical foundation for *zaum´* and sound poetry in general: they
are not simply a type of formal sound instrumentation or verbal music, the latter phrase being a contradiction in terms. They
remain tied to language and implicate meaning, even if on an
extremely primitive level. Jakobson's article "Aphasic Disorders

from a Linguistic Angle," first published in 1975, discusses this in detail:

> For the speaker and listener speech sounds necessarily act as carriers of meaning. Sound and meaning are, both for language and for linguistics, an indissoluble duality. . . . The degree to which speech sounds are a completely peculiar phenomenon among auditory events has been made clear by the remarkable experiments conducted in diverse countries during the last decade: these investigations have proved the privileged position of the right ear, connected with the left hemisphere, in perceiving speech sounds. Is it not remarkable that the right ear is a better receptor of speech components, in contradistinction to the superiority of the left ear for all non-verbal sounds, whether musical tones or noises? This shows that from the beginning speech sounds appear as a particular category to which the human brain reacts in a specific way, and this peculiarity is due precisely to the fact that speech sounds fulfill a quite distinct and multifarious role: in different ways they function as carriers of meaning.

In discussing *zaum'*, I have tried to show the radical orientation of transrational verse as well as its reflection in Jakobson's linguistic theories. In turning to the second period of his activity, which extends from 1919 to 1920, one sees his role as a critical partisan of Futurism in a direct political sense. The activist stance is clearly related to his close relationship with Majakovskij and the Briks, who had moved in the beginning of March 1919 from Petrograd to Moscow. It was during the late spring and summer of 1919 that Jakobson worked as Osip Brik's assistant at the Fine Arts Division (IZO) of Lunacharskij's People's Commissariat of Enlightenment (*Narkompros*). IZO was founded in early 1918 as part of the Bolsheviks' effort to consolidate administrative control and policy jurisdiction over the cultural life of the country, as well as to overcome their feeling of total isolation in cultural matters. Headed by David Shterenberg, a progressive artist with ties to the Futurists and Suprematists, it was run by such artists as Al'tman, Malevich, Kandinskij, and Tatlin, who served as deputy chief and head of the Moscow division. Majakovskij was particularly active in editing IZO's Petrograd newspaper, *Art of the Commune* [*Iskusstvo kommuny*], nineteen issues of which were published between December 1918 and April 1919; indeed, some of his best poems of the period were first published there as what might be termed "poetic editorials" (see Jangfeldt 1976). IZO's Moscow organ, *Art* [*Iskusstvo*], in which Brik was active, appeared in eight issues from January to December of 1919. Two of Jakobson's articles included in the current volume were first published there: his well-known appraisal "Futurism" (No. 7, August 2, 1919) and a rarely mentioned editorial manifesto entitled "The Tasks of Artistic Progaganda" (No. 8, September 5, 1919).

The Futurists regarded themselves as leaders of the Revolution in the cultural sphere, and IZO, with its two newspapers, gave them an outlet to champion the new art. As Bengt Jangfeldt writes in his monograph on Majakovskij and Futurism during this period, the Futurists "—rightly—saw themselves as the only radical and innovative cultural workers of their time; and they were in addition the only group ready and willing to cooperate with the political revolution" (1976, 36). They were subjected to what Jangfeldt characterizes aptly as "criticism both irrelevant and spiteful" from various directions— the Communist Party, right-wing intelligentsia and the academicians, and the Proletkul't—criticism that anticipates the later campaign against the Formalists. A typical editorial in *Izvestija* as early as December 29, 1917 cautioned against "the futurists, [who by] penetrating into the proletarian milieu, could bring the putrid poison of the decaying bourgeois organism into the healthy spirit of the proletariat" (quoted in Fitzpatrick 1970, 123). Criticism centered on the Futurists' destructive attitude toward the classics without understanding its rhetorical function, and on the nature of its avant-garde production, which was simply branded bourgeois decadence. As Shterenberg was quick to counter, IZO was a dynamic and activist organization devoted to revolution in the arts: "You shout about proletarian culture. You have taken a monopoly on yourselves. But what have you done all this time, when you have had every chance to act? . . . Nothing. . . . If we, destroying old forms of human culture, created new forms appropriate to new content, we have the right to state that we are doing great revolutionary work" (quoted in Fitzpatrick 1970, 123). As late as 1919 Lunacharskij continued to support the Futurists for their artistic activism, from which example the proletariat, in his opinion, could benefit: "The dynamism and methods of collective work which are so characteristic of futurist art certainly stand in some sort of relationship to what the proletariat may create in the artistic field" (1967, 301). Despite the considerable achievements of IZO in staging exhibitions and reorganizing art teaching, the attacks were so persistent that *Art of the Commune* was closed after the April 13, 1919 issue, and *Art* had only a few months to go.

Jakobson's piece, "The Tasks of Artistic Propaganda," appeared against this background and may be regarded as a unique blend of IZO-Futurist ideology with the Formalist theory of the history of art. It was published as the lead column in the September 5th issue of *Art,* beneath a large banner announcing "The Seventh of September is the Day of Soviet Propaganda," which is in sharp contrast both in typeface and in emphasis to his own headline title—"artistic propaganda." It opens by asking whether it is possible to "simultaneously inculcate in the masses all the aesthetic movements present at a given moment." The answer is a decided no, formulated according to the Formalist credo that any work of art is a deformation of previous works, which affords literary evolution a dynamic nature. It goes on to debunk the notion of popular appeal as a measure of a work's value, a conservative tendency that is opposed to "truly revolutionary artistic enlightenment," the task of which is "the revolutionizing of cultural, in particular, aesthetic habits" and "the overcoming of artistic statics." Few essays of the period so vociferously combine the political rhetoric of the period with a supposedly scientific theory for artistic evolution.

Jakobson's conclusion relies heavily on the premise of the Russian Formalists—apparent as early as Shklovskij's 1914 essay "The Resurrection of the Word"—that one of the basic functions of any aesthetic phenomenon is to revitalize the sign, thereby breaking conventional modes of perception and conceptualization (see Erlich 1965, 176ff.). In his essay "Futurism" of the same year (see pp. 145-152 below), Jakobson finds visual art particularly conducive to the "rehabilitation" of reality, since it is directly based upon perception: "Perceptions, in multiplying, become mechanized; objects, not being perceived, are taken on faith. Painting battles against the automatization of perception, it signals the object." However, even artistic forms, "having become antiquated, are also perceived on faith." As Jakobson puts it *The Newest Russian Poetry*, "form exists for us only as long as we sense the resistance of the material. . . . [When] form takes possession of the material, the material is totally dominated by the form . . . [and] form becomes seterotype and it is no longer alive" (cf. pp. 174, 189 below). Gleizes and Metzinger, stressing the Cubist search for painting that has "the hard brilliancy of a new coin," make a similar observation: "there are painters' methods as there are writers' methods; by passing from hand to hand they grow colorless, insipid, and abstract" (1912; in Herbert 1964, 56). From the realization of this fact follows the device of "deliberately impeded form" (*zatrudnënnaja forma*), which both Cubism and Formalism apply extensively. In increasing the tension between sign and object (or more narrowly speaking, *denotatum*), Cubism intensifies our perception and understanding of reality. This emerges clearly in the following statement by Gleizes and Metzinger, which Jakobson paraphrases in "Futurism": "From the fact that the object is truly transubstantiated, so that the most practised eye has some difficulty in discovering it, a great charm results. The picture which only surrenders itself slowly seems always to wait until we interrogate it, as though it reserved an infinity of replies to an infinity of questions" (1912, in Herbert 1964, 14f.). As formulated in semiotic terms in Jakobson's Prague essay of 1934, "What is Poetry?", the distinction between sign and object is essential for the dynamism of communicative systems:

> Why is it necessary to make a special point of the fact that the sign does not coincide with the object? Because besides the direct awareness of the identity between sign and object (A equals A_1), there is a necessity for the direct awareness of the inadequacy of that identity (A does not equal A_1). The reason this antinomy is essential is that without contradiction there is no mobility of concepts, no mobility of signs, and the relationship between concept and sign becomes automatized. Activity comes to a halt, and the awareness of reality dies out. (1934a, 175.)

Jakobson's partisanship of Futurism is also striking in his last critical essay of this period, on Dada (see pp. 163-172 below), written in 1920 from abroad for the pages of the Soviet newspaper *Vestnik teatra* [*Theatrical Herald*]. The first work in Russian on Dada, it is essentially a review of Richard

Huelsenbeck's *Almanach Dada* of 1920, which contained a representative sampling of the movement as a whole. Dada is seen, and rightly so, as one step beyond Futurism.

As an advocate of radical Futurism, Jakobson distinguishes two types. The first, a true artistic revolution with no holds barred, "refused to write beauty and art with capital letters" and admitted the utter relativity of all aesthetic schools. This pure brand rejected the past point-blank as a result of its "scientific," "historically-minded" awareness of the impossibility of any absolute sanctions on the range of devices in art, and became the first artistic movement which was "unable to create a canon." The "other" Futurism—and Jakobson has in mind the Italians—is, on the contrary, simply the thousand-and-first "ism," yet another artistic school based on the canonization of a set of arbitrary and conventional devices. For Jakobson, it was this transformation of Futurism in Western Europe from an aesthetic revolt into an "ism" that opened the way for the appearance of a new radical movement, Dada: "The demand arose for a new differentiation —'a manifestation parallel to the relativistic philosophies of the current moment—a "nonaxiom,"' as . . . Huelsenbeck announced."

Dada arises precisely as a "systemless" aesthetic rebellion, and Jakobson is perceptive in stressing that Dada makes no pretense of it own permanence or even aesthetic value, but simply rejoices in its own being, appealing neither to the past nor to the future for justification. It is the ultimate manifestation of the "device laid bare" for its own sake, the device constantly in conflict with the aesthetic norm and never crystallizing into its own limited canon. Dada offers nothing new in terms of devices but is content to appropriate three main principles from Cubism and Futurism: bruitism (sheer sound, the art of noises), simultanism, and the "new medium," i.e. collage (cf. Huelsenbeck in Motherwell 1981, xviii). Dada engaged in a free play with aesthetic means without itself becoming an aesthetic movement: "Poetry and painting became for Dada a circus side-show act," as Jakobson puts it. He regards this as the logical outcome of the total rejection of aesthetics and the position it enjoys in society, which is quite often a repressive one. Ultimately, Jakobson views Dada as a social rebellion only incidentally utilizing aesthetics as a means of attack. And this really is the main point, namely that Dada rests content with the continual "laying bare" of devices because it is quite uninterested in constructing a new aesthetics. As such it becomes nothing but a reflex of the times, neither one thing nor the other. And as such it is doomed to vanish and gladly accepts that fact; as Huelsenbeck writes, "the time for Dada has ripened, with Dada it will ascend, and with Dada it will vanish."

Jakobson's "Dada" is a curious piece. The Futurist in him enthusiastically greets an aesthetics of continual "laying bare," yet there is a lingering doubt that perhaps, after all, it leads nowhere. Jakobson nicely traces the evolution of this process, with an hilarious conclusion:

> What is important is that, having finished once and for all with the principle of the legendary coalition of contentless form and content, through a realization of the violence of artistic form, the toning-down of pictorial and poetic semantics, through color and texture as such, we come in Russia to the blue grass of the first celebrations of October, and in the West to the unambiguous Dadaist formula: "*nous voulons nous voulons pisser en couleurs diverses.*" Coloring *as such*. Only the canvas is removed. . . .

For Jakobson Dada is simultaneously the ultimate stage in the evolution of art and a socially-determined, non-aesthetic manifestation answering the spirit of the times and the crisis of Western values. The realization that all art is a convention, a realization resulting from a "scientific," i.e. relativistic, dismissal of earlier formulae such as "in the name of beauty we are creating a new art," leads to a radical mistrust of all convention and a valorization of revolutionary form as the ultimate goal of art. But when confronted by the obvious fact that a continual revolution in art either ceases to be a revolution and becomes a new order, or ceases to produce art and vanishes, the radical Futurist simply shrugs his shoulders. Such an argument clearly fails to answer the elementary question of why the evolving shifts in artistic conventions, the countless "isms" of the past, are in any way inferior to newer systems whose very revolt against convention is just as arbitrary as convention itself. Except, perhaps, the tautological reply: they are newer. Within that simple reply lies the revolutionary ethos of both Russian Futurism and Formalism.

III.

The original edition of this book, edited by Bengt Jangfeldt, was published in Russian in Stockholm Studies in Russian Literature, a series of the Acta Universitatis Stockholmiensis. It involved archival research of great depth and scope. It was envisioned as a collection of materials the purpose of which was to insure that Jakobson's works of the Futurist period be accessible in his native language. Obviously, an English translation has a different goal, namely a presentation of that legacy to the English reader who knows no Russian but is interested in the subject. I would like here to spell out the differences between the original Russian edition of this book and its English version.

The core of the volume (Part One), namely Jakobson's memoirs as tape-recorded, transcribed, and edited by Bengt Jangfeldt, remains intact, as does the extant epistolary record (Part Two). The selection of Jakobson's essays (Part Three) has been expanded for the benefit of the English reader by the inclusion of two of Jakobson's seminal works on his favorite poets of the time, who are often encountered in his memoirs, Xlebnikov and Majakovskij. The first consists of excerpts from Jakobson's first major monograph, on Xlebnikov, *The Newest Russian Poetry*, which was written in 1919 in Moscow, but published in Prague only in 1921, and which falls properly within the chronological scope of the volume. The second, on Majakovskij, "On a Generation that Squandered Its Poets," was written somewhat later, in 1930, in the wake of the poet's suicide, and remains until this day the most important critical appraisal of the poet's work. It seemed to me essential to include it in the present volume, in which Majakovskij plays such a central role. Both of these works were translated by the late Edward J. Brown of Stanford University.

Certain parts of the first edition have been omitted, in particular Jakobson's translations into Russian, for obvious reasons. Jakobson's own poetic output of the time has been truncated slightly: of the nineteen poems in the original Russian edition, only fifteen appear here. The omissions consist of some of Jakobson's juvenilia, which are better read in Russian with a certain sense of indulgence for the author's age. I have followed the rubrics of the original edition in presenting the poems that do appear here, namely: Juvenilia; Futurist Verses; Jocular Verses; and Verses to Elsa Triolet. Frankly, I find that typology somewhat artificial, since almost all the poems are full of humor and represent "occasional poetry" at its best. (The juvenile prose piece, "Excursions Around My Room," is a jovial coda to the poetry.) As a translator, I am pleased by the results

I obtained in some of the jocular poems, the originals of which were written in normative Russian. Whether the versions I have produced of Jakobson's futurist poems, in particular the most important one, "Distraction" (see p. 252 below), should be regarded as translations, transpositions, aberrations, or entirely independent poems, is an open question. They do, however, attempt to capture the spirit and rhythm of the originals.

One thing that remained intact from the first edition is the unique commentaries Bengt Jangfeldt compiled for the book. Few scholars have the knowledge and experience to so ably fill in the gaps in history. They are as fascinating as the text itself and could, indeed, almost be read independently as a history of the Russian avant-garde culled from little-known primary sources. I regard Jangfeldt's commentaries as an unsurpassed example of this genre of scholarship. Where I have added a note or two, or clarified something, it was for the sake of the English reader. One final note: the selection of illustrations here differs slightly from the first edition. Partly this is because certain of the illustrations in the original edition were of documents in Russian that would be of little interest to the English reader, partly because certain other photographs became available to me.

The translation of this book was a daunting challenge, given the diverse nature of the materials and genres represented. Jakobson's memoirs, based on transcripts of interviews, contain features of oral speech that are perhaps less grating to the eye on the page in Russian than in English, but I hope I have succeeded in rendering them felicitously. Jakobson's essays are characterized by the idiosyncratic style of his artistic milieu, which I have tried to render accurately but without too slavish a literality. His letters posed an enormous challenge, since we lack the other half of the correspondences, and many references are elliptical or obscure, but Jangfeldt's commentaries were useful in establishing the context in many cases. Jakobson's letters to Elsa Triolet were particularly difficult in this regard, given the intimacy of their relationship, but despite some obscurities, they remain compelling, indeed fascinating, human documents. In translating the poems, I tried above all to produce texts that were equivalents, however inadequate, of the originals, but that were also readable as English poems. For her help in answering numerous queries and preventing some terrible blunders, I should like to thank my dear friend and colleague Irina Belodedova.

Stephen Rudy
New York University

PREFACE TO THE FIRST EDITION

In his discussion of "Jakobson's Philosophical Background,"
Elmar Holenstein emphasizes the scholar's creative roots:
"Jakobson was not so much a philosopher or a linguist as he
was an aesthete, who had grown up among artists, painters,
and poets. Correspondingly, his earliest and most important
sources of information are to be looked for in the realm of art
and not in philosophy" (1987). Similarly, Vjacheslav V. Ivanov,
in his preface to the Soviet edition of Jakobson's works on
poetics, emphasizes that "in his mould Jakobson was by nature
rebellious, a romantic striving toward the new." Therefore,
Ivanov continues, Jakobson's attempts to create a new poetics
"are linked with the poets of Russian Futurism—Xlebnikov
and Majakovskij—and with those trends in Russian literary
studies which arose to meet this literary experimentation," i. e.
the Russian "Formal School" (1987, 12). The similarity of
Holenstein's and Ivanov's statements is not accidental: the significance of modern art for Jakobson's formation as a linguist
is obvious, and he himself repeatedly and resolutely underlined
the deep internal link between the scientific quests of the
young linguists and literary scholars and the creative experiments of contemporary poets and painters. In this regard,
Jakobson's personal aquaintance and collaboration with
Majakovskij, Xlebnikov, Pasternak, Malevich, Larionov and
others, is as important as the theoretical closeness.

The present collection of materials is devoted to these first steps in Jakobson's scholarly path. It covers his "Russian period" and his close ties to the representatives of Russian avant-garde art, both visual and verbal. Jakobson's autobiographical notes, here presented under the title "A Futurian of Science," are an important contribution to the scholar's biography. They are based on tape-recorded conversations I had with him in 1977 and are published here for the first time. Jakobson himself was adverse to the word "reminicences"; as K. Pomorska aptly remarks on his attitude toward this genre: "The element obviously unacceptable to Jakobson was the 'tense' of this genre: memoirs belong to the past tense; they push one's life into the past, thus putting an end to one's biography and, consequently, to one's life" (1987, 4). In many ways, they correspond more to Jakobson's *Dialogues* with Krystyna Pomorska (1980/1983), which, while highly autobiographical, are an attempt to evaluate the significance of avant-garde art and science at the beginning of the twentieth century. The correspondences between the two works are explained not only by their common thematics, but by the fact that Pomorska's and my conversations with Jakobson were conducted almost simultaneously and under the sharp impression that two new publications had made on him: *The Yearbook of the Manuscript Division of the Pushkin House* (M. P. Alekseev *et al.*, eds., 1976)—which included, among other things, the letters of Kazimir Malevich to M.V. Matjushin—and the collection *The Russian Avant-Garde* (N. Xardzhiev *et al.*, 1976), which contained the first chapters of Malevich's autobiography. In contradistinction to Jakobson's *Dialogues* with K. Pomorska, which concentrate on his scientific thought and its development, my conversations with him focused on his links with poets and painters, contacts that are described rather briefly in *Dialogues*.

Agreeing in full with E. Holenstein's statement quoted above, I decided to include in this collection Jakobson's own poems, and not only the well-known early transrational verses from *Transrational Boog* (1915), but his juvenilia, jocular poems, and futuristic verses, as well. The fascination of the schoolboy Jakobson with poetry and his early interest in problems of versification and the structure of poetic works explains a great deal in his further development as a scholar.

This collection also contains Jakobson's poems to Elsa Kagan (later Triolet), who played a most important role in his biography and to whom he was particularly close in 1916-1917. Therefore, apart from his letters of a theoretical nature to A. E. Kruchenyx and M. V. Matjushin, I have included here his extant letters of 1920-1923 to Elsa Triolet, which cast a new light both on Jakobson's early years in Prague and on the life of Majakovskij and the Briks in Moscow. Moreover, these letters offer rich material for understanding the intimate drama that formed the basis for Viktor Shklovskij's book *Zoo or Letters Not about Love* (1923).

As a matter of fact, the most vivid passages in Jakobson's reminiscences and letters are devoted to his close friendship with Elsa and with her older sister Lili and the men surrounding her, Osip Brik and Vladimir Majakovskij. In this respect the present collection supplements a series of publications about Majakovskij and his closest friends, who, through their talent and fates, occupied an almost unique place in the history and mythology of twentieth-century literature: *Love is the Heart of Everything: Correspondence Between Vladimir Majakovskij and Lili Brik, 1915-1930* (B. Jangfeldt, ed. 1986) and *"Dear Uncle Volodja . . .": The Correspondence of Majakovskij and Elsa Triolet, 1915-1917* (B. Jangfeldt, ed. 1990).

Among the poets mentioned by Jakobson in his "memoirs," the chief place is alloted to Majakovskij, Xlebnikov and Pasternak. It is hardly by chance that it is exactly to these three poets that he devoted some of his most penetrating individual studies. His book on Xlebnikov, *The Newest Russian Poetry. A First Sketch* (Prague, 1922), was his first schorarly work in general, the impact of which can be guaged by the review it received by the young linguist G.O. Vinokur: "for the first time the theoretical foundation for all the attempts to establish a science of poetry, which marked the life of the Moscovite and Petrograd philological youth for the last 5-6 years, is offered" (1921). Jakobson devoted two studies of an entirely different nature to Majakovskij: one on his prosody, *On Czech Verse, Primarily in Comparison with Russian* (Prague, 1923), the other on the poet's fate, "On a Generation That Squandered Its Poets" in the collection *The Death of Vladimir Majakovskij* (Berlin, 1931). Finally, in 1935, Jakobson analyzed the metaphoric and metonymic poles in the work of Majakovskij and Pasternak in his essay "Marginal Notes on the Prose of the Poet Pasternak," now considered a classic. Pasternak himself valued this work highly; in a long (unfortunantly lost) letter he told Jakobson that the essay made an enormous impression on him and that, after reading it, he "for the first time saw that he was understood" (see p. 63 below).

Vjacheslav V. Ivanov aptly characterizes Jakobson as "a romantic striving toward the new." It not by chance that Jakobson himself speaks of "the united front of science, art, and literature, of a life rich in new, still unknown values of the future" (see p. 3 below). He always emphasized his closeness to Futurism and its significance for his scholarly development; cf., for example, his letter to V.B. Shklovskij of October 23, 1928: "Actually, the strength of our science was precisely in the Futurist promontary of the word 'we'" (Shklovskij 1990, 519).

Indeed, the avant-garde nature, the *youthfulness* of his thought penetrates all the materials collected here, particularly the autobiographical remarks "A Futurian of Science," which draw a vivid picture of Jakobson's scientific and life path and his ties to world literature and art.

After Jakobson's death, Krystyna Pomorska asked me to take part in the future work on the study of his archive. However, the concrete idea for the publication of this collection belongs to Stephen Rudy, who, in 1988, on behalf of the Jakobson Foundation, commissioned me to edit and publish my conversations with Jakobson and supplement them with other materials relating to the period. I am deeply obliged to The Jakobson Foundation for providing me with materials from Jakobson's archive, as well as for financial support that made it possible for me to concentrate on my work on this book. In the course of that work I had numerous occasions to discuss various details of Jakobson's biography with Stephen Rudy, who generously shared both his knowledge and archival materials; it is to him, first of all, that I should like to express my thanks for his help and encouragement in the creation of this collection.

For advice and help in compiling the commentaries to this volume I should also like to thank Vladimir M. Vol´pert, Vjacheslav V. Ivanov, Vasilij V. Katanjan and Inna Ju. Gens, Mixail Ju. and Jurij M. Lotman, Tat´jana L. Nikol´skaja, Aleksandr E. Parnis, Evgenij V. Pasternak and Elena B. Pasternak, Roman D. Timenchik, Lazar´ S. Flejshman, Natalija F. Fridljand-Kramova, Jelena S. Jangfeldt-Jakubovich, Ben Hellman, Rein Kruus, Elena and Bengt Samuelson, Miloslává Slavíčková, Jan Benedict, and, finally, Professor Peter Alberg Jensen, who kindly accepted the first, Russian edition of this collection into the series Stockholm Studies in Russian Literature.

Bengt Jangfeldt

Stockholm, 1992

PART I

MEMOIRS

A FUTURIAN OF SCIENCE

The academic years 1912-1913 and 1913-1914 were for me years of literary and scholarly maturation. (Since those times I've become accustomed to think in the framework of academic years.) In those years it seemed absolutely clear that we were experiencing a period of cataclysms in the visual arts, in poetry, and in science, or rather, in the sciences. It was then that I heard the lectures of a young physicist who had just returned from Germany and was reporting on Einstein's first work on the theory of relativity; this was still before the general theory of relativity. On the other hand, my impressions of French artists alternated with those of the emerging Russian painting, which was partly abstract and then became totally abstract.

After the French prologue, which for me had as its head the name of Mallarmé—although I had then already familiarized myself with Rimbaud as well as several other, later poets,— there followed the discoveries of the latest Russian poetry, beginning with *A Slap in the Face of Public Taste*. These were unforgettable experiences. There clearly emerged a united front of science, art, literature, and life, full of the unknown values of the future. It seemed as if a science based on new principles was being created, a self-sufficient science, opening up endless perspectives and introducing into general use new concepts, which at the time did not seem to fit into the usual framework of common sense. We had teachers such as Umov and Xvol´son, atomic physicists whose lectures I heard and whose books I read.[1] The same occurred in every other field. The thematics of time and space, so mysterious and head-spinning, opened up. For us there was no borderline between Xlebnikov the poet and Xlebnikov the mathematical mystic. By the way, when I visited Xlebnikov, who was the great renewer of the poetic word, he immediately began telling me about his mathematical quests and meditations.

These same years just before World War I brought with them a passion for all sorts of evenings of lectures and discussions. A series of such discussions were connected with the so-called crisis of the theater, with problems of theatrical innovation: the experiments of Craig and Vaxtangov, Tairov, Evreinov, and Meyerhold were debated passionately. Every production, whether in Moscow or Petersburg, evoked agitation and arguments. There were as well, of course, such lectures and discusssions on literary, philosophical, and popular social topics.

The evenings of the Futurists brought together an amazing number of the public: the Large Hall of the Polytechnical Museum was completely packed! The public's reaction to them was various: many came for the sake of scandal, but a broad segment of the student public awaited the new art, wanted the new word (by the way—and this is interesting—they weren't particularly interested in prose). This was a time when readers gravitated almost exclusively towards poetry. If anyone from our wider circle of acquaintances had asked what was happening in Russian literature, there would have been references to the Symbolists, especially Blok and Belyj, partly, perhaps, to

Annenskij or to those poets who followed the Symbolists, but no one would hardly have recalled Gor´kij; his work seemed already completed by 1905. Sologub's late prose was in great disfavor, and the one work people recognized was *The Petty Demon*—this was also literature already three years old—and his short stories. People read Remizov, but somehow just in passing, and in general thought that the main thing was poetry, and that poetry had a genuinely new word to say. Apart from these large public evenings there were many closed groups, circles, and private gatherings, where the main place was alloted to the new word.

. . .

I saw Majakovskij for the first time in 1911. However strange it my seem, the various snapshots from my memory often coincide with memorable dates in the poet's own biography.

At the time I personally was much closer to artistic circles than to writers and poets. But I had two friends. One of them was my schoolmate at the Lazarev Institute of Oriental Languages, Isaak Kan,[2] who very early on had begun looking for new forms in painting. The epoch of abstract painting was still in the future, but problems of emancipating color and volume were already being addressed. The French painters were seductive. People already paid homage to the names of Matisse and Cézanne. Although Picasso's canvases already adorned the walls of Shchukin's private mansion, we did not have entrance there and learned about Picasso a bit later. But there were others. In the Tret´jakov Gallery there hung several important new French artists—that is, new for that time—of Post-Impressionism. We went from a fascination with the Impressionists precisely to Post-Impressionism, which, actually, carried within it a rejection of Impressionism. We were fascinated by Cézanne and van Gogh, and also—no less than van Gogh—by Gauguin and a series of other innovators.

Another friend of mine was Sergej Bajdin,[3] a painter who was in the close circle of admirers and students of Mixail Larionov. (In the last years of Larionov's life, when I met with him in Paris, he recalled in detail—he had a phenomenal memory—Bajdin in particular as one of the new abstract artists, who already in 1913, at the time of the exhibitions "Target" and "No. 4,"[4] was an honest to goodness, talented abstract artist.

It was with Bajdin and Kan that I went to the funeral of Serov.[5] We still liked Serov as we had before, despite our adamant hostility toward both the World of Art and the Union of Russian Artists. We went together to the opening of the World of Art exhibition in January 1911, where there were two new pictures by Serov, the novelty of which aroused both public enthusiasm and bewilderment. One was "The Rape of Europa"; the other—a nude portrait of Ida Rubenstein.[6] We stood before these canvases amidst a crowd of visitors who were debating and for the most part condemning them. Among them was a portly society lady, the wife of the Georgian Prince Gugunava, an artist I knew who was either a relative or in-law of my close friends the Zhebrovskij family.[7] I shall never forget the loud grumbling of the Princess: "She's shameless! It would be one thing if she had something to show, but she is nothing but a scrawny cat!"

At the funeral, as was usually the case at the time, there were huge crowds of students which followed the procession right to the cemetery. We had been at the home of Serov, where he was laid out. His unusually beautiful profile in the coffin made a tremendous impression on me. The procession got under way, and when we reached the cemetery I suddenly heard a fresh, stentorian voice. We were standing rather far away from the grave and the family of the artist. We asked who was speaking and were told that it was one of Serov's best students. It was Majakovskij: he remembered Serov with great emotion and vividness and solemnly swore that what Serov was unable to accomplish would be realized by the younger generation.[8] Until then I had not heard of Majakovskij.

The next time I saw Majakovskij was at the Knave of Diamonds exhibition at the beginning of 1912.[9] I recall that I did not recognize Serov's student: there entered a dishevelled young man in a shabby velvet jacket who immediately began wrangling with the organizers of the exhibition. He was literally thrown out of the place. They were afraid there would be a scandal. The organizers of the exhibition rather stunned me and grated on my nerves: after all, it seemed, they were artists and innovators, why were they behaving like such cowards? Of these artists I knew Adol´f Mil´man the best; he was the older brother of a great friend of mine in those days, Semen Mil´man. I asked him what was the matter. "Ah, they're nothing but hooligans," he replied. Adol´f Mil´man was a landscape artist, somewhat in the style of Derain. He belonged to the Knave of Diamonds, was himself skeptical toward Cubism, but introduced me to everyone who was in the Knave of Diamonds then—Mashkov, Konchalovskij, Lentulov, Jakulov and others. By the way, my acquaintance with them was quite superficial at the beginning.[10]

A while later I saw Majakovskij together with a rather heavy-set man who wore a lorgnette. This turned out to be Burljuk. I saw them at the concert of Raxmaninov that Majakovskij was later to describe in his autobiography.[11] I recall how he stood by the wall with an obviously pained look of boredom on his face. This time I recognized him. His face was astonishing, and I studied it closely.

Soon after this the Knave of Diamonds organized a debate, which Majakovskij attended, on February 25, 1912. This was, it seems, his first appearance at a public debate.[12] The debate made a tremendous impression on me, since it was the first time I absolutely sensed all those ferments, all those new questions of art, which had ripened and become, as it were, a new organic part of me, dear and indissoluble.

Then, in late summer, *A Game in Hell* appeared. I immediately got this poem-brochure and tried to grasp it.[13] It struck me—struck me by the fact that at the time I did not have the slightest idea how innovative verse could be. To a significant degree it was parodic versification, a parody of Pushkin's verse. I was immediately thrilled by it. At the time I knew nothing about Xlebnikov and hadn't even heard of Kruchenyx. But in our small circle it was at this time that we began to have conversations about the appearance of Russian Futurism.

I was already fairly well-informed about Italian Futurism, since my teacher of French language at the Lazarev Institute was Genrix Èdmundovich Tastevin.[14] He and I were on very friendly terms. I really didn't need to study the French language, since I had spoken French since early childhood. Instead of the homework assignments he gave my schoolmates, he gave me special topics, in keeping with what I was interested in. It was actually in this way, I may be so bold as to say, that my scholarly interest in literature began.

The first topic Tastevin had me write on was Mallarmé's poem "L'Azur." Thibaudet's book on Mallarmé had just been published in Paris, and copies were available in Moscow.[15] It made a great impression on me by its interpretation of poems, by its attempts to get inside the structure of poems. I was completely unused to this. In general I must say that in the beginning of my studies at the Lazarev Institute (which, actually, was an institution for instruction in Eastern languages for the middle school through lyceum level), I thought that I would study natural sciences (my father was a chemical engineer and inclined me in that direction), perhaps astronomy or geology. I vacillated all the time, but never considered the possibility of studying anything other than science. Still in childhood, when I was asked what I wanted to be, I would answer: "An inventor, and if that doesn't work out,—a writer." Becoming a writer struck me as easy. In the third class I edited a lithographed journal called *Student's Thought* and wrote poems and prose for it,[16] but to become an inventor was what attracted me the most. From the natural sciences, sometime in the fourth class, I went on to a fascination with literature, in particular poetry, and decided that I should become a literary scholar. But everything I encountered in works on literature instantly seemed to me to be grossly insufficient and entirely not what was really needed. And it seemed to me absolutely essential for the study of literature to immerse oneself in the minutiae of language.

Thus I decided to become a linguist; I was fourteen or fifteen years old at the time. After having borrowed my uncle's copy, I finally bought my own copy of Dal''s explanatory dictionary and read it continuously. I also acquired Potebnja's *Notes on Russian Grammar* and *Thought and Language*, and in general turned more and more in the direction of linguistics.

Tastevin was a charming man and related to me in a very cordial way. He was the secretary of the Symbolists' journal *The Golden Fleece*, a cultural activist of the type of the Bohemian intelligentsia, hardly a typical teacher-pedant of the time. I recall how once we were walking down one of the school's corridors—the times were reactionary, with strict pressure exerted on students and teachers alike, with a whole series of governmental bans imposed on us. While we were discussing the Symbolists, a superviser came up to us and said: "Is it possible that you do not know that it is forbidden for students to walk in this corridor!" Tastevin became silent. I was terribly offended.

After working on the poem "L'Azur," I wanted to write about one of Mallarmé's sonnets that Thibaudet considered the most difficult, "Une dentelle s'abolit." As a first step I brought Tastevin my translation of the sonnet into Russian verse, intentionally diverging from the classical versification of the original, and then wrote a long analysis of the poem.[17] This was at the very beginning of 1913, already after my first work on Trediakovskij.

Part of the background to this is that in 1910 Andrej Belyj's book *Symbolism* appeared. It contained several essays on verse, one in particular analyzing the strophic arrangement of Pushkin's "Ne poj, krasavica, pri mne . . ." [Do not sing, oh beauty, before me . . .] and another on the history of the Russian iambic tetrameter. These experiments fascinated me extremely. I was sick at the time with jaundice, and, lying in bed with a fever, I decided, under the influence of these experiments, to draft an analysis of Trediakovskij's verse. I preserved this draft quite by accident.[18] It was a statistical analysis of Trediakovskij's long poems according to the model of Belyj's investigations and was meant to advance the thesis that among Russian poets of the eighteenth century the main deviations from the stress scheme—the main "half-stresses" as Belyj labelled them—that is, the main unstressed syllables in downbeats of the verse, occur in the fourth syllable, whereas in the nineteenth century the main deviations occur in the second syllable. I demonstrated, supplementing Belyj's argument, that in the case of Trediakovskij both types of "half-stresses" are developed to an extreme degree, that is, as it seemed to me then, the beginning of the establishment of a definite metrical type was preceded by a chaotic period in which both types were mixed.[19]

At the very end of 1912 *A Slap in the Face of Public Taste* appeared, and on one of the very first days of the new year I settled down to read this collection.[20] It was one of my very strongest artistic experiences. The collection opened with the poetry of Xlebnikov, and it was his work that fascinated me the most. I learned everything there by heart: "Snake Train," "I and E," "On the Island of Ösel," and the various smaller poems published under the title "Przheval'skij's Horse," as well as the play "A Maiden God."[21] All of these made a simply staggering impression on me: his understanding of the word, of verbal mastery, corresponded to what I was dreaming of at the time. It was at the same moment that I first encountered Picasso's work, during a debate at the Knave of Diamonds where Burljuk showed slides of his pictures on the screen.[22] Everyone was shouting, the majority out of indignation or mockery. These pictures overcame me even more when, along with Mil'man, I went to Shchukin's mansion, where they were hung in a special room, surrounded by African sculptures, which, it is said, Picasso himself selected.

In January 1913 there was a scandal, when a madman named Balashov slashed with a knife or razor Repin's picture "Ivan the Terrible and His Son" in the Tret'jakov Gallery (in Stalinist times the picture was jokingly called "Ivan the Terrible Administers First Aid to His Son"). There was a lot of commotion about this. There were accusations against the Futurists and the occasion was used to launch an attack on them. The Futurists, of course, had had nothing to do with the escapade. It was then that the Knave of Diamonds organized a debate.[23] At the debate Repin himself got up and spoke, saying: "It is disgraceful to attack an artist!" He attracted the audience's deepest sympathy; he was an excellent speaker. The main speaker was the poet Maksimilian Voloshin. And suddenly Majakovskij made a sharp speech; he always assumed a very sharp tone in relation to the members of the Knave of Diamonds, whom he considered out-and-out compromisers between Cubism and much more conservative art. On the fact that Voloshin had been invited to speak, he said: "There's something about this in Prutkov's poetry." (In general he loved quoting Prutkov.) Then he read the poem about the priest's wife who called in a lackey because a bug had fallen on her: "If a bug crawls on your neck,/ Crush it yourself, don't have a lackey do it." Reciting these ambivalent lines strikingly to loud applause, he compared the Knave of Diamonds to someone who lives in doubt and, unable to resolve it, calls for the help of a substitute who lacks any relation to the new art.[24]

These were impassioned times. There was a second debate on February 24, 1913. I remember it quite well. They didn't want to allow Majakovskij to speak. Various members of the audience took an active part in the discussion, some for, some against, but they still wouldn't let him in. Then he appeared at another door of the Polytechnical Museum and everyone started shouting. His voice was strikingly stentorian, yet at the same time extraordinarily sympathetic, hypnotizing one in his favor, a voice of colossal range. He spoke passionately in defence of the new poetry, in particular, of Xlebnikov.[25]

I recall that at the time two poems by Majakovskij in *A Slap in the Face of Public Taste* particularly struck Kan, namely "Night" and "Morning." He would read them with great success to young ladies, pretending that they were his own. But they didn't affect me very much. I would harangue him that the poet of the future, the true Futurian, was Xlebnikov. The others made on me a much weaker impression. But I knew by heart the poem by Benedikt Livshic published there. I didn't like Kandinskij at all; as a matter of fact, he later protested against having been included, declaring that while he was in favor of innovation, he was against scandals. I was already acquainted with his book *On the Spiritual in Art*, which seemed to me to be too closely linked to German art of the recent past and its foggy, abstract slogans. I was terribly proud of the manifesto *A Slap in the Face of Public Taste* itself. After this I persistently turned my attention to anything that Xlebnikov wrote.[26]

During Christmas vacations I would always go to Petersburg. I regularly went to the Union of Youth exhibitions; they had one practically every year. I recall standing on the landing of the staircase, and right in front of the entrance to the exhibition there were several artists—Shkol´nik, Rozanova, and Boguslavskaja, with whom I later became friends, along with her husband Puni. She was quite beautiful at the time and quite elegant in her own way. Someone said: "I wonder whom Pushkin would be with if he were alive today?" She answered with a confident, enthusiastic voice: "He'd be with us, of course!"

It was a time of fierce confrontations and challenges, but for the youth of the time they were equated not so much with the reactionary artists as with the police, since the police were constantly interfering. But even though the police interfered, they didn't always like those for whom they were interfering. When Bal´mont came back from abroad, a small group of us went to listen to him recite his poems.[27] He declaimed his poems in an unforgiveably flaccid and tedious manner: "Thirteen years! Thirteen years! Is that really so much?" and so on. Semen Mil´man whistled, and a policeman detained him. He wanted to issue a summons, which would have been dangerous, since Mil´man was still a Gymnasium student and he was not allowed to leave his house at all at night under the current regulations. Kan and I tried to vindicate him in every way possible with the policeman. The evening had been organized by the Ladies Society. We said: "But why? People applaud, they express their opinion. It's possible to applaud, right? Then why can't one whistle?" Suddenly the policeman, having threatened Mil´man enough, said: "You know, if I weren't in uniform, I'd whistle too. I'm so sick of these members without members and of those who applaud them!"

I recall quite well the evening in honor of Bal´mont, who had recently returned from abroad, organized by the Society of Free Aesthetics in the building of the Moscow Literary Circle on May 7, 1913. I absolutely wanted to attend this meeting, but it was forbidden for schoolboys in uniform to attend such gatherings. In general, schoolboys, who were required to wear uniforms, were threatened with a whole host of rules and regulations. At the time there was a joke going around on this score. There was a lecturer named Ermilov, who gave lectures on all sorts of "liberating" topics. In particular, he had a lecture entitled "When Will the Real Day Come?" after Dobroljubov's famous article, and on the posters there was a warning that students would be denied admission. Someone added sarcastically: "When will the real day come; students *in uniform* are forbidden to attend." So we actually took off our uniforms. I borrowed from one of my cousins a civilian jacket—I still didn't even own one—and went to the gathering in honor of

Bal´mont.

Someone had told me ahead of time that Majakovskij would be speaking at the meeting.[28] He spoke in an excited and effective manner, with an highly expressive word-order: "Konstantin Dmitrievich, you have heard words of welcome in the name of your friends, now hear your enemies' welcome. There were times when everyone repeated 'Rock, o swing' and so on, we all lived with this estate poetry, but its time has gone, and now"—and he began to read excerpts from his urban poems, if my memory doesn't fail me, from "Noises, Noiselets, and Noisiks." "You have," he said, "boring repetitions—'Love, love, love, love, love, love,' whereas we have"—and here he recited Xlebnikov's "Ljubxo," with its heaps of neologisms based on the same root. In response to his scathing attacks there followed a rebuke by Brjusov: "We came to welcome Konstantin Dmitrievich, not to judge him." Bal´mont himself answered with reconciliatory verses (which, by the way, he later gave the autograph of to Majakovskij) to the effect that "we are both in the azure," that is to say, that they were both sons of poetry. When Majakovskij spoke, there were a lot of catcalls. Among those booing were two people who later became close members of Majakovskij's entourage. I knew them personally and defiantly clapped throughout before their eyes.[29]

· · ·

I made Xlebnikov's acquaintance at the end of December 1913. I had decided it was imperative that we meet and talk. I had an incomparable admiration for him.

The second almanac *A Trap for Judges* had already come out. At the time I borrowed a copy of the rare first issue of *A Trap* from some friends and began reading it.[30] I had figured that it didn't mean much to them, but they asked for it back and I had to return it. The first *Trap for Judges* astounded me, and when I read Gorodeckij's review of the second *Trap*, in *The Impressionists' Studio*, in 1910, Xlebnikov's poem "Incantation by Laughter" was cited there in its entirety and simply stunned me.[31]

Xlebnikov rented an apartment somewhere at the end of the world, at a place called something like Kamenoostrovskie Peski. I recall that as I was looking for his apartment there was a raw chill in the air, penetrating even for a Moscovite, so that I had to hold my handkerchief to my nose the whole time. The author of "Laughter" had no telephone, and I had come unannounced. He wasn't at home, but I asked them to tell him that I would return the next morning. The next day, December 30, 1913, I turned up at his place, along with a special copy I had made for him of a collection of excerpts I had compiled at the Rumjancev Museum from various collections of incantations, some transrational, some half-transrational. A part of them had been taken from Saxarov's anthology: songs about demons, incantations, and children's counting-out rhymes and tales as well. Xlebnikov immediately began to look at them with undivided attention, and soon was to use them in his poem "A Night in Galicia," where the mermaids "are reading Saxarov."[32]

In the meantime Kruchenyx came in. He had brought from the typographer the first, just published copies of *Roar!*[33] The author gave me one, with the following dedication: "V. Xlebnikov to Roman O. Jakobson, who has established our kinship with the Sun Maidens and the Bald Mountain, in the sign of coming Conflicts." This was related, he explained, both to the verbal conflicts of the Futurists and to bloody martial battles. Such was his dedication.

I hastened to share with Xlebnikov my own premature reflections on the word as such, as well as the sound as such, that is, as a basis for transrational poetry. The response to these discussions with Xlebnikov, as well as to ones I had soon after with Kruchenyx, was their joint manifesto "The Letter as Such."[34] In reply to my bluntly posed question as to which Russian poets he liked, Xlebnikov answered: "Griboedov and Aleksej Tolstoy." This is quite understandable, if one recalls such poems as "Marquise Dessaix" and "Seven." When I asked him about Tjutchev, he responded with praise but without great enthusiasm.

I asked Xlebnikov whether he had ever been a painter, and he showed me his early diaries, which were about seven years old. There were various signs drawn in colored pencil. "Experiments in colored speech," he explained in passing.

Aleksej Eliseevich Kruchenyx and I immediately became fast friends, and we soon began a lively correspondence. Unfortunately, many of the letters were lost, including all of his letters to me. We frequently wrote one another on theoretical topics. I recall that he once wrote me about transrational poetry: "Transrational poetry is a good thing, but it's like mustard—one's appetite can't be satisfied with mustard alone." He valued only the poetry of Xlebnikov in a genuine way, but not all of it. He wasn't interested in Majakovskij.[36]

Kruchenyx would come to visit me in Moscow. At the time he rented an apartment somewhere in Petersburg, and he invited me over one time. He lived in poverty, and the landlady brought in two pancakes. He cut off half for me: "Try it, you'll see, it's not harmful. You know, as they say: 'The old lady's not harmful.'"

Later Kruchenyx and I together published *Zaumnaja gniga* ('Transrational Boog'). The last part of the title was from *gniga* ('nit'); he would become offended if anyone called it *kniga* ('book'). By the way, it's not true that it came out in 1916. Kruchenyx put the date 1916 so that it would be a book of the future. But it actually appeared earlier; in any event, all the work on it was done in 1914, and I wrote my part before the war had begun.[37]

Kruchenyx would often have quite unexpected ideas, unexpected mischievous comparisons, and he had a colossal sense of humor. He declaimed poetry and parodied it remarkably. When I visited him in Moscow, shortly before his death, when he had already reached the age of eighty, he still acted out his unpublished poems superbly, using a chair as a prop, changing his intonation and pronunciation, piling on various amusing verbal plays. He was very pleased by my visits; it was apparent that he cherished his Futurist past and his collaborators.[38]

That morning at Xlebnikov's, I asked him if he would be free to celebrate the New Year: "May I invite you to join me?" He eagerly agreed. So we went, the three of us—Xlebnikov, Kan and I—to the Stray Dog. The place was packed. I was struck by the fact that it wasn't at all like the Moscow taverns: there was something Petersburgian, something a bit more affected, a bit more made-up, even slick. I went to wash my hands, and a young man turned to me and asked, with a certain foppish courtesy: "Wouldn't you like to powder yourself?" He had with him a little book with powdered pages one could rip out. "You know, it's hot, and it's quite unpleasant when one's face shines. Here, try it!" And we all powdered ourselves with the little book's pages for a laugh.

We sat all three at the table and chatted. Xlebnikov wanted to write down someone's address, and at Kan's request he wrote a quatrain in his notebook, which he then instantly crossed out. It was a description of the Stray Dog, the walls of which had been painted by Sudejkin and others. I recall one line: "Sudejkin's vaults hang aloft." This is again the same motif that entered into *A Game in Hell* ; later one finds in Majakovskij's "Hymn to a Judge"—the "vaults of laws." The verbal link between *Sudejkin* and *sud'ja* ('judge') offered the occasion for the pun. Xlebnikov also wrote down for me a variant of two or three lines from "Incantation by Laughter."

A young, elegant lady came up to us and asked: "Viktor Vladimirovich, people say different things about you: some— that you are a genius; others—that you are mad. What is the truth?" Xlebnikov smiled somewhat transparently and quietly, moving only his lips, slowly answered: "I think neither the one, nor the other." She brought one of his books—I think it was *Roar!*—and asked him to sign it. He quickly became serious, thought for a moment, then painstakingly wrote: "I don't know to whom, I don't know for what."

People started calling out for him to read; soon everyone joined in. At first he refused, but we talked him into it, and he read "The Grasshopper" in a very low voice, but at the same time quite audibly.

It was quite crowded. The walls and the people pressed all around. We drank several bottles of strong, sickly-sweet Barzac. We had arrived there quite early, when there were still hardly any people, and left around dawn.

My admiration for Xlebnikov grew and grew. This was one of the most impetuous impressions of a person I've had in my life, one of three absorbing sensations of having unexpectedly encountered a genius. First there was Xlebnikov, a year later Nikolaj Sergeevich Trubetzkoy, and some three decades later, Claude Lévi-Strauss. In the case of the latter two it was a first encounter with a stranger, of a few words let drop almost by chance that I happened to hear. In the case of Xlebnikov, I had already read him and had been astounded by the experience, but suddenly in the quiet of a New Year's celebration I saw him as someone completely different and as someone inconceivably, indivisibly linked to everything that I had found in reading him. He was, to put it briefly, the greatest world poet of our century.

• • •

Those of my schoolmates at the Lazarev Institute who had a passion for literature and culture were quite interested in the manifestos of Marinetti that had recently appeared. We were acquainted with them through Tastevin and through the newspapers, despite their lambasting of the Futurists, which we considered typical of conservative journalism, whereas Futurism attracted us as a living movement. At this time Tastevin published a book about Futurism that contained translations of Marinetti's manifestos and negotiated with him about his coming to Russia.[40]

Marinetti arrived at the end of January, 1914. And we were ready for him—if not to "throw rotten eggs," as Larionov proposed,[41] then in any event to greet him with open hostility.

Marinetti was a great diplomat and knew how to promote himself in certain segments of the public. He spoke French with a strong Italian accent, but quite well. I heard him speak on two or three occasions. He was a limited person, with an enormous temperament, who knew how to read effectively but superficially. But none of this charmed us. He simply didn't understand the Russian Futurists.

Xlebnikov was profoundly against him, as was Larionov at first. Then Larionov and Marinetti began to drink together. They drank because they couldn't understand each other's language. Larionov simply showed him his paintings and his own drawings and those of his collaborators.

I shall never forget one of Marinetti's appearances. Discussion was conducted in French, rather sluggishly. The conversation was exclusively on the topic of Italian Futurism, of its relation to the Italian literary tradition and to the French. This all dragged on somehow. Marinetti was very polite, continued the discussion. But Larionov got fed up listening to it all, even the moreso since he didn't understand a thing, and said to Marinetti: "Let's go have a drink!" But Marinetti didn't speak a word of Russian. Then a brilliant idea occurred to Larionov, and he flicked his fingers on his throat—which in Russian is "an invitation to pour something behind the collar"—but Marinetti, of course, had no idea what it meant. Then Larianov said: "What an idiot! Even this he doesn't understand!" He thought the gesture was international.[42]

After this we all went to drink at the Alpine Rose, a German-Russian restaurant not far from Kuzneckij Most. There we sat, drinking vodka. They needed me, since practically none of the Russians spoke French, and I acted as a sort of interpreter.[43]

Marinetti struck up a conversation with me and said: "Ecoutez, ne pensez pas—j'aime la Russie, j'aime les russes, je pense que les femmes russes sont les plus belles du monde, par exemple"—and he named Natal'ja Krandievskaja, the wife of Aleksej Tolstoj, and someone else—"et je me comprends dans les femmes. Mais je dois dire que les poètes russes ne sont pas des futuristes et qu'il n'y a pas de futurisme en eux." He asked me whom I considered to be a Futurist. I replied—Xlebnikov, to which Marinetti responded that he was a poet who wrote in the stone age, not a poet who knew our time. I answered with all the impertinence I could summon up, being still a child but already a Futurist: "Vous le dites, parce que vous vous comprenez dans les femmes mais pas dans les poèmes."

He reacted quite cordially to this and later send me a copy of his book *Zang-Tumb-Tuum* from Italy with a warm dedication. Since I was then writing poems under the pseudonym Aljagrov,[44] he sent me the book under that name.

Then Majakovskij entered. There was a free place near me, and he sat down. He asked me: "Are you a Stroganovite?" (that is, a student from the Stroganov School of Painting), since we students from the Lazarev Institute had somewhat similar uniforms, with gold buttons and so on. Conversation turned to the topic of Larionov, and he said to me: "We all went through the school of Larionov. This is important, but one goes through school only once." So that it was clear he was cutting himself off somewhat from Larionov.

Majakovskij offered me a cigarette, and I managed somehow to brush against the box, and the cigarettes scattered on the floor. I started picking them up. He said: "Never mind, never mind, my friend, we'll buy new ones." This was my first brief conversation with Majakovskij. But we somehow already—both he and I—considered ourselves acquainted.

The atmosphere in the Alpine Rose was very friendly. When we were getting ready to leave there was a parting toast, and someone asked: "Will you come to visit us again soon?" Marinetti answered: "No, there will be a great war," and said that "we will be together with you against the Germans." I recall how Goncharova, quite strikingly, raised her glass and said: "To our meeting in Berlin!"

• • •

In 1913 Malevich paid me a visit. What prompted him to do so, whether we had exchanged opinions before this, whether he had heard about my views and school-boy experiments from someone, or whether we had run across each other before, I can't recall. But I remember that we met in the room that our servant, following tradition, called the "nursery." I was a student at the Lazarev Institute, sixteen or seventeen years old, and my brother, also a student at the Lazarev, was five years younger than me.

Malevich spoke to me about his gradual departure from representational to abstract art. There was not an abyss between these two concepts. It was a question of a nonrepresentational relation to representationality and of a representational relation to nonrepresentational thematics—to the thematics of surface, color, and space. And this corresponded profoundly—this he already knew, in general outline, about me—to my thoughts regarding, for the most part, language, poetry, and poetic language.

We had a discussion, and then he said to me: "I am painting new pictures, nonrepresentational ones. Let's go to Paris in the summer, and you can give lectures and explain these pictures at their exhibition."[45] Partly he made this proposition because he didn't speak French, but moreover, because he trusted me as a theoretician more than he trusted himself, despite all my naïveté at the time.

I lived in Lubjanskij Thruway, in the same building where Majakovskij later lived.[46] The Polytechnical Museum, which had a large auditorium for public lectures, was quite near-by. It was there I first heard the Futurists, as well as a whole series of foreigners who came to Moscow to lecture. It was around the Polytechnical Museum that I usually took walks and thought up my own declarations and manifestos, which I wrote for myself alone: a declaration of the emancipated word, and then, the following step, of the emancipated verbal sound. (I had several large notebooks with my theses and declarations, but they all were lost when the Germans invaded Czechoslovakia.) The theme was that the verbal sound could have more in common with nonrepresentational painting than with music. This topic vividly interested me both then and much later: the question of the relation of word and sound, the extent to which the sound retains its kinship with the word, and the extent to which the word breaks down for us into sounds—and further, the question of the relation between poetic sounds and the notation for those sounds, that is, letters. I was not in agreement when after "The Word as Such" there followed "The Letter as Such"; for me it was "the sound as such."

This brought me closer to Malevich, who in one of his letters published in *The Yearbook of the Pushkin House* addresses this topic directly.[47] This is a reflection not only of our earliest conversations, but also of my visit to him in Kuncevo in the summer of 1915, when I was already a student at the university.[48] In Kuncevo he was living with a friend, the artist Morgunov.

I visited Malevich, at his invitation, together with Kruchenyx. We had dinner. Then there transpired a scene that amazed me. Malevich was terrified of having anyone find out what his new works were like. He talked a lot about them, but refused to show his new works. Kruchenyx then made a joke that Malevich and Morgunov were so afraid of openness, so afraid that their inventive secrets might be recognized and stolen, that they painted in total darkness. As a matter of fact, the blinds were drawn!

I had another meeting with Malevich. This was at Matjushin's apartment in Petrograd, probably at the end of 1915. The conversation involved some sort of discontent, some sort of split in avant-garde circles, though the issue was muted by terminology. The question of terminology, however, did not interest me; what interested me was that there be no compromises. They spoke about Majakovskij as a great poet, but as a poet of compromise, a poet on the border between Impressionism and Futurism. Majakovskij seemed unacceptable to this entire group. Burljuk, Majakovskij and Livshic seemed to them to represent some sort of right wing.[49] Apart from Matjushin and Malevich, Kruchenyx and myself, Filonov was also at this meeting; although he was not a nonrepresentational artist, one found in his work significant structural affinities. They asked me to recite my transrational verses, and the artists—both Filonov and Malevich—approved of them greatly, precisely for the fact that they diverged even more strongly from every-day speech than Kruchenyx's "*dyr bul shchyl.*"[50]

My letter to Kruchenyx with the enclosure of a poem that is an indirect satire on Majakovskij is linked to the meeting just described.[51] Kruchenyx had quite a few of my poems, which were for the most part transrational. Two are printed in *Transrational Boog*, and one was published several years later in a collection entitled *Zaumniki* ('Transrationalists').[52] The latter were verses of an almost propagandistic, ad-like character. But there were also poems on the verge of transrationalism, and I recall how Kruchenyx criticized them. There was, for instance, the line: "*Ten´ blednotelogo telefona*" ('The shadow of a pale-bodied telephone'). Kruchenyx said: "No, no, that *blednotelogo* ('pale-bodied') is too old-fashioned." I immediately changed it to "*ten´melotelogo* telefona" ('the shadow of a chalk-bodied telephone').

I was very much to Matjushin's liking. I remember well his large apartment, where on the shelves and chests of drawers stood his sculptures. These were sculptures made from roots, from half-fossilized branches that he had found by the seashore, transrational sculptures, practically unworked. He was a dreamer-organizer and a very enterprising man, with a multiplicity of various plans.

I was quite fascinated by the theme of a completely transformed perspective, transformed by the treatment of the parts of an object that remained. And then another problem fascinated me, one that arose very strongly and very early in Russian art, the theme of collage. It is quite difficult to say what came about under the influence of Western stimuli, and what arose independently in both cases, or even what passed from Russian art to the West. An example of the latter is undoubtedly constructivist architecture; although it practically was not realized in the form of buildings, its entire thematics and problematics, all the models and drafts, were there.

It was a very unusual epoch, with an exceptionally large number of gifted people. And it was a time when, for various reasons, the youth of the day suddenly became the law-givers. We didn't feel ourselves to be beginners. It seemed quite natural that we, the boys in the Moscow Linguistic Circle, should ask ourselves the question: "How should one transform linguistics?" The same thing occurred in all other fields.

For me the connection to art, to which I didn't have any active, actual relation, where I was only an observer, was very important. In general, what we today wisely call *interdisciplinary cooperation* has played a very great role in my life. I always had to look from this point of view: what is different in language? What does this not correspond to in poetry? As I see it now, this is what brought me to the attention of several artists, Malevich in particular. When I read his notes, I see how strongly our conversations affected him, and how he, from his own, artistic side, began to think about what did not appear to be painting, and what, at the same time, was incomparably closer to painting than music.[54]

In 1923 my book on Czech poetry was published, in which, strictly speaking, phonology in the new sense of the term first appeared, that is, phonology in the sense of the science of the structure and function of sounds (a term I picked up in a foot-note in one of Sechehaye's books).[55]. This must have had an influence on Malevich, and in The State Institute of the Arts (GINXUK), which he directed from 1923 to 1926, there was organized a Section of Phonology for the Study of Poetic Language.[56]

It is quite curious how, in my life, close collaborations between people from relatively distant fields came about. I was struck when I was shown in Paris excerpts from the diaries of the prominent Czech artist Joseph Šima in which he relates how significant for his work were the conversations the two of us had in Prague in 1925, just before the creation of the Prague Linguistic Circle. He was particularly struck by the topics of paired relations, of binarism, and of distinctive features.[57]

There were many such instances in my life when it was pre-cisely with artists and theoreticians of art that I had the clos-est ties. Of the theoreticians the closest one of all to me was the Czech theoretician of visual arts and architecture Karel Teige, with whom I associated a great deal.[58]

There was, in the course of our entire generation, an extremely close tie between poetry and the visual arts. There were the problems of the very, very similar basic features, occurring in time in poetry and in space in painting, and then of the various intermediate forms, of various forms of collage. Indeed, it was this transition from linearity to simultaneity that fascinated me greatly, as is obvious, for example, in my let-ter to Xlebnikov.[59]

• • •

It was Sergej Bajdin who introduced me to Larionov. Larionov related to me quite well, but—as always—somewhat vulgarly. There was something about him of a petty bourgeois from Kolomna.

Larionov was both quite intelligent and quite witty. His essays were remarkable in their theoretical subtlety and in their understanding of the relations between literature and art. He understood quite well what was going on. He had gone through an intense period of Primitivism, then there was his period of barbers and Venuses. Then Rayonism began, which was already a transition toward nonrepresentational art, but then he landed in Paris, where he worked on decorative art for Diaghilev. Moreover, he was very Russian and never actually learned to speak French. It was all foreign to him, and he didn't become what he might have become—one of the great masters of our time.

Rayonism seemed to me a very temporary experiment. After Cubism there could only be a transition to one thing, to the play with independent surfaces and colors.

Goncharova was under the strong influence of Larionov. She was a subtle painter, who understood color beautifully, and was an intelligent woman.

I was in very cordial relations with Rodchenko and with his wife, Varvara Stepanova. Rodchenko was an easy-going fellow. He had a colossal self-possession and grasped everything remarkably quickly. He was a marvelous photographer; it is amazing how well he understood Majakovskij's *About That*, the semantics of the poem.[60] I valued him chiefly as a photographer rather than as a painter.

David Burljuk understood painting remarkably well. I spent several hours with him at the Hermitage. What he showed me in pictures, for example a nagging texture or chiaroscuro, was quite out the ordinary. Besides which, he would amuse himself by asking the question "To which picture does this or that relate?" and would explain: "Here you are, Romochka, you could be in that picture." He assigned me to Rubens' studies for paintings.

For Burljuk painting merged with life in a remarkable way. So too Brik's evaluations of young scholars merged completely with life. He would say that everyone in essence has their own profession, and this profession was partly fortuitous— "but what profession emerges from his character?" He would say, for instance: "Vitja [Shklovskij], he's a sergeant-major, from among the soldiers. He says: 'I don't need any of this philology; for me the most important thing is that everyone looks like a good lad!'" And, actually, Shklovskij later became a partisan; he was absolutely that sort of man.

Of Bogatyrev, Brik would say: "Bogatyrev is the type of bird that collects little seeds and is glad that it's finally collected a whole pile of seeds. When he collects folklore, he is so carried away by the exchange of songs for kerchiefs, collars, aprons and such things that it turns out that his main job is to be a dealer in old clothes rather than a folklorist." Later Bogatyrev was to tell me how, when he worked in Sub-Carpathian Russia, he had the feeling: "Look at how much I got for these kerchiefs!"

About me Brik said: "Roma, he's a diplomat. War is about to break out, they're already bringing out the cannons, and he goes to inquire at Court about the state of Her Excellency's health." At the time there wasn't even the slightest talk that I might engage in diplomatic service.

• • •

The people around my parents were always more or less connected to various bourgeois enterprises. My father had business with and was in very friendly relations with a certain merchant of the Old Believers' sect named Prozorov. Once this Prozorov said: "We will have nothing to do with your son, you'll never make a merchant out of him." My father asked why. "He's still a lad [I was seven or eight at the time], I come by, you're not home yet, he entertains me and says: 'You know what occurred to me? Why do they sell things for money? Why don't they just give them away? If they traded everything for free, how nice it would be.'"

When I was accepted as a student at the Historical-Philological Faculty of Moscow University, it was for me a huge event. I had no doubts: I would major in linguistics, of course, linguistics as it is connected with folklore and literature, but above all linguistics—both general linguistics and Slavic philology, in particular Russian. I was totally enthused with this, so exhausted was I by the atmosphere of the high schools of the time in which there was so much superfluous discipline, routine and so stuffy an atmosphere.

Once I went into the school library. What did I come across immediately? The *Bulletin of the Academy of Sciences* (not of the section of Russian language, but the general one), where there was an essay by the mathematician Markov: a chain analysis of *Eugene Onegin*, an attempt to link mathematics with the analysis of a text.[61] It was hard to understand, but I was instantly fascinated by it.

Suddenly an old man came up to me, Pavel Dmitrievich Pervov, a famous teacher who wrote articles on the grammar of Latin and Russian; he taught Latin and Greek at our school.[62] He saw me and asked: "Ah, so you're here too. What are you, a student?" "Yes, of the philological faculty." "Well, what are you studying, history or philosophy?" "No," I said, "linguistics." "Listen, then there's some hope for you yet; I always thought so, but in recent years you became such a blockhead that even I took you for one. But now I'll send you my works." And he actually did send me his offprints.

So everything went remarkably well. I immediately landed in a very scholarly milieu. I instantly became good friends with Bogatyrev, with whom I had stood in line to register at the university in the fall of 1914. We almost immediately decided to create the Moscow Linguistic Circle, and set off on our first fieldwork expedition, in which we were almost killed.[63]

Bogatyrev took me to the Commission on Folklore, where I later read my first lecture, as well as to the Dialectological Commission. It seemed that there was a completely different atmosphere there.

I also became friends with Buslaev, who had a famous grandfather.[64] He was part of an academic tradition, had an exceptional memory and was quite talented. Once he got angry with me: "You start almost as if you're an unskilled laborer. You work like a workman; you brush aside all the general questions." I then answered him, quite reasonably, that it is impossible to approach general questions without knowledge, that that's not the way to do things and is impossible.

At the time I was mostly busy attending seminars, lectures and discussions and paid less attention to taking exams, so that by the end a huge number of exams had piled up for me to take. But it was clear that I would continue to pursue scholarly work. How, in what form, who knew? We were at war, and moreover it was clear that after the war ended things would be very different from what they had been before it started.

Here several factors played a decisive role: the fact that I still maintained my connections with artists, that I had begun to establish contacts with poets, and the fact that for me there had always been a distinct tie between poetry and linguistics. All of this predetermined what was to follow. I hadn't the slightest idea of would would happen. I didn't think much about whether or not I would teach.

Everything went step by step. It was a period of new acquaintances—with linguistics of the Moscow School, with the heritage of Fortunatov, when I was a freshman, and then with the tradition of folkloric research, with field work and expeditions. And then I tried to connect all these experiences with the new approach to poetics, my early fascination with the question "why?", with the question of teleology: for what purpose do these phenomena happen—finally, with the question of structure. There was also the influence of Husserl's phenomenology. All of these things taken together prepared me for my future work.[65]

• • •

I became more closely acquainted with Majakovskij only during the war. At the end of the summer of 1916 he came to Moscow. This was a time of a great, passionate friendship between Elsa and me. Once she invited me, along with Majakovskij, to the Tramblé Cafe on the Kuzneckij, which was a cafe of the European type.[66] We sat there and Majakovskij proposed playing a game, using our fingers instead of cards, if I'm not mistaken. But Elsa had warned me earlier that I had better not do so: "Under no circumstance, I forbid you." Then he started to put me to the test, as one would a new boy at school, to tease me in various ways, to ask me various trick questions. I was able to answer them, and Elsa was pleased with the result.

I think it was during this same visit, in any event in the last
months before the February Revolution, we all dropped by
Elsa's. Apart from Majakovskij and me there was a man named
Mara Levental´, who in his own time was famous for having
won a colossal sum in the State Lottery. Elsa writes of him in
her novel *Wild Strawberry*: "He's not a man, but a monument
to himself."[67] There was also a young woman, an Armenian, by
the name of Begljarova.[68] Where should we go out? Then
Levental´ proposed: "The girls still haven't heard Vertinskij?
Let's go hear Vertinskij!" And we all went. We sat in the second row. When Vertinskij came on stage in his clown's costume and saw Majakovskij, he practically fell into a faint. He
was frightened, lost his head, and ran off the stage. A little
later he returned, sang his songs, and after his appearance
Majakovskij related to him in a very friendly way. He invited
us out and we all went to dine at the Literary-Artistic Club.[69]
One had to be a member of the Club, but they all had various
acquaintances there. There was a certain bourgeois type by the
name of Janov whom I knew, and I asked him: "Would you
mind if I signed under your name?" He said: "What are doing
going around with such lackeys?" But he let me sign under his
name. We sat down, peacefully conversing. Majakovskij, of
course, was carrying on, as he liked to do.

Once, at the beginning of 1917, I asked Elsa out to Komissarzhevskaja's Theater. They were playing Sologub's "Van´ka the
Steward and the Page Jean."[70] She said: "Fine, but first I have
to change. And in the meantime read this." And two little
books fell into my hands, both of which amazed me. One was
the first of the *Collections on the Theory of Poetic Language*,
which corresponded profoundly to what I was doing and writing at the time, but had still not published.[71] I had already written, for instance, an article on transrational language. Before

this I knew Shklovskij's essay "The Resurrection of the Word," which I had particularly liked.[72] But these essays I didn't know at all, nor that such collections existed, and that Osja Brik, with whom I was practically unacquainted, was connected to it. Lili Brik was Elsa's older sister. When I was a student at the Lazarev Institute, she was already too old for me; besides which, my parents would aggrevate me with her: "Look what marvelous compositions Lili writes; they give her such enraptured comments!" Later, when I told Lili about this, she laughed and said: "There was a teacher who was in love with me and helped me write them."

The second book was the first, censored edition of *The Backbone-Flute*, which had, however, the censored lines written in by hand. This too made a tremendous impression on me. I must say that my attitude toward Majakovskij changed step by step. *A Cloud in Trousers* astounded me. I recall how once I was at Bajdin's house one evening—he was already lying in bed— and I read him aloud *A Cloud in Trousers*, and he said: "Yes, this is a great poet."

Before *A Cloud in Trousers* I was disposed against Majakovskij; I considered him to be an Impressionist. I must say that I didn't react genuinely to his *Vladimir Majakovskij, a Tragedy*. This was a much better work, but it struck me as cheap Symbolism. At the time the only poet who existed for me was Xlebnikov. But I loved *A Cloud*; I knew it by heart, and later heard Majakovskij himself read it on numerous occasions.

Soon after these two little books landed in my hands, I went to Petrograd, in the middle of January, 1917. Elsa gave me a letter of introduction to Lili. Zhukovskij Street, where they lived, was not far from the train station, and when I arrived I went straight to them and ended up staying there for five days. They wouldn't let me leave. The only other thing I did was go to the University, to listen to Shaxmatov's lectures. In her letter Elsa had particularly asked that they make me read my translation of *A Cloud* into French. I read it, and they liked it a lot. Then Majakovskij came by, and I read it to him. He had me read it many times, and one time asked me to repeat my translation of the following lines from his poem:

> You entered
> brashly as "Take it or leave it!",
> tormenting the suede of your gloves,
> and said:
> "Know what?
> I'm getting married."

In French they read:

> Âpre, comme un mot de dédain,
> tu entras, Marie,
> et tu m'a dit,
> en tourmentant tes gants de daim:
> "Savez-vous,
> je me marie."[73]

"Wait a minute," said Majakovskij, "marie, marie, what is that?" I translated it for him literally. "Oh, so they're different words; that's good."

I then became extraordinarily good friends both with Majakovskij and with Brik. I had already heard the whole story from Elsa, that is in her version, of how Majakovskij was acquainted with Elsa, how her father was terribly opposed, how Lili was also opposed after she heard about it from her father, and how Elsa tried to reconcile Lili with the fact that she had such a friend and that he would be coming by, and Lili said: "Just as long as he doesn't read any poems."[74] But then, of course, he became one of the Briks' close circle. For a long time in Moscow I had in my hands Elsa's diary (it was later lost), in which she had written: "Roma has returned from Petersburg, and, unfortunately, he's also already one of the Briks'."

Elsa and I were drawn together very much by the French language. We had a teacher of French in common, a certain Mademoiselle Dache. She was the daughter of a French family that had come to live in Moscow. She grew up in Russia, it is true, studied at a French gymnasium, but spoke French without a burr, with a rolled "r." This same rolled "r" remained in both Elsa's and my French pronunciation. Grammont, by the way, considers that the correct, classical pronunciation is precisely with such a rolled "r."[75] And in Russia—partly in aristocratic circles, but not only there—it was considered in bad taste to imitate French pronunciation too much. People would say: "You should learn proper French, how to speak and write well, but remember that you're not monkeys, but Russians. Imitate the pronunciation, but not too much, so that it won't seem like you're trying to play at being French." And in both our pronunciations the rolled "r" was even stronger, since we hadn't heard the other "r," except perhaps when French writers or actors would come to visit Russia and we attended their performances. Thus, for example, I heard in childhood Verhaeren, Richepin, Sarah Bernhardt and others.

Because Mademoiselle Dache loved French literature and would give it to us to read, both of us also loved French literature, and there was always something connected with France in our relations. Often Elsa and I, speaking in Russian, would insert French into our conversation. No one ever thought that she would become a French writer, or that I would become linked one way or another to French science.

Sometimes we improvised jokes in French and once, in connection with something funny that had happened, I composed some impromptu verses, and Elsa played and sang them as a little chanson:

> C'est demain, mon escapade,
> vite—je quitte mes air malades.
> Un docteur, étant aimé des femmes,
> vite m'entraine vers des lieux infames.
> A la fin de la nuit,
> comme toujours, je m'ennuis
> et je n'ai plus rien à dire.
> Il m'agace avec son bête de rire . . .

and so on.

I must say that because of Mademoiselle Dache we had a strong French orientation, cultural, literary, and artistic. Who would one want to look at of the artists? Why, of course, the French!

In his early youth Mademoiselle Dache's father had taken part in the Franco-Prussian war, and she would often talk about the alleged German atrocities. Both Elsa and I had a strong pro-French and anti-German inclination. So that it was natural that she would meet and marry the French officer Triolet. Later Elsa wrote in a very interesting way about Mademoiselle Dache in her book *La mise en mots.*[76]

• • •

I returned from Petrograd to Moscow entirely convinced that a revolution would occur. Almost no one wanted to believe it. But it was completely clear from the mood in the universities.

In February I was again in Petrograd. Lili prepared a dinner with bliny; this was the founding of OPOJAZ. Present were Èjxenbaum, Shklovskij—who in general was at the Briks' quite often—Polivanov and Jakubinskij, who called me an "armored

Moscovite," since in Moscow there was a single linguistic orientation. About Petrograd we Moscovites would say: "Here
and there, wherever you want," or "As you wish." I recall that
Majakovskij, who was also present, asked me about Polivanov:
"And what does this one study?" "Chinese language."—"Aha,
he catches whales, I respect that." [A pun on *kitajskij* 'Chinese'
and *kit* 'whale'—tr.]

I had met Shklovskij earlier at the Briks', but I met the rest
for the first time that evening. Both Osja and Vitja began to
push me forward a lot.[77]

At the end of March or the beginning of April
Majakovskij, Burljuk and I went together to Petrograd.[78] This
was a few days before the arrival of Lenin. On the train there
were huge political arguments, and someone shouted "Down
with the War!" Majakovskij, in his stentorian voice, replied:
"Who is shouting 'Down with the War'? Former policemen,
who don't want to go to the front?" Later, when I told him this,
he winced.

The Provisional Government had organized days of Russo-
Finnish rapprochement. I ended up at the opening of an exhibition of Finnish art—of painting, architectural plans, and so
on—with Volodja and Osja. There were various welcoming
speeches, followed by a formal dinner.[79] At this reception I was
called upon to act as an interpreter between Gor´kij and a certain famous Finnish architect, who spoke French. The architect
was quite drunk, as was Gor´kij. In general quite a few people
were drunk.

The Finn said: "Tout le monde pense que vous êtes un
génie—génie—et moi je vous dis: vous êtes un imbécile.
Traduisez, mais traduisez éxactement! Non, non, non, vous ne
traduisez pas comme j'ai dit! Imbécile, comment se dit ça en
russe?" Such was the style of the conversation.[80]

Majakovskij was then called on to read. He read his own poems and then suddenly said: "Now I shall read the verses of my friend, the brilliant poet and scholar of verse." The verses were as follows:

> I myself will die when I feel like it,
> And enter in the list of voluntary victims
> My family name, name and patronymic
> And the day when I will be dead.
> I'll pay off all my debts at the stores,
> Purchase the latest almanac,
> And await my already-ordered coffin,
> Reading *A Cloud in Trousers*!

Osja was extremely embarrassed, since he did not consider his poetic activity to be a social fact.

Then a few of us went out; Osja was not among them. Lenin arrived, and Osja went to the station. When he returned later, he said: "He seems to be crazy, but he's very convincing."[81]

We went on to our favorite spots: Volodja, me, the artist Brodskij (who later became an official Soviet artist), and a certain Gur´jan, a relative of my neighbors in Moscow, a prominent attorney and a grand *bon vivant*. We went from place to place, and in the end Gur´jan invited us all to his place at around two in the morning. Various drinks and hors-d'oeuvres were served. Majakovskij and Brodskij decided to play pool. Pool was one of Majakovskij's weaknesses, or rather one of his strengths, since he played beautifully. They battled against one another with real verve. I lay on the couch and even took a snooze. Then they began to discuss where to go next, and someone said that in a few hours, at eight o'clock, Lenin would be speaking at Kshesinskaja's Palace. "Let's go listen to him!" And so we went. There were torn curtains. Someone sat on a piano. There was a mixture of chairs and complete chaos.

There was a large crowd, and quite a few sailors. Everyone was waiting. And when finally the speaker was announced, it wasn't Lenin but Zinov´ev. We got bored and finally left.[82]

During this or my previous visit, Majakovskij said to me: "Come on, you want to take a ride?" I said yes. He absolutely loved to go in a fast cab in a circle past the University and the Academy, on the Strelka. He said: "But let's divide the fare in half." "Fine," I said, "but I don't have any cash on me."—"You give me your word?"—"Yes."—"'Til our next meeting." We sat in the cab, and he started reading me some verses that he had just written: "If I were as little as the Great Ocean..."[83] When we met at the Briks' the next time, I tried to give him the money, but he said "What's this?"—"I did give you my word."—"You're crazy!"

• • •

Before my arrival in Petrograd in the middle of January I hadn't met with Lili at all, and there was a very long interval from my childhood until the time I began seeing Elsa again. Elsa and I had become particularly close in 1916. But I only began to know Lili again when I happened to end up in their literary circle (one could hardly call it a salon).

There were relatively few people there, strictly speaking, people who revolved around Osja's latest interests. I don't even know how Osja became a Formalist, why he became interested in sound repetitions and the like.[84] I was quite astonished when Elsa showed me the collection on the theory of poetic language; I thought to myself: here are people who are doing what needs to be done!

Whenever I hadn't been at the Briks' for a while, I would ask, jokingly: "Tell me, what is one supposed to talk about at the Briks' these days, and what is forbidden? What is considered correct and what—superstitious?" There was a pretty definite mood at their place, a sort of dogma of its own.

When I came alone to Petrograd, I would stay at the Briks'. They had a very crowded apartment. They lived there because Brik was a deserter from the army, and they couldn't move into another apartment, since it would have to be registered with the police. So I would sleep on the divan in a room more like a passage-way, which Osja used as his study. It was all extraordinarily Bohemian. There was a table laid all day, where there was kolbasa, bread, cheese, and tea all the time. A samovar would be brought in. Whoever wanted to talk would come in. It was quite unique, something completely unlike anything else I'd ever seen. Interesting pictures hung on the walls. And there was a huge sheet of paper that took up a whole wall, where all of the guests would write something for Lili. I recall that there was one caricature of Lili and Osja, who was sitting and working, with the inscription: "Lili revolves around Osja."

At the time I happened to be around, Kuzmin would come by often to play cards. Kuzmin was most amusing in company; he sang well and played on the piano. It was at the time that he wrote two poems for Lili, which were published in a separate edition.[85]

Lili would say: "It's pleasant to have Kuzmin over; he sings his little songs and always has something amusing to relate. But, you know, if you want to have someone over and because of that are forced to invite his unpleasant wife, *that's* not good. And with Kuzmin one has to invite Jurkun." Kuzmin was having a real affair with Jurkun.[86]

And Kuzmin would say to me: "How is it, Romochka, that you love Elsa so; after all, she looks so much like a woman!"

I also saw Mandel´shtam there, but he came only on business.

There was also an artist, Kozlinskij,[87] and a certain man whom Elsa was quite fascinated with, Gurvic-Gurskij. He was a very talented engineer, with a great knowledge of art and literature.[88]

Natan Al´tman would also drop by. They were playing cards *bon ami* or "cheaps," as they called it, so as not to have to pay right away. Al´tman didn't have any money on him, so when he lost, they would put pledges into play along with the cash. Volodja quipped: "Al´tman's governesses are in play."

They played cards a lot. Majakovskij played fantastically, but was terribly nervous during the game. He would win; he was able to do so particularly at poker, a psychological game. He would clean out his opponent often. But afterwards—I was a witness to this on several occasions when he stayed at my place overnight in Moscow—he would walk up and down the room weeping, so overwrought were his nerves.[89]

Moreover, he was terribly afraid of Lili. She was against the fact that he played so often and with such animation. I even wrote some humorous verses on this score—not about poker, but about chemin de fer—which he also played and sometimes took terrible losses at, not even reckoning up how much he had lost:

> With Volodja we shuffled along timidly
> Wondering whether we'd get it hot
> From Lili, from Lili, from Lili . . .

and so on. I liked to play poker more than chemin de fer. Mainly it was Volodja who taught me how. But he didn't insult me in the process. Once we were playing chemin at the premises of the Linguistic Circle and he came up with the lines: "It's time, my friend, to drop by the Circle./ Let's play at *vikzhel'* for a change." *Vikzhel'* was the abbreviation for the All-Russian Executive Committee of Railroad Workers, and the invented verb *vikzhel'nut'* meant to play chemin de fer.[90] I won and he lost, then he took me not only for what I'd won, but for a rather large sum on top of that, which I paid, even though my financial means at the time were extremely limited. He said to me: "Listen, I can't give you the money back, but I'll invite you to live together with us for the entire summer." So we ended up in Pushkino.[91]

At the time it still hadn't been decided that we would go to Pushkino. The first plan, as I recall, was totally wild and fantastic—Voronezh; this is mentioned in the game of bouts-rimés we played.[92] We thought to go, the four of us—Lili and Osja, Volodja and me. Then we went to Voskresenskoe, where I knew people. But when we arrived there, it turned out that almost the whole village had died of spotted typhus. Majakovskij became terribly frightened. Then we took a walk in the woods. He didn't want to get near anyone. We spent the whole time playing different card games, using our fingers instead of cards.

• • •

By education Brik was a lawyer.[93] He was quite unique. For his doctoral thesis he wanted to write about the sociology and juridical status of prostitutes and would frequent the boulevards. All the prostitutes there knew him, and he always defended them, for free, in all their affairs, in their confrontations with the police and so on. They called him "the whore's papa" or something of the sort; I won't vouch for the word. They were very impressed that he wasn't interested in them,

that he never wanted anything from them. He did it all purely in a friendly, comradely way.

Osja knew how to sit and work, and no one bothered him.
When I first landed there, he was terribly carried away by
poetry and didn't want to hear about anything else. He studied
metrics and poetics fanatically. He arrived at amazing ideas—
about Benediktov, about Gogol's "The Nose." Later, in the
period when he began to depart from poetics and studied the
sociology of art, he had, for example, a marvelous interpretation of Zola's novel *L'Œuvre* as an artist's testament, which he
compared with the diaries and letters of the Russian Itinerant
artists.[94]

He had one ability which was exceptional. He knew
Ancient Greek a little. Suddenly he arrived at some sort of
conclusions about Greek verse and invited Rumer to come
by.[95] The latter heard him out and said: "It's amazing: this is
the latest discovery, which was only recently made." For Brik
all of this was like doing crossword puzzles.

Osja was terribly ironic, but not ironic in a mean way; he'd
just smoke and talk. I recall how once, in 1918, he, Lili, and
Volodja were sitting in my rather cramped room, and
Majakovskij was reading the still unfinished draft of *Mystery-
Bouffe*. After the reading he started to say that he didn't know
whether people would understand that it was genuine revolutionary art. Osja said: "You think that this is communist art,
right? 'You are the first to have entry into my heavenly king-
dom. . . .' You think that *that's* a theme?" The line was gone by
the second version.

Brik was one of the wittiest people I have ever known. And
he was witty for the fact that no one ever saw him laugh. He
always spoke in complete earnest. Once in Berlin I was talking
with Brik about Shklovskij's recently published book, *Zoo*.

Brik said: "Vitja's a strange fellow. He hasn't studied grammar. He doesn't know there there are words that are inanimate in gender, and that VCIK [The All-Russian Central Executive Committee] is an inanimate noun. Inanimate objects don't have a sense of humor, so one can't make jokes with VCIK."[96]

Brik didn't do a lot that he might have done. It's amazing, but he had no ambition. He wasn't even interested in finishing his own works. But, on the other hand, he generously shared his ideas. And he very much valued a person's ability to work, as well as a person's talent; this is the way he related to the members of the Moscow Linguistic Circle. He liked people who came up with unexpected things. He liked me a lot in general, but when I came to him and told him that I was in danger of being considered a deserter, he answered: "You're not the first, nor the last." And he didn't do a thing for me.

Brik joined the Cheka soon after my departure.[97] It was from Bogatyrev, who visited me in Prague in December 1921, that I learned Brik was in the Cheka. And he told me that Pasternak, who often visited the Briks, had said to him: "Still, it's become rather terrifying. You come in, and Lili says: 'Wait a while, we'll have dinner as soon as Osja comes back from the Cheka.'" At the end of 1922 I met the Briks in Berlin. Osja said to me: "Now there's an institution where a man loses his sentimentality," and began relating to me several rather bloody episodes. This was the first time he made a rather repulsive impression on me. Working in the Cheka had ruined him.

• • •

When Majakovskij began writing the poem *Man*, in the spring of 1917, he would say to me: "This will be a man, but not a man of the Andreev type, but a simple man, who drinks tea, takes walks on the street . . . . It's just about such a man that I will write a genuine poem."

Once Majakovskij read me an excerpt from the section "Majakovskij in Heaven" or something quite near to it in the poem. "The lines are good, aren't they?" The lines were indeed remarkable. "Yes, but they don't fit." They did destroy the effect of the whole, and he deleted them.

He practically didn't write anything down and threw everything away. If at the time I had had an archival relation to things, it would have been enough for me to simply ask the maid to bring me whatever he threw away in the wastebasket, and it would be a rare collection today. By chance I preserved a first-draft version of *150,000,000*; I left at the time for Revel´, and asked him to give it to me. He gave it to me, not only as a keepsake or to show to people, but because, as he put it, "they won't publish it here."

On February 2, 1918 Majakovskij gave a public reading of *Man* at the Polytechnical Museum. I was with Elsa. I had never heard Majakovskij give such a reading. He was very agitated, and wanted to convey everything and read several sections in an amazing way, for example:

> A laundry.
> Laundresses.
> Many and wet . . .

The lines "Drugist! Drugist!" sounded very much like Blok.[98] Nothing had ever produced such a strong impression on me as this.

He said that he would never again sell his works and simply give away his books. He asked Andrei Belyj, who had been at his previous reading at the poet Amari's, to speak.[99] Belyj spoke with great enthusiasm about the fact that after a long,

long interval there was a great Russian narrative poem, and that he understood that this was genuine poetry and that there were no such boundaries as Futurism, Symbolism, etc., but only *poetry*.[100]

• • •

Once, soon after the October Revolution, I was visiting Elsa at her apartment on a street near Pjatnickaja.[101] I suggested we go to the Cafe of Poets.[102] At the time it was still difficult to get around Moscow at night, but we went anyway. Volodja was very pleased to see us. He read "Our March," "Left March," and "An Ode to the Revolution." I didn't like "An Ode to Revolution" at all, with its abundance of dry rhetoric, which showed even in the way he read it.

The public was quite diverse. There were actually former members of the bourgeoisie, who listened to such lines as "Eat your pineapple. Chew on your grouse. Your last day has come, bourgeois!" There were people off the street, who hadn't ever even heard of poetry. There were interested young people. At the time squatters had already appeared, for the most part anarchists, who had seized houses and apartments. At the reading a certain anarchist in some sort of strange para-military uniform suddenly spoke. He said: "Here you've read all sorts of poems, but now I'll tell you how I got married." And he read, with excellent fairy-tale technique, the technique of a village storyteller, a famous *lubok* text, which exists in various versions from the eighteenth century—a mocking poem about a pathetic bridegroom and his pathetic, ugly, poor, repulsive wife. I was still a folklorist at heart, so I went up to him and asked: "I'd like very much to write down what you just narrated to us so magnificently."—"No, I came here just

to have a rest and make merry. Drop by my place sometime."—"Where is it?—"It's called the House of Instant
Socialists."[103] I planned to go, but somehow never got around
to it. Soon afterwards they dispersed the anarchists.[104]

I was sometimes asked to read. I read my translations of
Majakovskij into French—*A Cloud in Trousers* and "Our
March." Majakovskij would read in Russian, and I in French:
"Barbouillons dans les vagues du second déluge/ l'huile des
villes de l'univers. . . ."[105] Later I read my translation of
Majakovskij's poem "They Don't Understand a Thing" into
Old Church Slavonic.[106]

Toward the end of the evening, when there were only a relatively few people left, Chekists suddenly came in to verify
people's papers, to find out what sort of people were there.
Whether the document I had was insufficient, or whether I
had no documents at all, I don't recall, but they were beginning
to pester me, when two people intervened on my behalf: on the
one hand Kamenskij, who said, "He's one of ours, he works
with us," and on the other hand, quite strongly and insistent-
ly, "the Futurist of life" Vladimir Gol´cshmidt. So they left me
alone. Gol´cshmidt was a terrific strongman and would break
boards over his head at the Cafe of Poets.[107]

• • •

On May Day, 1918, I was supposed to read at the Cafe of
Poets, where there were very interesting decorations by
Jakulov, but I had to go away somewhere, and someone read
my French translations in my place.[108] Nejshtadt read his
German translations and my Old Church Slavonic translation,
which he later printed with mistakes, having totally mixed up
the text.[109] The actress Poplavskaja, who, if I'm not mistaken,

was attracted to Xlebnikov, also read some of my French translations.[110]

Majakovskij rarely appeared at the Cafe Pittoresque. Once I was sitting there with Shklovskij. Esenin, whom I did not know personally, came up to us. Shklovskij introduced us. "Oh, so it's you, Jakobson . . . Majakovskij, Xlebnikov. . . . Understand, the essence of poetry is not in rhymes, nor in the verse. It is there so that the eyes can be seen, and so that something can be seen in the eyes."

David Burljuk in the spring of 1918 lived in one of the anarchist houses; there were lots of cases then of people moving into anarchist houses. These were private residences of aristocrats or simply wealthy people that had been seized and plundered. Volodja told me that Burljuk used some sort of porcelain or crystal from these houses. It had been noticed, but he hid it and carried it all off. Moroever, he had brothers who were serving in the White Army. His brother Nikolai had either died fighting in the White Army or had fallen into the hands of the Reds and been shot; one didn't talk about him.[111]

• • •

Majakovskij was very jealous because of Lili's attachment to a man named Jacques.[112] Jacques was a real swashbuckler, quite intelligent and cultured in his own way, a fast liver and a squanderer. Once, shortly before the February Revolution, I arranged a large party at my mother's house. There were various officers, generals, and, in particular, Volodja, Vitja and Osja. It all had an absolutely dissolute, pre-revolutionary character. Jacques begin teasing me for flirting with his aunt, who was a young woman. I said jokingly: "How dare you say this about an honorable woman!" And he replied, "Who dares to call my aunt an honorable woman?!"

After the Revolution Jacques was on very friendly terms with Gor´kij for a certain time. He was a person who was always ready to be of help. Once Volodja happened to meet Jacques on the street in the company of Gor´kij. They started bantering with one another, and ended up in some sort of fight. After this Gor´kij conceived a terrible dislike for Majakovskij.[113] At one time Gor´kij had been Majakovskij's protector, and Majakovskij had admired Gor´kij greatly. Osja said to me: "Volodja thought that his *War and the World* was a real accomplishment, but he took a lot of undigested phrases from Gor´kij. Gor´kij had made a tremendous impression on him, that suddenly someone could talk in such a way about the War."

Later Majakovskij had a long enmity toward Gor´kij. I don't know a single person about whom he would speak in a more inimical way than about Gor´kij. And I must say, the same applied to Gor´kij. He spoke with me several times about his attitude toward Majakovskij. Gor´kij very much wanted me to publish a critique of Majakovskij in his journal *Beseda*, and relayed the request through Xodasevich.[114]

Majakovskij despised Gor´kij, and this became particularly evident to me twice. Once, in the spring of 1919, Majakovskij had won at cards, and I went with him to have coffee and cakes at a private, quasi-legal cafe in Kamergerskij Lane. I was sitting at one table with Volodja; Bljumkin sat at the next table. We struck up a conversation, and Volodja suggested to Bljumkin that they organize an evening and speak out against Gor´kij. Suddenly Chekists came in to verify people's papers. They came up to Bljumkin, and he refused to show them his documents. When they started pressing him, he said: "Leave

me alone, or I'll shoot!"—"What do you mean, shoot?"—
"Well, just like I shot Mirbach!" They got confused, and one
of them went to call to find out what to do. Bljumkin got up,
went up to the one standing by the door, threatened him,
brandishing his revolver, pushed him aside, and left.[115]

Bljumkin was an educated man. He talked with me at the
time about the *Avesta*. He had studied ancient Iranian languages and had an interest in philology.

The second time was in my apartment in Prague [in 1927],
when I invited Majakovskij and Antonov-Ovseenko over for
bliny.[116] He read his poems, in particular one about Gor´kij.
Antonov-Ovseenko started defending Gor´kij energetically.
Then Volodja said: "Fine, but just let him come back. What's
he sitting abroad for?" And he began speaking bitterly about
the fact that Gor´kij was, in general, an amoral phenomenon.

• • •

When the "King of Poets" was chosen, I was on the jury.
Majakovskij had proposed me. We didn't actually do anything
but count the votes. Majakovskij read various poems, but it
was clear that the audience preferred Severjanin. The mood
was such that people wanted a little every-day joy in life.
When the vote was counted and Severjanin won, Burljuk
stood up with his lorgnette and said: "I declare the present
meeting to be dismissed."[117]

• • •

Majakovskij and I worked on his "Soviet Alphabet" together.
When he had the first line of a couplet, but the second would-
n't come to him, he would say: "I'll pay you so much, if you can

think up a good one!" There are quite a few of our joint verses there.

It amused him a lot. There existed a school-boys' past-time—indecent alphabets, and several of these verses recall them somewhat. Some of these alphabets existed in manuscript form and even were sold underground. The association was obvious, and for this reason Majakovskij was attacked terribly for his "Alphabet."

One typist from a good family, whom he asked to type it up in some sort of office where she worked, refused with tears in her eyes to type such indecencies as:

> Wilson's more important than other birds.
> He'll stick a feather up her butt.

This was quite typical for these indecent alphabets. So that, when she became offended, it was obvious that she knew them.[118]

I often saw Majakovskij drawing posters for ROSTA. Once I even helped him with some sort of rhyme.[119] But the work didn't interest him much. He tried to do it in a business-like way. I never spoke with him about whether he considered the work to be serious or simply hack-work. It never went any-where, was never published, it was only displayed in shop win-dows! And the majority of the puns were too difficult to understand. It was above all a hack-work source of earning some money.[120]

The agitational poems were already something else; they were more like a preparation for a future time. But Majakovskij thought all along that he would return to genuine work.

In his poetry there are many elements of parody. Compare, for example, "Drink Van Houten's cocoa!" in *A Cloud in Trousers* with the later lines "Where's strength?—In this cocoa." This is practically a verbatim repetition, a complete parody, just as *The Bedbug* was a total parody of *About That*.[121] He often lost his head, didn't really know what to write or how to write. If you take, for example, Esenin's poetry, it is poetry to *himself*!

• • •

In the summer of 1918 I lived in the countryside close to Voskresenskoe, where I was busy writing. When I came to Moscow, I learned that the staff at the People's Commissariat of Foreign Affairs were looking for me.

Negotiations were going on between the R.S.F.S.R. and Skoropadsky's Ukraine.[122] Rakovskij was heading the negotiations.[123] The chief question was that of the borders.[124] The Ukrainians proposed basing them on the linguistic boundaries established by Russian scholars, and presented the map of the Moscow Dialectological Commission, where a series of transitional dialects were described, most of the territories of which would be assigned to the Ukraine.

They sought out the authors, of whom there were three: Ushakov, Durnovo, and Sokolov. But in view of the fact that it was summer, none of them were in Moscow. Then Bogdanov, who was Secretary of the Ethnographic Division of the Rumjancev Museum, pointed me out, since I was also a member of the Dialectological Commission. They sought me out and asked: "What actually are these borders?" I answered that they were hardly unquestionable, that they represented a working hypothesis, that one should approach the question not from an historical point of view, but should attempt to establish where these transitional dialects related, and that one could easily challenge the results. "Can you write all this down for us?" I said that I could. "Can you do it quickly?" I answered, "Today."—"But could you add the signature of one of the authors?" I told them that Ushakov lived in the Podolsk District, which was rather far away. "We'll give you a car and chauffeur, drive out to him!"

I went. Ushakov and I discussed the entire matter. It turned out that the map actually did contain mistakes and inaccuracies and that it was impossible to formulate the borders on the basis of it. We composed a letter together. I stayed at his place overnight, and in the morning the car took me back to Moscow.

This time I was received by Vladimir Friche, who was, it seems, a Deputy Commissar.[125] He thanked me warmly and offered to pay me an honorarium for my work. I told him that I didn't need any money, but that my father was sick and I had to send my parents abroad. He immediately wrote out a passport for them and they left soon after.

• • •

I advised my parents to go to Sweden, but instead they lingered in Riga. Then the Red Army entered Riga, and they sent me a desparate telegram asking me to come to save them.

For part of the journey I had to travel in a wagon crammed with Red Army soldiers, among whom some were actually dying. A louse from one of them jumped on me, and in exactly thirteen days I came down with spotted typhus. This kept me in Riga, even though I wanted to return to Moscow, where I was an advanced graduate student at Moscow University preparing for a career as a professor.

My father and brother moved into a different apartment, while my mother stayed in this one, though she didn't usually come into the room where I was lying, since she was afraid of being infected. I had a local nurse, who we paid. I lay for three weeks in total delirium. Only a year later did I come back to my senses. It was only with great difficulty that I began to recall what was real and what I had seen in my delirium.

Suddenly three Latvian Chekists with rifles came to search the place—two men and a woman—to clarify how it was that bourgeois people lived in the apartment. It was explained to them that a sick man was lying there. They didn't believe it. They entered. I jumped up on the bed when I saw them and announced deliriously: "In the name of the People's Commissar I order all three be subjected to the highest punishment!" They became frightened and demanded my documents. The document had been signed by Trockaja, and they left.[126] It was one of the tricks by which my life was saved.

This was in early spring of 1919. After I had recuperated, I left for Moscow in the second half of March, still so weak from my illness that I couldn't even make it up the steps of the train.

In Moscow I entered the Division of Visual Arts (IZO), where I worked under Brik. Osja related to my work in a very obliging way. If I considered the work I was doing at home to be more important, if I missed two or three days at work, he didn't object. My title was "scholarly secretary," and I helped out in various publishing matters.

The literary-publishing section of IZO was supposed to publish an encyclopedia.[127] The head of the section was Kandinskij; Shevchenko[128] worked there, as did the Italian Franchetti, who later emigrated to Italy.[129] Brik and I took part in the editorial conferences, when the section's publications, in particular, this encyclopedia, were discussed. Several people related to it quite hotly—Kandinskij had just written his autobiography,[130] and many had written various articles. But Brik, with characteristic venomousness, said, when they showed him the list of who would write about what: "This I understand— Byzantine art, specialist on Byzantine art. The Fifteenth Century—a specialist on the fifteenth century; that's harder to understand, but alright. But here, what does this mean: 'Articles beginning with the letter B'? What sort of specialist is that? Aha, I get it—a specialist at copying from the Brokhaus and Efron Encyclopedia. . . ."

The editorial board asked me to do an article for the encyclopedia, and I proposed to them an article and even wrote a note with the content: "Artistic semantics." Everyone was very pleased except for Kandinskij: "What is it? It's incomprehensible!" Kandinskij was a kind man in his own way, cultured, a bit of an eclectic despite all of his innovativeness, a combination of a German and Russian, which didn't go together all that well. But he was a talented man.

The journal *Art of the Commune* was already coming out in Petrograd,[131] and it was decided that a newspaper should be published in Moscow. They had no editor, and I brought them an editor, Kostja Umanskij, who was still a boy with peach-fuzz on his cheeks. But he set to work and made a fine job of editing the paper. He was a very capable person and later published a book in German on avant-garde art, not a bad book for the time.[132] After that he became a diplomat and was the first Soviet ambassador to Mexico.

I left IZO quite soon, in August 1919.

· · ·

After my return from Riga I worked with Xlebnikov. Together we were preparing a two-volume edition of his works.[133] He received me very warmly, and we saw a lot of one another.

When we were alone he talked a lot, though for the most part he was laconic. And he had interesting things to say, for example, how phrases constructed without the slightest humor and without the slightest ironic intention, would become mocking expressions, such as, "the Senate made clear." It is an actual expression, but later "made clear" acquired the meaning that "it would have been better to obfuscate." He cited several such examples.

He would speak, jumping from topic to topic. He was very happy that I was preparing his book, because he knew my attitude toward him and he knew that I had a good memory.

The so-called "Testament of Xlebnikov" is not a testament at all, but merely a list, which we composed together, of what he wanted to be included in the volume. We decided that he should write a few words about himself. I suggested calling this preface "Svojasi" ['My Place']. He liked the idea a lot. For a time I wavered: perhaps instead of "Svojasi," it should be "Mojami" ['My Me'], but the latter didn't sound as good.[134]

Xlebnikov was sharply critical of Burljuk's editions of his writings. He said that his edition of *Creations* was totally corrupted, and often became indignant over the fact that he published things that were not at all meant for publication, in particular the lines: "Eternity is my pot / eternity's a swat / I love the boredom of intestines / I call fate piss. . . ."[135] And he would correct a great deal, both in manuscript and in printed texts. He was against Burljuk's chronology, which was fantastic, but it didn't bother him that much; what bothered him for the most part were the texts and the separate publication of fragments that belonged together.

It was very interesting working with him on this book. We met often. I was at the Briks' constantly, and occasionally Xlebnikov would visit me. Once we were far from the center, at one of the small exhibits that IZO had put on, an exhibit of the works of Gumilina.[136] We spoke about painting; it was a very interesting conversation. Then we went to my place on the Lubjanskij Thruway. I invited him to come upstairs. We continued talking, but I suddenly felt completely exhausted, lay down and fell asleep. (This was shortly after I had contracted spotted typhus.) When I woke up, he was already gone.

This was our last meeting. He soon left town.[137] One could never predict his movements. He would suddenly feel like going off somewhere; he had a nomadic spirit. If he had not left then, it's possible that we might have finished this two-volume collection. It was impossible to explain. It wasn't that he was starving; they fed him at the Briks', after all. Perhaps Lili said something to him that insulted him; that would happen. . . . He was a very difficult person to have as a guest.

My introduction to Xlebnikov's works was called "Approaches to Xlebnikov"; it was later published in Prague under the title *The Newest Russian Poetry*.[138] I read it at the Briks' in May of 1919, at the first meeting of the Moscow Linguistic Circle since the October Revolution.[139] Xlebnikov was not in Moscow; he had already left for the South. Majakovskij was present and took part in the discussion. Lili was late for some reason or other and asked, "How was it?" and Majakovskij answered with some warm words.

At the time Xlebnikov and I were on very friendly terms. It was clear that I was closer to him than the Briks were. He was somewhat intimidated by them and kept himself apart.

Xlebnikov's relations with Majakovskij were quite complex. Majakovskij spoke with him in a somewhat affectedly polite way, very respectfully, but at the same time kept him at a distance. He related to him in a strained way, but at the same time was delighted by him. All of this was very complicated. There is actually a very strong influence of Xlebnikov on Majakovskij, but there is also a very strong influence of Majakovskij on Xlebnikov. They were quite different. I think that Majakovskij was won over by certain small fragments in Xlebnikov that were unusually unified and strong. But from Xlebnikov I never heard a thing about Majakovskij, or at any rate I don't recall it.

I'll never forget how, when I was working on Xlebnikov's long poems, there was lying on the table a page of the manuscript with the fragment: "From the beehive of the street / Bullets like bees. / The chairs shake. . . ."[140] Volodja read it and said: "If only I could write like Vitja . . . ."

I reminded him of this once, and reminded him in a cruel way. I was very angry with him over the fact that he did not publish Xlebnikov at a time when he could have done so and had received money for that purpose.[141] Not only did he not publish him, he even wrote the phrase: "Paper for the living!"[142] He replied: "I never could have said anything of the sort. If I had said it, I would have thought so, and if I thought so, I would have stopped writing poetry." This was in Berlin, when I had to make arrangements to locate Xlebnikov's missing manuscripts. It was an idiotic story, which, of course, tore Majakovskij apart and made him terribly bitter. He didn't recall what had happened to the manuscripts and knew nothing about it. As a matter of fact, he had absolutely nothing to do with it. The story goes as follows.

I was afraid for Xlebnikov's manuscripts. After my parents' departure, their apartment was given over to the Moscow Linguistic Circle. There were boxes with the publications of the Circle, various book shelves, and my father's fireproof safe, which went unused. It was into this safe that I put all the manuscripts. There were other things there as well, in particular, my own manuscripts.

After Xlebnikov's death I received a letter from the artist Miturich with the request to help him find out what Majakovskij had done with Xlebnikov's manuscripts. I was totally perplexed. I knew that Majakovskij had nothing whatever to do with it. He never had them in his hands, except for the incident I just mentioned, when he simply read them on the spot. I immediately wrote from Prague to my friends in the Circle, in particular Buslaev, to whom I had given the key to the safe. He was unable to find the key. Then I informed him that I wanted him to open the safe somehow; it didn't matter to me whether it was destroyed in the process. He wrote me that this would cost a lot of money. I answered that I would pay for everything and sent the money somehow. They opened the safe and found the manuscripts.[143] They had all been preserved. What had been lost, since I had not put them in safe, were my notebooks with Xlebnikov's works in which he had made corrections by hand or filled in various blanks.

There was never an instance when Xlebnikov would speak sharply about someone. He was very restrained and very much, so to speak, a loner. He was a distracted man, a sort of homeless eccentric in the extreme.

In general people were delighted by Xlebnikov; they understood that he was a great poet. But at the Briks' at the time one could never say that Xlebnikov was greater than Majakovskij. (But then again, how can one possibly say such things?) For me the title of Burljuk's lecture, "Pushkin and Xlebnikov," was entirely natural.[144] I accepted him completely and entirely: I think people have still not recognized him genuinely, that he will be discovered in the future. In order for that to happen, what is needed is a good edition of his works; it is impossible to read him in Stepanov's edition. Kruchenyx understood him profoundly, though on the other hand he took a lot on faith:

"Do you really like 'A Vila and a Wood Goblin'? It simply is."

Xlebnikov meant the most to Aseev, who was in rapture over his verse. But he was completely alien to Pasternak; I heard this from him more than once. Pasternak said that he simply did not understand Xlebnikov at all.

• • •

Majakovskij liked Pasternak a lot, whereas my attitude toward the early Pasternak was rather ambivalent: an interesting poet, but of a completely different caliber. I remember how Volodja read, with great enthusiasm, the poem "I was born yesterday. I don't respect myself . . ." from the collection *Above the Barriers.* He knew many of the poems from *Above the Barriers* by heart and read them aloud with enthusiasm, but it was *My Sister Life* that made the greatest impression on him.

Pasternak had already read a whole series of poems from this collection to Majakovskij, and once Majakovskij invited him to the Briks' to give a reading. There was a dinner with drinks, a real dinner, almost ceremonial, which at the time was a rarity. Besides the Briks and Pasternak, Majakovskij and I were present.

He read, with unbelievable animation, the entire cycle *My Sister Life,* from the first page to the last. It produced a completely flabbergasting impression, especially "About These Verses," as well as all the swaying, windy poems, such as "In the mirror there is a steaming cup of cocoa," and in particular, "My Sister Life" itself. Everyone received it enthusiastically.[145]

From that moment on I valued Pasternak very much. Trubetzkoy blamed me for considering him a great poet. He had been a schoolmate of Pasternak at the university and considered him a second-rate poet. But nevertheless I wrote, being completely convinced of it, that the two genuine poets, from an historical point of view, were Xlebnikov and Majakovskij. Later I added the names of Pasternak, Mandel´shtam, and Aseev.[146]

After this reading Osja said to me: "The funniest thing is that Pasternak thinks that he's a philosopher, while, actually, from a philosophical point of view it's all nonsense. These are great poems, but philosophically speaking, both his and Volodja's poems aren't worth anything." In general, Brik thought that poets weren't very intelligent: "Take a look at Pushkin's letters to his wife; a porter writes more interesting letters to his wife. Volodja writes the same sort of letters to Lilichka that Pushkin wrote to his wife. It's complete vulgarity, since everything genuine went into the poems."

I recall how after a meeting of IMO, we were walking with Malkin along one of the Moscow boulevards.[147] Volodja asked Pasternak quite ironically in reference to me: "Roma doesn't understand why for him this is verse, whereas for me it's simply prose: 'Holy server of the world, redeemer of all sins, the sun in your palm is on my head.' Where's the rhyme?"[148] And Pasternak, to my amazement, said: "For me poems without rhyme are nonexistent." It was striking how they both defended this proposition before me in detail. Earlier such a concept could not be found in Russia, not even in Blok.

Pasternak was very talkative, even chatty. He was quite vain, but at the same time was full of his own grief. He lived by it, and it could be quite exhausting. He was constantly on edge, but completely sincere and open: "What will come of this? Whose fault is it? What should we do?" He was a very lively person, but also a person who was a bundle of nerves, no matter in what area—in music, in relation to women, in relation to poetry, in relation to events, in relation to the duty of a poet.

We did not carry on a correspondence. But when I sent him my article about him,[149] I received a letter from him that was forty pages in length. It perished; when I left Czechoslovakia in 1939, I gave it to one of my students, who destroyed it out of fear. In this letter Pasternak spoke of himself, of his life, and about the fact that my article produced an enormous impression on him, that he saw that he was understood. He discusses this in his letter to Josef Hora. He also wrote about what an incredible experience it was for him to see his poems, which Hora had translated, and his prose, which my wife had translated, in another Slavic language.[150] They were not the same, yet not different. For him it was a moment when he was unable to break away from his earlier poems and could not move on to something new. These Czech translations opened up for him that possibility, since they showed him that such a shift was possible.

Later in the same letter he wrote: "You know, Roman Osipovich, I come more and more to the conviction that it is among us, and not only among us, now, and perhaps not only now, that the life of the poet—and perhaps not just the poet—has become unwanted."[151] That is a remarkable phrase.

Pasternak liked the fact that I wasn't a poet, but a linguist who was close to poetry—which, actually, is what also created my closeness to poets, rather than to linguists. I was particularly close to the Russian poets—Majakovskij, Xlebnikov, Pasternak, Aseev, and Kruchenyx—though I never related to the last as a poet; we corresponded as two theoreticians, two "transrational" theoreticians. Later I was close to the Czech poets—Nezval, Seifert, and Vančura, partly to Biebl,[152] and in Poland—to Julian Tuwim and Wierzyński; in France—to Aragon.[153]

• • •

My parents lived on the third floor of Staxeev's house (no. 3) on Lubjanskij Thruway. I lived in the same house on the floor above, where I rented a room in the apartment of our friends, Doctor Gur´jan and his family,154 though I would have meals at my parents' when they were still in Moscow. When they left, during the summer of 1918, I settled various of my linguist friends in their apartment, for example, Afremov and his family.155 The dining room was left as it was, with the same furniture, only various bookshelves were added for the Moscow Linguistic Circle, and this became the premises of the Circle.

It was there that I hid Viktor Shklovskij, when they were hard on his heels. He was a left-wing Socialist Revolutionary (SR) and had been blowing up bridges. I left him on the couch and said: "If anyone comes here, pretend that you're a piece of paper and rustle!" He actually quoted this in his book *A Sentimental Journey,* as the words of an "archivist."156 He tried to leave and save himself, and noticed somewhere that they were looking for him. At the time the Church of Christ the Saviour had not yet been destroyed, and there were thick bushes all around it. He had hidden and slept there, and came to me all covered in prickles.157 Then he appeared and told me that he had managed to get from someone documents under the name Golotkov, but that he had to type in answers to various points. He did this on my typewriter, and I was struck by his quick-wittedness: he looked at the date given on the paper and correspondingly wrote in the old orthography, since at that time the new orthography was still not wide-spread. Then he got ready to go, already as Golotkov, stripped naked, made up his face, shaved his head, and was completely changed in appearance.158 At the time my teacher, Professor Nikolaj Nikolaevich Durnovo, happened to drop by to see me. Seeing a naked man who was shaving and making himself up, he

didn't say anything—one didn't ask questions in those days—
and was hardly surprised. He started talking to me about his
discoveries in some Old Russian manuscripts (I think he mentioned the Ostromir Bible). But suddenly he did become surprised: the guy standing there naked made various astute
philological observations.

Shklovskij understood that he wouldn't be able to get too
far, but he managed to drop by the apartment of Larissa
Reisner, who knew him. He explained to her that he would be
captured and that would be the end of him. Having made him
promise that he would behave himself, she left him at her
place, and herself went to get him a document, signed, if I'm
not mistaken, by Trockij, stating "whoever permits himself to
lay hands on the carrier of this document will be punished."
This is how he got out of his situation.[159]

In 1922, when Shklovskij came under suspicion and was to
have been arrested in connection with the trial of the Socialist
Revolutionaries, he fled to Finland.[160] While he was in
Finland, there were various unpleasantries, and he had to
prove that he was not a Bolshevik. He wrote to Repin, asking
him to help him out. Repin replied with a letter that I kept.
(When Shklovskij later returned to Moscow, he left it with
me, and I gave it to the Slavic Library in Prague [Slovanská
knihovna, the entire collection of which was seized by the
Russians after the war].) The letter was brief, written in
Repin's characteristic large script: "How could I forget you? I
liked you a lot; your features reminded me of Socrates. [I am
not sure now whether it was Socrates or someone else.] But
you write, asking that I certify that you are not a Bolshevik,
and you write the letter in the Bolshevik orthography. How
can I possibly defend you?" And he did nothing for him.

• • •

Once Majakovskij told me that it was too crowded at the Briks': "When I want to write, I need my own room." On the fourth floor of Staxeev's house, above my parents' former apartment, on the same landing where I lived, there lived a certain Bal´shin.[161] He was a petty bourgeois, a very kind man, but not very profound. At the time he had turned to me with a request: "I'm afraid they're going to reduce the living space in my flat. Don't you have some sort of good, peaceful tenant for me?"—"I do."—"Who is he?" I said: "Volodja Majakovskij." Bal´shin had not heard of Majakovskij. "Where does he work?" I said that he worked at ROSTA, but didn't say that he was a poet. "Is he a quiet person?"—"Yes, he's quiet."—"Well, introduce him to me!" I introduced them to one another, and the following scene took place before my eyes.

Majakovskij agreed immediately. The door led directly to the entrance; one could come and go easily. Bal´shin announced how much it would cost, and Majakovskij said: "What's with you, what's with you, that's too little!" and offered him a larger sum. Then Bal´shin arranged for him so that everything would be fancier, and, in particular, hung various horrible old pictures on the walls. When Majakovskij arrived to live there, he said: "Take away the ancestors!" And Bal´shin did.[162]

Bal´shin had also put there a piano with golden, so-called wedding candles. These Majakovskij accepted. Later he told me: "This is what happened: at night the electricity went out and I was working on a poem." (He was writing *150,000,000* at the time.) "I was really in the mood to write, and it was dark. I remembered the candles and by dawn had burnt them all down." Bal´shin was terribly annoyed by this.

Bal'shin speculated on the black market, and he had a telephone. He had paid quite a bit of money so that the phone could be moved from room to room. And he was terribly angry at Majakovskij: "He's always on the phone talking with his Lilichka, talking, talking. . . . Then he goes out and locks the door, leaving the telephone behind. I hear the phone ringing for me, but I can't get in to answer it." So then Bal'shin again hired a worker, this time to fix the telephone in the wall, so that Majakovskij couldn't take it to his room. Majakovskij returned late at night, went to grab the telephone, tugged at it, but it wouldn't budge. He tugged harder; it still wouldn't budge. Then he simply pulled it out with a chunk of the wall and brought it into his room.

Bal'shin, even though he cursed Majakovskij, liked him a lot. He cried like a baby when Majakovskij shot himself. He had become strongly attached to him, and Majakovskij to him, in his own way.

• • •

I spent the summer of 1919 in Pushkino together with Majakovskij and the Briks.[163] We were at our leisure. We sat, we read, we wrote. At the time I was studying Majakovskij's rhymes, and Leva Grinkrug, who was also there, said ironically: "We're all fascinated by Majakovskij, but why make lists of his rhymes?"[164] At the time I was interested in the question of shifting rhyme from the ending of a word to its root, as well as the structure of rhymes in relation to their meaning, and in relation to syntax. I had touched briefly on this in my essay on Xlebnikov, but I never was able to return to the topic in detail except in my lectures.

From our conversations in Pushkino I recall a lengthy discussion we had about the need to develop the published works of OPOJAZ and the Moscow Linguistic Circle. There was a certain rivalry between these two institutions, and Brik, who was at first more linked to the Petersburg group, now went over to us. There was a lot being done in the Moscow Linguistic Circle then on poetics, and it was different from what was being done in OPOJAZ. The Moscow Linguistic Circle, was, moreover, first and foremost a linguistic circle, and linguistics played a very great role in it. Majakovskij was very much interested in the structure of poems, spoke with me a lot about it, and asked me a lot of questions about it.

In Pushkino I wrote the first draft of my analysis of "And grief grief—little grieving", which later, in America, came out as part of a large study on parallelism.[165] I was then working a lot. Several works remained unfinished—on rhyme, on the cries of street hawkers ("The greengrocer's come, the greengrocer's driven up, peas, carrots, cucumbers he's grubbed up!"), and so on. They interested me as a minimal, elementary manifestation of poetry.

At the time I was working with Bogatyrev. We wanted to write a book on the structure of folk theater. Our work later became, to a certain extent, the basis for his book on the same topic.[166]

Once the four of us—the Briks, Volodja, and I—were dining together on the balcony. We were eating kasha. Brik had just returned from Moscow. With a certain affected seriousness and at the same time slightly ironically, he said: "Volodja, today Shiman came to me at IZO and lay before me a whole series of sketches made by Gumilina of you and her," with a hint that they were of a very personal and erotic nature; I don't recall the terms he used, but it was clear what he meant.[167] Lili probably knew who Gumilina was, but she started up: "Who is this? What is this? What's this about?"—"It was his wife," said Osja, "—she committed suicide." There was a generally rather tense mood, and Volodja, with affected cynicism, said: "Well, with such a husband, who wouldn't throw oneself out the window?" And Osja said: "So I said to him: 'Why are you coming to me? Perhaps Majakovskij is interested in this stuff? It doesn't interest me at all.'" All of this struck me, particularly Majakovskij's tone. In my opinion, it's quite clear that this suicide figures in the scenario *How Are You?* [168]

I had seen Gumilina with Majakovskij earlier. Elsa hinted that she was attracted to Majakovskij and gave me her story "Two in One Heart" to read; it was lyric prose, quite striking. Gumilina was a talented woman, a very good artist. She herself and Majakovskij were depicted in all her pictures. I recall one picture quite well: a room just before morning, she is in a shirt sitting on the bed, combing her hair. Majakovskij is standing by the window, in trousers and a shirt, bare-footed, with devilish hooves, exactly as in *A Cloud in Trousers*—"And thus,/ enormous,/ I stood by the window,/ and my brow melted the glass. . . ." Elsa told me that Gumilina was the heroine of the last part of the poem.

I first saw Gumilina at Elsa's in the beginning of fall 1916, when "Two in One Heart" had already been written. Volodja was angry that Elsa had invited her. We had a party, and we all had a lot to drink. Volodja was there, Gumilina, her brother, as well as a very good-looking young girl, Rita Kon, who was then studying ballet.

• • •

I first heard about *150,000,000* in the beginning of the summer of 1919, in Pushkino. Majakovskij had asked me to become the secretary of IMO (the publisher "Art of the Young"), and in the publishing plan he included: "Ivan. A Bylina. An Epos of the Revolution" without an indication of the author.[169] He told me: "You'll see what that is!"

We were going once from Pushkino to Moscow on some sort of business. Volodja didn't want to sit in the compartment—he was terribly afraid of spotted typhus—and we were standing between the wagons, on the ties. Suddenly Volodja asked me: "Listen: tá, ta, ta—tá, ta, ta—tá, ta, ta—tá, ta, ta—tá, ta, ta—tá, ta, what's that called? Isn't it an hexameter?" I said, yes, it sounded like a hexameter. "What do you think, to begin an epos like that—would it be fitting or not?" This was, as I later learned, the rhythm of the beginning of *150,000,000*: "Stó pjat´desját´ milliónov mástera ètoj poèmy ímja."

When we reached Moscow, I wanted to get off, but Volodja said: "Wait until all these people get out." I said: "Why?"—"I don't like crowds."—"You? The poet of the masses!" He replied: "The masses are one thing, a crowd's another."

Majakovskij had a passion for gathering mushrooms. I went with him to hunt for mushrooms; this was natural, since there was very little food to be had at the time. Suddenly he drove me off: "Go in that direction; we'll talk later." At first I thought that he was afraid I might intercept some special mushroom patch he had found. But actually, as he later explained to me, he considered being in a forest, hunting mushrooms, the best place and activity for thinking up verses. He was writing *150,000,000*.

In the fall I learned more details about *150,000,000*; in general he kept it a secret. I learned these details from his landlord Bal´shin, who told me with indignation about Majakovskij: "You see, he sits with his Lilichka on the floor painting posters; they paint and paint, and then he starts shouting at her against Wilson, as if it weren't all the same to

Wilson." That's how I learned that there was something about Wilson in the poem.

Then he invited me over and read me the beginning, which made an enormous impression on me. The second time he invited me over with Shklovskij,[170] who was staying overnight at my place, and read us the part about the start of the Civil War in all of Moscow and all of Russia. I said that I didn't like it, that this was a big step down in his work. If he had to do it, then in any case let it not be so abstract and propagandistic, but better totally concrete everyday scenes from popular prints. And he did so; he included several such scenes, such as: "But immovable, / Narkompros / grew up in Ostozhenka, / stood upright / and still stands." Nevertheless, this part didn't come out very well. But on the other hand, I liked the last part very much: "Perhaps it is the hundredth anniversary of the October Revolution." This is a requiem.[171] He read it beautifully.

He read *150,000,000* for the first time at the Briks'.[172] I recall how their very good-looking cook and housekeeper sat on the floor and listened with amazement. This was still not the final draft, but the draft which I brought to Prague and later gave to Bonch-Bruevich through Bogatyrev. (Bogatyrev collected Russica for Bonch-Bruevich, and this saved his life: when the war began, he was permitted to return to Moscow.)[173] In this text there are many divergences from the later, printed text, which are, by the way, hardly coincidental.[174] For example:

> To be a bourgeois
> is not just
> to have capital
> and squander gold,
> It's to be
> the heel of corpses
> on the neck
> of the young.

It's a closed mouth
full of lumps of fat.
To be a proletarian
doesn't mean being
Dirty
or being the one
keeping factories going.
To be a proletarian
is to love the future,
having blown up
the filth of basements,
to believe in it !

In the printed text this went:

Not to Trockij
Not to Lenin
a tender verse.
I praise millions
in battles,
I see millions,
millions I sing.

Lunacharskij was at this reading. This was necessary in order that he would speak in favor of having it published. (Afterwards, it wasn't published for a long time, and when it finally was, Lunacharskij, as is well-known, got it from Lenin.)[175] There followed a discussion. Lunacharskij spoke about the fact that it made a very strong impression and that he was glad that a poet was coming forward so strongly for the revolution.[176] But, when one listened to it, one wasn't sure whether it was rhetorical or sincere. I took part in the discussion and said: "Anatolij Vasil´evich, aren't we being like viewers in the Artistic Theater, who for the most part think only about whether the columns on stage are real or made of cardboard?"[177]

Lunacharskij reacted to this in a very kind way. In general he had the style of a Russian benevolent intellectual. I remember how at the very beginning of 1920, just before my first trip to Revel´, I was picked as a professor of Russian orthoepy, on the one hand in the First Drama School,[178] and on the other in Serezhnikov's Institute of Declamation.[179] Lunacharskij was invited as an honored guest to the opening of the Institute. They served some sort of pirog. Pirog was then a rarity, and everyone attacked it. "Wait a minute, wait a minute," Serezhnikov shouted, "the People's Commissar wants some of the pirog! Pass the pirog to the People's Commissar!" But they had already gobbled it all down.[180]

Majakovskij read *150,000,000* for the second time in the Moscow Linguistic Circle.[181] I remember it quite well. He had brought along Gaj-Men´shoj.[182] There was a fairly large crowd: Nejshtadt, Vinokur, Buslaev and others. After the reading there was a discussion. During the discussion Volodja took notes. I said something about the poem's connection with byliny, someone spoke about Derzhavin, someone else about Kol´cov, and when Volodja answered, he said: "People say: byliny, Derzhavin, Kol´cov, but actually it's not the one, the other, or the third, but one hundred and fifty million."[183]

• • •

There was never any idyll, only a battle, all the time. There were moments of break-throughs—for example, when the parks in Moscow were painted in various colors on the occasion of May Day—but in the general complexity one had to be constantly on the alert. Majakovskij also went into an embittered mood when he had to speak in various institutions. Once, when he was drawing posters for ROSTA, in a moment of respite he drew the following caricature: on one side a fortress, with three lines of defenders, with the Red Army breaking through all three rows; on the other side Lunacharskij, with three rows of secretaries around him, with Majakovskij trying to break through all three rows unsuccesfully.[184] Or he would go to the State Publishing House, to Vorovskij, and shout: "And how do you publish me? Pushkin gets decent type! And me, I'm just some sort of sewn-in muddle!"

Majakovskij's attitude toward Lunacharskij was ambivalent. On the one hand, he was a man who recognized his importance and often tried to help him. On the other hand, Majakovskij saw in him a strong bureaucratic principle and, moreover, an opportunistic streak, the type of opportunism that finds a curious reflection in the lines of both of the last plays (*The Bedbug* and *The Bathhouse*), where there is a direct mention of Lunacharskij Street,[185] and where the phraseology of Pobedonosikov parodically reflects that of Anatolij Vasil´evich.

Majakovskij was terribly afraid that the revolution would become philistine, that it would be overgrown by vulgarity. He had a total hatred of such an overgrowth. The poem "The Fifth International" was to have been devoted to this theme. And it seemed to him for a long time that in the near future one could raise what he called "The Revolution of the Spirit" against philistinization, against conservatism in architecture, against growing numb on the operas of Verdi, and so on.

But at the same time,—although he announced that this would not happen,—he was afraid that vulgarity would be victorious. He had a sharp and far from happy prognosis. He sensed the invasion of vulgarity into private life, into art, into culture, into everything. We spoke several times about the poem that he was writing to one of the Internationals, but which he never finished. When he was writing this poem, he was quite unsure and quite irritable about whether the peom would cause attacks and quarrels. It seemed to him the most important thing he had done, the most important in its broad grasp of themes. In general, the question of the "Revolution of the Spirit" was for him for a long time the basic question of the October revolution; it was precisely from the point of view of the "Revolution of the Spirit" that Majakovskij defined his attitude toward October.[186]

I recall how he read me one of the versions of the "International," and he read it remarkably. It was all deeply thought through as poetry. In talks about this poem he insisted on the cunning combination of logic and transrationalism. When I said to him that the course of the poem was becoming very rationalistic, even journalistic, he became angry, grinned, and said: "But didn't you notice that all of the solutions of the mathematical formulae and so on I give are completely transrational?"—that this was only apparent; an apparent fear of poetry, a fear of verse, but actually it was all constructed as a satirical transrationalism.

Separate stanzas seem quite logical:

> I
> permit
> poetry only one form:
> brevity,
> exactness,
> the exactness of mathemathical formulae.

And then, suddenly, there are completely transrational phrases:

> *Axiom*:
> All people have a neck.
> *Task*:
> How can the poet use it.

He insisted on the unexpectedness of combinations, in particular, on what follows when, in his words, the most interesting thing starts, when events at the end of the twenty-first century start. And he asked me: "What do you think, what will come, what should follow this? Can you guess?" and told me in advance: "A picture of unbearable boredome, a picture of unbearable vulgarization—a vulgarization inescapably demanding a new revolution."

It is quite curious how this changed all the time with him, even not in the course of years, but in the course of a conversation:—"What is it, immediate events, conversations with Lenin are at hand? Or is it something that will happen in five hundred years?" In any event, this was a sacred theme. Of course he understood that this theme was becoming more and more unacceptable for the Soviet norm. And he was unable to find the possibilities that would have enabled him to raise what were for him the most pressing questions. This was an extremely difficult theme, which became even harder beginning with the title: which International was it? So it changed all the time: the "fourth," the "fifth," and so on. This "new rebellion / in a future / of communist satieity" is a theme that haunted him then. It was not just a theme—it was *the* theme.

Majakovskij had absolutely no idea of what was to come. In this respect he was totally blind, as, by the way, was Brik. Brik imagined that there would be democracy and discussion within the party; he absolutely did not imagine there would be a total liquidation of fractionalism. Volodja actually imagined that the commune

> is a place,
>   where bureaucrats will disappear
> and where there will be many
>   poems and songs.[187]

He believed in this. And he believed that he would make a great accomplishment when he wrote his "Fifth," if not "Fourth" International. He asked me about Einstein, and I never saw him so full of enthusiasm. He really believed that the dead would be resurrected, an idea from Fëdorov.[188] Volodja was so full of admiration for Einstein that he tried to persuade me that we should send him a telegram through ROSTA with "greetings to the science of the future from the art of the future."[189] I don't recall whether it was sent or not.

He couldn't tolerate the thought that Russia would come to Socialist Realism, that they would play "La Traviata," "Onegin," and so on, and that the country would be deeply conservative and reactionary in relation to art.

He had the most incredible attitude toward everything. He absolutely couldn't imagine that there would be a cult of the machine, a cult of industry. All of this didn't interest him at all: actually, he was a terrible romantic. But Xlebnikov understood: "But when my turn comes, / my flesh will become dust."[190]

I saw a lot of Majakovskij when we were neighbors. Either he would drop by my place, or I would drop by his—one had only to cross the landing, that was all.[191]

In the spring, I believe in April, of 1920, Majakovskij came by my room and said: "I've written a play; would you like me to read it?" And he began reading: "So who spends their time celebrating holidays. . . ."[192] He read it through, and I was seized by annoyance. It seemed to me to be some sort of dadaistic propaganda, with the propaganda interfering with the dadaism and the dadaism interfering with the propaganda. It came out with the slightest wittiness and was simply boring. Sparing his vanity, I said: "Volodja, this is a repetition of the least best lines of *Mystery-Bouffe,* and isn't very interesting." He was quite upset.

At the time there still rang out motifs from *Mystery-Bouffe*. But what there sometimes blazed with poetic and rhetorical wit, seemed simply untolerable in such short texts, which, for the most part, remained unpublished for a long time.[193]

II

Shortly after Majakovskij read *150,000,000* in the Moscow Linguistic Circle in January 1920 I ended up in Reval quite by chance.

Earlier, when I had spotted typhus, I had forgotten to apply for a deferment from military service, in order not to be sent to the front during the Civil War. I had the right to a deferment, since I was an advanced graduate student at the university. This was strictly a formality; they gave them away at the time for nothing, but it was the law.

But I had missed the opportunity, and I was summoned and told: "You have to appear immediately with the proper documents, or else, you know, you will be considered a deserter." That day I was scheduled to have my usual poker game, in which Majakovskij almost always took part. Also playing was an acquaintance of mine who occupied a rather high position in Glavles, the Department of Forestry; it was a military institution, and people who worked there were not called to the front. When we had finished playing, he said to me: "Well, when will we play again?" I said: "I don't know. It turns out I'm a deserter, and I have to take certain measures immediately."

"Oh, forget about it, I'll take care of it for you." So suddenly, out of the blue, he made me secretary of the Economic-Informational Division of Glavtop, the Main Committee for Heating. This was at the beginning of the fall of 1919.

I worked at Glavtop for two or three months, until it became clear that I would not be called to the front. I even called on Pokrovskij[194]—a most unpleasant figure,—but they gave me the deferment, and then I left Glavtop. My boss told me at the time: "Oh, what a shame it is that you are leaving. You could have made yourself a great career here; you have enormous capacities for this sort of work." In general he was a curious person, absolutely outside the party, Petr Mixailovich Shox, a good economist.

At Glavtop they would give out ration coupons sporadically, and once they gave us rations for marinated mushrooms. Then I decided: no matter what, I'm keeping only half for the house (I gave them to our landlady), and with the rest we'll have a drinking party. We gathered at the Moscow Linguistic Circle. I got a hold of some alcohol through friends of Majakovskij. The sale of alcohol was strictly forbidden and was punishable by execution. But there were sellers—Caucasians or Georgians. Majakovskij spoke with them in Georgian, so they trusted him. They were called "Spirtashvili."[195] I bought the alcohol from one of the Spirtashvilis, and we arranged the party by pooling our resources: the marinated mushrooms, some sort of biscuits (we couldn't get any bread), and vodka.

In the Circle there was a fireproof safe that had been left there by my father, the same one in which Xlebnikov's manuscripts were kept.[196] Petr Mixailovich Shox climbed on top of this safe and said: "Comrades! Bolshevism is not a political problem, it is not a social or economic problem, it's a cosmic problem. How can the world tolerate so much stupidity?"

When I left Glavtop, Vitja Shklovskij invited me to give a lecture in OPOJAZ. I was terribly pleased, since Glavtop had exhausted me incredibly; I was exhausted from it all because it was so against my grain. For a while I lived at the Shklovskijs', that is at his parents' place; his father was a teacher in some sort of school for workers.[197] Later I moved to the place of an acquaintance, Nadja, a very dear young lady who later became an actress and dramatic writer.[198]

I attended the meetings of OPOJAZ. We met in the House of Writers, which Kornej Chukovskij was in charge of. He warned Shklovskij that everything should be quiet, that there should be no scandals: "You know, we're very tolerant." Shklovskij answered him: "Yes, yes, I know that you have a 'house of tolerance' [i.e., a brothel]."

There I met the most various people, for example, Akima Volynskij, a specialist on Dostoevskij, and other older literary scholars. I gave two lectures. The first was against Brjusov's book *The Science of Verse*. When I left after the lecture, a man of the Petersburg style, very polite and self-possessed, approached me; it was Gumilev, who excused himself before me for having been unable to come to my lecture and said that he would definitely come to my lecture on Xlebnikov; the first was in the Circle, and it was very successful. Polivanov, Jakubinskij and others spoke. This was at the end of November or the beginning of December of 1919.[199]

Then I returned, spending the New Year's in Moscow. As I left, Nadja asked me to deliver a letter to an acquaintance of hers. The letter was too important to send by post. (Mail then was without stamps, most of the letters were simply thrown away, little got through.) This acquaintance was Gennadij Janov, who occupied a rather high position under Chicherin in Narkomindel, the People's Commissariat of Foreign Affairs.

I knew him: he was five years younger than me and an acquaintance of my brother.[200]

I showed up at his office. He worked at some reception office in the Commissariat of Foreign Affairs. There were armchairs, rugs, the place was clean—for those times this seemed like a great comfort; we had already grown unaccustomed to this. I give him the letter. He read it, then asked me: "And what are you doing, Roma?" I told him in a couple of words how I had been working at Glavtop, that I was back in advanced studies at the university, and that I had to look for some sort of work, since studying wasn't sufficient to live on. "Listen, how would you like to go abroad?" This was a strange question, since at the time there was a total blockade. "Which abroad?"—"Reval."— "Well," I said, "that isn't too far abroad. Well, what the hell, I won't refuse, but when and for how long?"—"We need a person who knows languages; our first diplomatic representatives are going there." (I later asked him why he had proposed it to me so simply, without knowing, actually, anything about me. "It was practically impossible to find someone," he replied. "Why?"— "They're afraid that the White Guardists will blow them up the minute they cross the border." But I wasn't afraid.)

I returned home to my friends the Gur´jans. Their mother was at home. I said: "You know, in two days' time I'm going abroad."—"Oh, stop playing the fool! You're always thinking up such things! Why it's not even funny!"

I left; all my books and manuscripts were left behind. . . . I didn't know for how long it would be, how it would be, or what it would be; I didn't know a thing. This was at the beginning of 1920, between Tat´jana's Day, which I spent in Moscow, and Shrovetide, when I was already in Reval.[201]

When I was on the train, there were two others sitting with me in the same compartment: one, who was supposed to be my chauffeur in the Press Office,—Mixail Levidov, a pleasant and cultured person, who later perished, at the end of the 1930's[202]—and the other, Gaj-Men´shoj, who was being sent by the Comintern to Reval. Both greeted me in a very friendly way. Gaj kept himself somewhat apart, but generally he was a kind person and very direct.

Both of Gaj-Men´shoj's names were pseudonyms. He was an American Jew of Russian origin, the son of emigrants from Russia. He spoke Russian with a slight American accent. He got through to Moscow after traveling the entire length of Siberia during the Civil War. He worked at *Pravda* and in the Comintern, and his main friend and protector was Zinov´ev. He played a large role in *Pravda*, where he was one of the main collaborators. It seems that at *Pravda* he was Men´shoj, and in the Comintern—Gaj. He had only been in Reval a short time. I recall him quite well at a reception for the leaders of the Italian Communist Party, who came to Moscow for the first time. With them was a certain young Italian, a futurist, the sole futurist-communist, Arturo Cappa, who was terribly upset that Marinetti had gone to the right.[203]

Gaj-Men´shoj was one of the first to go; he had become disillusioned quickly and thoroughly. Having returned to Moscow, he began to write, thanks to Martov, articles under a pseudonym in *The Socialist Herald*, a Menshevik journal that came out in Berlin. His thesis was that the Soviet regime was being reborn into a fascist regime, that Russia would become a very chauvinistic country, basing itself on brute force. He was captured, was in exile at Solovki for a while, and was later shot.

Men´shoj and Levidov fell asleep, but I couldn't get to sleep, so I went and walked in the corridor. There I met Klyshko, who had worked for a short time in the mission as its first secretary. Earlier he had worked under Vorovskij in the State Publishing

House as an assistant in an administrative capacity.[204] Klyshko was a very passionate communist even in pre-Revolutionary times, and also a devote Orthodox Christian. He tried to convince me that he didn't see a contradiction in this, that now, in Russia, where the Church was completely apolitical, such a combination was entirely possible. I told him that I had once been in the State Publishing House. "With whom?"—"With Majakovskij." He immediately began attacking Majakovskij in a rage, saying that it was precisely such parasites who were most dangerous for us, who played various games in order to get themselves the best royalties and make themselves a name, people who had nothing in common with the revolution. I argued with him quite openly all night long.

We traveled a long time. For the greater part of the trip—thirty-five kilometers or more, if I'm not mistaken,—we had to go on sleds, since the rails had been destroyed in the Civil War. The entire staff of the diplomatic mission was traveling with us, typists and others. We were met at a border town, Narva, where the Minister of War of Estonia gave us dinner: buttered bread with kolbasa and ham—in that terrible year of starvation. . . . The higher-ups contained themselves, but the girls literally threw themselves on the food, as if they hadn't eaten anything for two years, totally ignoring any commands to behave themselves properly.

• • •

After a while I took a leave and went to Moscow. After my return from Reval I made the acquaintance of two young Polish scholars. (They were communists, and both were "illegally liquidated" in the late 1930s.) One of them invited me to go to Prague as part of the Red Cross Mission. The Mission's task was the repatriation of former Russian prisoners of war, who had been stranded in Czechoslovakia since Austro-Hungarian times. The other task was to attempt to establish diplomatic relations with Czechoslovakia. "You know Czech, don't you?" I said that I knew it from the course I had taken on the comparative grammar of Slavic languages.—"Where would we ever find such a one!"

The head of the Mission was Dr. Gillerson, who took me on with pleasure, and took me on, moreover, on conditions that were, I must say, most honest. He asked me why I wanted to go. I told him the truth: when I became an advanced graduate student at the university, they told me it would be desirable for me to have a closer acquaintance with other Slavic countries and languages, and that I wanted to work at the university in Prague. He replied: "If it's possible for you to combine the two, then that's fine." Later it turned out that he was against my working in the university, since there were some sort of counter-revolutionaries there opposed to Moscow. And then he asked me to make a choice: "I'll let you choose what you want." I chose the university, but we remained in good relations. He later ended up an émigré himself and died in Prague just before World War II.

At the end of May 1920, I again went to Reval, where the Red Cross Mission was awaiting its departure for Prague.[205] Two young men, practically boys, came to Reval: one was Levin, who many years later, after returning home, perished; the other was the diplomatic courier Teodor Nette. They came up to me and asked me whether I knew Professor Jakobson. I replied: "Professor Jakobson doesn't exist, but I am Jakobson." (I was then twenty-three years old, but I looked much younger, practically like a boy. When, just before this, I was giving my opening lecture at the First Dramatic School, they asked me to show my entrance ticket at the door. I told them that I didn't have a ticket: "I'm giving the lecture."—"Don't play the fool!"—They didn't believe me.)

We had to wait for Gillerson, and Nette, Levin, and I spent several days and nights in Reval. We departed Reval in the first days of July by sea to Stettin, and from there traveled to Prague by train, with a stop in Berlin.[206] Nette and I shared the same cabin and instantly became fast friends. He told me the story of his life. He had worked from childhood in a shoe-maker's shop together with his father, I don't recall in which Latvian town, and while still an adolescent landed in jail with his father for taking part in the revolutionary movement. Later he took part in the revolution and worked in Soviet Latvia during the brief period of its existence. In Nette a masculine cast was combined with a rare kindness, heartfeltness, shyness and purity of soul. He loved poetry adamantly, both Latvian and Russian. He spoke Russian fluently, but with a slight Latvian accent.

At night in the cabin I started talking to him about Majakovskij. He was slightly skeptical about Majakovskij, as was the rule at the time, especially in the circles of the Commissariat of Foreign Affairs. Then I took out the typescript of *150,000,000*, which had a lot of manuscript corrections by the author, which I was supposed to try to have published abroad. At first I read a section of it, but Nette couldn't calm down until I read him the entire poem. He was in an extraordinary state of enthusiasm, and said that these were the first real verses of the revolutionary years that could not help but sting one to the quick. He was indignant that people judged Majakovskij, and I had to swear to him that when he went back to Moscow I would give him a letter to personally deliver to Majakovskij. He read me the famous Latvian poet Rainis.[207] I didn't understand

Latvian, but it was interesting to listen to the rhymes, and he translated some of the lines for me.

We arrived in Prague on the tenth of July, and I left the Mission in September. Nette stayed there until the end of the year. We wandered around the city together. He was enraptured by the beauty and grandness of its old architecture, which reminded him at times of old Riga. In general, Nette tended to get carried away by things. Thus, for example, he found a small, typical Prague cafe, very comfortable and charming, the cafe Derby. There was an old piano in the cafe, which was played by some sort of has-been, who was, however, a very talented pianist. And it made such an impression on him that he brought me there.

It happened that later, quite a while later, I lived for a few years near this cafe, and it became my hang-out. I didn't have any money, ate only three or four times a week—it was very hard to go by the sausage shops on the days I didn't eat—and my room wasn't even heated. So I would sit there for several hours at a time with a cup of black coffee (black coffee was cheaper) and a single roll. They would bring me an ink-well and a pen, and it was there that I wrote my book on Czech verse.[208] I was considered a regular, so to speak, and they treated me marvelously.

However strange it may seem, this cafe later played a role not only in my life, but also in the scholarly life of Prague. It was there that the Prague Linguistic Circle was created, and the meetings of the Committee always took place in this cafe. It was there, for example, that Mathesius' theses were written.

Once Nette learned that a communist bookkeeper in the Commissariat of Foreign Affairs had committed some sort of financial embezzlement, and he was sentenced, it seems, to capital punishment. Nette broke into tears, and Levin said to him: "Listen, you probably shot barons?" Nette answered: "But those were barons, while this is a comrade."

Nette was quite attached to me. Even when I left the Mission for the first time, in order to work in the university, he was always hanging around me. He would ask me about literary and cultural life, and would say that being a courier was only a temporary job for him, that he wanted to study.

To help characterize him: once I received a very sharp letter from a certain person in Reval. It was a letter I deserved; I had had a personal confrontation with him. When I showed it to Nette, he said his next route lay through Reval and that he would go to the man and give him a slap in the face.

I fulfilled my promise to Nette and through him sent a letter to Majakovskij with a few lines about him. In May or June 1921 I ended up in Berlin at the same time as Nette. He told me how much he had liked Majakovskij, how cheerfully Majakovskij had received him, and how they both "chatted about Romka Jakobson."[209] He made me very happy with news of the publication of *150,000,000*, made me a gift of the "anonymous" book,[210] and I drafted the first announcement about it for the Berlin newspaper *Nakanune*.[211] In October of 1922, I ended up again in Berlin, arriving almost directly at an evening of Majakovskij reading his poetry. After it the five of us sat together drinking wine—Volodja, Lili, Osja, Shklovskij and I—and Majakovskij reminded me, with an affectionate grin: "Your Nette with the letter—he's an eccentric, but very nice." Lili remembered him as well.

Nette left Prague at the end of 1920 or beginning of 1921. I later saw him a couple of times, when he was bringing the diplomatic post to Prague. As earlier, we were tied together by a strong friendship and of course reminisced about Majakovskij, whose verses he now knew from cover to cover.

Nette, who already in 1920 had dreamt of leaving his job and taking up full-time studies, spoke about his plan with even greater insistence.[212] But he was so dedicated a person and it was so easy to be confident of him, that he delayed his entrance into the university time and again. He conceded reluctantly and met an untimely end; during one of his trips he was killed by Latvian fascists.

Thus is explained the line about me in Majakovskij's poem to Teodor Nette. They actually travelled together several times in the compartment for diplomatic couriers, and in view of the fact that their main theme in common was their acquanitance with me, they really "chatted" about me. Majakovskij later read me the poem.

Even when I was working for the Mission, I was fed up with my position there. Skaftymov, who was the dean of the philological faculty at Saratov University,[213] wrote and offered me a professorship there. I then wrote my great friend and teacher Ushakov a letter about the fact that I was tired of being so distant from Russian scholarship and that I had received an offer. He answered me with a post card: "When you want to dance, you have to remember not only the stove you're dancing away from, but also the wall you're dancing toward."

They related to me well in the Mission. Everything was done in an improvisational way. Later the first Envoy, Mostovenko, arrived, in the beginning of the summer of 1921.[214] I often dropped by Levin, the secretary of Gillerson, who would give me something to eat; he would get a large dinner, with plenty of knedliche, but would eat few of them. Once he said to me: "Sit here a while; I have to meet with the Envoy." I eat something, had a beer, and lay down on the couch. When he returned, he woke me up and told me: "You know, Mostovenko wants to see you."—"Why?"—"He said that he needs a person who knows Czech language and is generally familiar with Czech culture, history, and so on, and that he spoke about it with Chicherin." And Chicherin told him: "Take Jakobson."[215] Mostovenko proposed that I become a free-lance worker for the Diplomatic Mission, and I worked there part-time until 1928.

Antonov-Ovseenko received me most warmly.[216] He was a follower of Trockij, and when he returned from Germany, where he had said farewell to Trockij, he told me what Trockij had said to him: "I know the end has come, but it is necessary for me to perish having kept my armour clean." Later, when purges began and they demanded that he fire all non-party members, and me especially—I had plenty of enemies there— he felt quite guilty before me. He said: "Stay here." And he approved of my working in the editorial board of *Slavische Rundschau,* so that I would, as it were, not be breaking the new rule.

I was, I must say, a reckless youth; I always had a "futuristic ferment." They sent us forms that we had to fill out. There was a question: "With which party do you sympathize, if you are not a member of the party?" I left it blank. Then the form was returned to me, and I was told that one could not leave an item unanswered. So I answered: "None."

I already knew that I would leave the Mission. I could have left earlier, if I had not had a lack of faith in my own abilities. For example, I couldn't bring myself to take the Ph.D. exam for a long time, even though I needed a Czech doctorate.

• • •

During his first visit to Prague, in 1927, Majakovskij stayed in a hotel for prostitues on Václav Place; rooms weren't available anywhere else.[217] There were various curtains and double beds, and he said: "I feel like Madame de Pompadour."

They arranged an evening of readings for him at the Mission.[218] Quite a few people came. In general he was received rather so-so, though Antonov-Ovseenko and the councilor Kaljuzhnyj greeted him quite warmly. Majakovskij said: "When a worker starts working, he takes off his jacket," took off his jacket and began to read. For the most part he read his poems about his trip to America, including the poem "Homeward!" Then he turned to Bogatyrev and to me and said: "Here sit two people who genuinely appreciate poetry. For them I should like to read 'A Shallow Philosophy in Deep Places.'"

Afterwards there was a public reading, where he read the poems of other poets, in particular Sel´vinskij, from memory and rather freely. He read Aseev's "Bull" and "Blue Hussars." Bohumil Mathesius, a cousin of the linguist Mathesius, did a translation of *150,000,000* with my help,[219] and Josef Hora read a section from the translation. Then Majakovskij was asked to read the poem in Russian, and he refused point-blank. I was surprised. He wouldn't read it for anything. In general, he rather disliked reading his older poems.[220]

At the time Majakovskij was complaining a lot about the State Publishing Company: "What fools we have," he would say. "They think that if I write poems with short lines, I'm doing it for the money. But it is closely linked with the verses." They got particularly mad when he had a very short line consisting of one word. How to pay him was an eternal squabble. They finally agreed to pay him by the word. He said that it was particularly jolly when he ended up with three words of the type: "and for you."[221]

During this visit Majakovskij read me his verses about Paris with the lines:

> I would like
> to live
>   and die in Paris,
> if there weren't
> such a land
>   as Moscow.

He said: "This line can't be changed. One couldn't, for example, write 'I'd like to live and die in Berlin, if there weren't such a land as Warsaw.' Those are not two different worlds, but Paris and Moscow are." I immediately asked Majakovskij whether, when he was writing the poem, he knew the similar lines from Karamzin's *Letters of a Russian Traveler*: "I want to live and die in my beloved country, but after Russia there is no more pleasant land for me than Paris." Majakovskij was fascinated by this. No, he didn't know Karamzin's line: "But it goes to show my lines are not accidental."[222]

Once Majakovskij asked my wife, Sof'ja Nikolaevna, to show him the town. She took him along a long street. He looked around with interest. "Well," he said, "shall we turn around?"—"What do you mean, turn around?! You wanted to see Prague!"—"I've seen it. First from one side, and now from the other. They're different things, after all." And when Adolf Hofmeister asked him: "What drew you to Prague?" he answered: "I like details."[223]

• • •

In 1929 Majakovskij was received very coldly at the Mission; whether it was because of him or because of me, I do not know. But he was already in bad standing then. People coming from Russia would tell me that it was considered both advantageous and chic to rag him, that whoever felt like it would attack him.

At the time he read *The Bedbug* to the director of the Vinohradský repertory theater, Kodiček, and I hoped that he might do a production of it. But they decided that it wouldn't work. He read remarkably.[224] Later we went and had a drink. But Majakovskij was dying to get to Paris and spoke openly about it, particularly with my wife, with whom he was great friends: "You know, you fall in love, and everything else immediately gets thrown aside." When he left, he told her: "Look, I suddenly learned: one should love and not be jealous."

At the time he spoke with me in the tone of the poem "At the Top of My Voice," that poetry was done for, that what was being written wasn't poetry, that God only knew what was going on, that what was being done was absolute servility.

III

Majakovskij was never happy, even when he was writing the poem "I Love"; it also has the theme of time:

> Women make themselves up.
> Men do cartwheels according to Müller's system.
> But it's too late.
> The skin proliferates in wrinkles.
> Love flowers,
> and flowers—
> and then withers and shrinks.[225]

He was a very seriously and deeply unhappy man, and one felt it. Sometimes, when he was slightly tipsy, he had a certain wittiness of his own. . . . . He was really a kind of eternal adolescent, and had a sort of interrupted development. Xlebnikov was different: he wasn't unhappy, he was epic, he took life as it is.

Majakovskij was a lyric poet on a grand scale, and he truly believed that he would return to lyric poetry all the time. I heard this from him a dozen times.[226] He was very open with me; he knew that whatever he told me would remain strictly between us as long as he lived. And he did talk a lot, very openly.

But he broke. I think he broke in the year he met Tat´jana Jakovleva. Elsa wrote me then in detail—look, she said, what a stupid thing to have happened: he meets a girl, thinks he'll have a pleasant time, and he ups and falls in love, and so seriously. And this was at a moment when he couldn't stand living alone anymore, and when he had to change in some fundamental way.[227]

Majakovskij could do nothing more. He was in too great a despair. All he had were unanswered questions. What he wrote in his farewell letter—"I have no choice"—was the truth. He would have perished all the same, whatever happened, no matter where he was, whether in Russia, Sweden, or America. He was a man absolutely unsuited for life.

• • •

People find this difficult to believe, but Majakovskij was extremely sentimental. He was terribly cruel and aggressive to people in front of a large circle, but as he writes in *A Cloud in Trousers*:

> It's fine, when a yellow shirt
> Shields the soul from investigation!

Once he offended me over something, over some nonsense: he said something that made me angry, and I left. Then he ran to me in IZO, where I was working under Brik, called me onto the stairway and started begging me with tears in his eyes not to be offended or angry with him. I had already completely forgotten it all, which I told him, but he didn't believe me.

He was incredibly afraid of Lili. She could give him a dressing-down, and he was finished. And, after all, she kept him at a distance for a long time. But she had an iron self-possession. She was totally carried away by his poems, and in general he seemed to her to be a completely unusual man. But he was a person who was not at all for her; she made him over completely.

I knew some of the people who surrounded her, and I must say they weren't the people for her, they weren't on her scale. She fascinated them. I wouldn't say that she was beautiful, but there was something quite unusual about her—both the color of her skin and of her hair. She was a woman of unusual elegance.

I personally think that apart from Osja she loved no one. And Osja was a person who could occupy himself today with sound repetitions, tomorrow the art of love, the day after tomorrow the organization of an unusually rational catalogue of profiteers for the Chekha. At the beginning of April of 1917 Volodja said of him: "Here's a man without the slightest sentimentality."

Majakovskij had a great deal of brotherly tenderness for Elsa too, I would say. People think that it's not true, as she relates in her memoirs, that she came to him in Petersburg, because he had written her such desperate letters. But it's a fact.[228] Many such things happened.

And together with this was an unbelievable roughness, as well as an unbelievable egocentrism. Osja said of him: "Volodja thinks that if someone is his friend, then he can send this person to Vagan´skoe Cemetery for cigarettes."

Il´ja Zdanevich once told Volodja how much he liked him, and Volodja told him how much he liked him, and then Volodja said to him: "Give me twenty roubles; I need them today." Zdanevich said: "Is this really what friendship consists of?" Volodja: "If not that, then what?"

· · ·

At the time in these circles one didn't gossip. Majakovskij never gossiped, neither about himself or about others. In general he didn't converse. He would joke or read poems. He would talk about certain literary topics or about publishers. He didn't like conversation. He was a rather silent person. Osja was too. He would speak about topics that interested him, scholarly or professional ones.

One knew very little about one another's personal lives. When I think about how we lived in Pushkino. . . . Personal life was rather candid, but at the time it was not the topic of the day. At the dacha we rented there was an old run-down garden. We found some sort of wickets, not even in a sufficient number, and would play croquet not far from the fence. Lili was in a state of near undress. Someone stood by the fence and stared at her, and she shouted: "What, haven't you ever seen a naked woman before?"

Majakovskij was proud of the fact that he had never written scabrous poems, with the exception of certain couplets.

· · ·

Volodja liked to speak of himself as a futurist. He was quite touched, in the first place, that I had so many memories connected with Futurism, and, in the second place, that I didn't relate to it as if it were "past."

Two examples. Once I was telling him about the futurist evenings I had attended, mentioned some of the jokes that were made, and so on, when Lili came into the room; this was in Pushkino. Lili related to it all somewhat ironically. But Volodja said: "No, it's touching."

Later, in 1922 or 1923, in the corridor of the Berlin hotel, Majakovskij turned to me and asked: "And what are you now—a Comfut [Communist Futurist]?"[229] I said: "No, simply a futurist." He burst out laughing; he was pleased by what I'd said. He never renounced Futurism and never became a realist. When one would speak with him about realism, he would cite his lines: "We are also realists, but not at grass. . . ."[230]

. . .

Majakovskij had a phenomenal memory, which, however, did get worse with the years.[231] At the beginning he could recite whatever one liked without a scrap of paper, for example *150,000,000*. And he remembered an incredible number of other poets' poems, although he often garbled them when he read them aloud. In particular, he had memorized Blok, whom he valued.

Once Lili said: "I don't have Blok, but sometime I'd like to have a look at his poems." Then Majakovskij went to Blok and told him: "We'd like to read your poems." Later he told me: "I talked with Blok, he received me well, and gave me his poems with a dedication. I brought the book to Lili. We started to read them and, well, what shall I say: it's as if the rhymes were bad and the lines weren't so good, but they did make an impression."[232]

. . .

Majakovskij didn't like children, because he saw them as a continuation of present-day *byt*. It's interesting in relation to whom this appeared. He was sitting with me in Prague. The one-year-old Kostja Bogatyrev ran into the room, and Majakovskij said: "Take him away!"[233] He hated stories of his childhood, of his early years. When his sister came to visit in Pushkino and started talking about his youth, he would go into a rage.[234]

But he loved dogs. This is apparent from the last part of *About That* and from a series of other poems, but it was particulalry apparent in life. He played joyfully and tenderly with his dog Shchenik, and once he said to me: "Shchen is an animal. I like animals. Shchen is like people, but he can't talk. That's pleasant."[235]

. . .

Once Majakovskij said to me that Russians lacked a genuine sense of humor. The Ukrainians had a real sense of humor; a truly rare sense of humor could be found in Gogol´, with his Ukrainian and first-rate sense of humor. And if one were to take Russian writers, it was those who were connected with the Ukraine in one way or another who were humorists. Whether it was Averchenko or Burljuk, or whether it was Chexov, who was from Rostov, Ukrainian features would appear all the time. But among the Russians it wasn't humor, but satire, for example Saltykov-Shchedrin, and that was something completely different. But he, Majakovskij, in his own words, had a Ukrainian sense of humor, and he would recall that his grandfather was from the steppes, and so on. He would say that he didn't have a Russian sense of humor, that Russian humor was darker and more gloomy.

· · ·

Majakovskij had a portrait of a woman which was done in a rather neo-impressionist manner. Someone asked him why it remained unfinished, to which Majakovskij responded: "Well, there was no time—we started kissing."

· · ·

In 1918 or 1919 Majakovskij and I were walking along the street in Moscow, when suddenly he asked me: "Listen, can I ask you something that may strike you as strange?" I said: "Ask away."—"You're walking along the street alone and suddenly you notice that you're thinking of something incredibly stupid, silly, and meaningless, and that you're thinking about it in a concentrated way. Does that ever happen to you?"—"Oh yes, it happens all the time."—"Thank God, I thought it happened only to me." This is very characteristic for Majakovskij's psyche.

· · ·

When I once said to Majakovskij that "this is good, but worse than Majakovskij," he said that was impossible: "If I knew that I was going down, it would be the end."[236]

· · ·

Brik's copy of Pushkin's works was a broken set of Wolff's edition, which had the pages falling out, since when he worked on it, he would tear out the pages. I recall how I was drinking tea one morning with Volodja, and he said: "You know how they say at the butcher's shop: I got a good chunk of meat today—'Poltava.'" Majakovskij loved Pushkin very much.

• • •

In Flinsberg, in the summer of 1923, Majakovskij read me *About That,* which I had read but had not listened to. At the time he was gambling a lot, and in particular, had won a lot of money at cards from some sort of rich émigré who had managed to bring a collosal amount of platinum out of Siberia.

Majakovskij told me several times, in various contexts, that nothing made him more indignant, angry and full of hatred as anti-semitism.

• • •

Once, in 1917, I was at the Briks' in Petrograd. Lili said: "Do you read philosophy?" I said yes, of course. "Well, here's Kierkegaard; have you read him?" "No," I said, "I haven't." "Listen, do read him, I have by chance one of his books in German. I'm reading it and translating it for Volodja. It's a remarkable thing!"[237]

• • •

It was forbidden, under threat of capital punishment, to possess weapons without a special permit. And I had a Spanish walking stick that had a dagger inside. It was easily recognizeable, and it certainly wasn't worth dying over. But party members had the right to carry weapons, so I brought it to Brik, who said: "I'll keep it until the fall of Soviet power." There was still no sort of cow-towing to the party at the time.

• • •

[When Majakovskij was writing *About That*] Nadja, the former cook of my parents who remained living in the apartment and loved him very much, would bring him food. She made exceptional pirozhki and was always ready to feed him. When she learned that he had killed himself, she rushed into the room; she told me this herself, when I saw her in Moscow in 1956. Someone shouted: "Don't go in there! There are GPU men there!"—"Who will stop me," she replied, "Vladimir Vladimirovich is dying!" She ran in and saw, as she told me, "he's lying, all terrible, and is roaring like a lion." I thought it was a folkloric invention. But, as a matter of fact, in a volume of reminiscences about Majakovskij, [Lavinskaja] relates that a photograph had been taken that depicts him in his death throes.[238] Later, when I asked Lili about it, she said: "Yes, of course, I even have a copy of the photograph."

PART TWO

LETTERS

1. TO A.E. KRUCHENYX

[Moscow, end of Jan.–beginning of Feb., 1914]

I am granting your request in full, Aleksej Eliseevich, and am sending you a poem "in words" of a sort,[1] written three weeks ago.[2] In it the word is not "selfsome,"[3] but has perished from an explosion of the heart in a striving for laconism and arhythmicality. All the words in it are of masculine gender (as you requested). My language is not selfsome, for the selfsome word presupposes a certain stasis on the part of the author, which is, incidentally, unrealizable (elementary truths). Please publish the poem under the name Aljagrov with the following title: "To the Futurist *prugvach* Aleksej Kruchenyx." *Prugva-bukva*[4] is the clever neologism of the mentally-ill Platon Lukashevich (from Radin's *Futurism and Madness*).[5] There are many interesting quotations there. By the way, you are well acquainted with the verses of madmen and endlessly correct in what you say about them. If possible, please print [the poem sent] in prose lines without misprints, especially in the punctuation. Incidentally, please write me as to when our collection will appear, etc.[6] At the same time send my remarks and, most importantly, a copy of *Roaring Parnassus*.[7] By the way, the newspapers, magazines, store windows are flooded with articles on Futurism, some of which have pretensions to seriousness. The Musagetes[8] have taken to Futurism—in a few days

Stepun[9] is devoting half a lecture to it. Vjacheslav Ivanov delivered a lecture, supposedly on Čiurlionis, but actually on the Futurians.[10] I didn't go, but here's the approximate content of part of it: the most sympathetic of youths, irrational tramps, prodigal sons who, after abandoning the paternal home, remained solitary on a tall mountain top, rejecting harmony. We shouldn't poke fun at them, but erect a monument to their madly bold feat; nevertheless, let us raise a hymn to divine harmony, etc., etc. No one is a prophet in his own land, but they won't find themselves a fatherland or a refuge anywhere; they are the sole true Russian anarchists. . . .

You asked me where I happened to come across poems composed of vowels. The magical formulae of the gnostics are interesting models of such.

Remember, you said that poetry is any sequence of letters in direct or inverted order, and called this a demonic or or "underground" point of view?

You know, poetry up to now was a stained-glass window *(Glasbilder)*, and like the sun's rays passing through the panes, romantic demonism imparted picturesqueness to it.

But here's victory over the sun and the f-ray (from your own works).[11] The glass is blown up, from the fragments—in other words, pieces of ice (this is from Andersen's fairytale)[12]—we create designs for the sake of liberation. From demonism, from null, we create any convention whatsoever, and in its intensity, its force, is the pledge of aristocratism in poetry (here I'm at my peak). But you laugh and say: a fine dream, etc. It's not a dream, but the breath of which Martynov speaks,[13] the joy of creation of which you write, the ability to color that Marinetti points out. And as to the human point of view, I spit on it! Marinetti, by the way, craves a meeting with you Futurians[14] and a debate, even if through the medium of a translator.[15] Smash him and his junk and trash to bits — you're so good at it! And it's most important. Incidentally, *I very, very much ask* you to answer all the above, it's very important to me: no one's gone as far as you and me,[16] how can we lose sight of one another? If you flinch, if you don't answer, all I can do is repeat your own words: oh, damned old reflex!

In Moscow no one knows of the existence of your new books. I pointed this out to the clerk at Obrazovanie,[17] asked him to put them in the window. He answers: "Thank God no one knows!" What's one to do? The above phrases are relative: don't forget that I'm using words. What's Xlebnikov up to? Give him my best.

I wish you the very azure (thus, they say, I. Severjanin[18] closes his letters). Please answer as soon as you can.

Roman Ja.

Address:
Lubjanskij Thruway
Staxeev's House
   Apt. 10

P.S. If possible, publish [the poem] in the collection *Onanism*, but without a title.[19]

2. TO A.E. KRUCHENYX

[Moscow, after August 1, 1914]

Thank you for Belyj;[1] you, of course, are right, but what is one to do—the square and the newspapers stink of Germans and vulgarians, and I was infected for a moment. But then, think back—can't one catch cold even from Dostoevskij's underground?

However, it's a question of something else. Did my letter really irritate you so that you didn't want to answer my other questions? I still ask you to answer. It is not a matter of Belyj or of philosophy, I repeat.

If you're thinking of publishing another children's book or something of the sort,[2] then here's a couplet by a nine-year-old:

"Teptil´ brentil´ kosu dral	"The warmer pulled the jingler's braid
Merin kuricu ukral."	The gelding stole the chicken."

Other verses and drawings have also come my way. The most interesting are two compositions of a little boy "in all languages,"[3] quite transrational scribblings.

Don't be angry and write.

Roman Ja.

3. TO M.V. MATJUSHIN

[Moscow, mid-January 1915]

I gave the pictures to Malevich and made his acquaintance, as well as that of Morgunov (at the former's place).[1]

It seems that they're working a lot, but I didn't get to see their things.

I took *The Little Heavenly Camels* to the office of *Russkie Vedomosti*.[2] I'll send you the photos of Bajdin's pictures later; there's been a delay.[3]

Now, as to Xlebnikov: his prediction actually came true. On the 20th, the Germans sank the Formidable.[4] I refrain from commenting further.

For some reason I didn't succeed in Petrograd in relating to you fully a certain thought: it seems to me that we're not with Don Quixote, but with the peasants and hooligans beating him; for he's a romantic, genuflecting, praising the old. Our towering illusion is whether or not it's a knight we're battling.

How's Kruchenyx? For some reason he's not answering my letters, and I've got to write him on an extremely urgent matter. So please convey this to him.

I don't know whether Malevich managed to write you about this, but we're wondering whether it isn't an extremely opportune time to publish a collection, even if in a minimal number of copies.

It would be a gibe at the gravediggers of the new. It would concentrate, for example, the main works of the present, that is, "first-quality goods" (as the Moscovite shopkeepers say) of Futurism, ones achieving a maximum of tension.

Being of substantial size, the collection could include: 1) works and 2) articles on music, poetry, painting and so on (blows and substantiations).

If such a collection is impossible, one could to a certain extent replace it with a collection of current verses. After the war, one would think, they will be surpassed, and will thus recede into the background. As a result, if there isn't a collection, there will be a certain void. If this idea strikes you favorably, please let me know, and I'll draft more detailed considerations in that regard.

From the latest news here: Goncharova is doing decorations for the Kamernyj Theater,[5] Severjanin during a poetry evening discarded the word "Reichstag" from his verses and changed "Hauptman" to "Huysmans."[6]

I await a letter from you.

Greetings to Ekaterina Genrixovna[7] and Ol´ga Konstantinovna.[8]

Roman Jaljagrov

4. To E.Ju. Kagan

[Prague, mid-September 1920]

Dear Elena Jul´evna,

I just received your letter. On September 12th I received from Elsa a short letter from London, which travelled for almost two weeks, where, among other things, Elsa says that she will write from Paris, when she gets from me a confirmation that I am still in Prague. I was in depair, since in such a case I will get a genuine letter from her no early than in a month's time, so I immediately telegraphed you: I ask you to convey to Elsa that I am waiting impatiently for the promised letter. The telegram was hopelessly distorted. I was given your telegraphic reply to read, but they refused to leave it with me, since they continued to doubt that it was to me, and apparently sent it back to you. The address bewildered me, and I took the word "written" as an answer, that is, I decided that you wrote Elsa in Paris. Why did I telegraph you, instead of telegraphing Elsa directly in Paris? I was afraid that Elsa's husband would look askance at such a telegram from a man with whom he is unacquainted; moreover, before my departure [from Moscow] Lili warned me severely not to forget that Elsa had married "a Frenchman."[1]

I have absolutely no news from Lili, as well as from our native country in general, due to the laziness of my friends. I send letters there, but it is a very long path; you should better write to Osja's and my friend Grigorij Vinokur in Revel´, at the Hôtel Petersburg.[2] He will forward your letter with pleasure, and you'll get an answer. In recent days I've managed to exchange letters with many old acquaintances who have emmigrated abroad, in particular with Izja Kan.[3] But nothing overjoyed me as much as the few lines from Elsa. In your letter—when you write about Elsa, I sensed a note of anxiety, of dissatisfaction. You know, Elena Jul´evna, how dear you all are to me. And so I await Elsa's letter with even greater impatience.

Roma.

5. TO ELSA TRIOLET

[Prague] Sept. 17 [1920]

Dear Èlechka,

As soon as I saw the edge of the envelope in the half-darkened corridor, I instantly recognized your handwriting. I became so happy. When I wrote the first letter to Elena Jul′evna from Reval, I was full of energy, in good form, was thinking of the past incidentally, by the by. But now for a hundred and one reasons I'm going through a period of decline (I still permit myself to hope that it's not final), and perhaps for the first time in my life I've begun to think in terms of the past. It ends with our acquaintance, and I absolutely don't remember whatever came before—probably I was playing with a rattle. And sudddenly, at the peak of my decline—a few lines from you (I'm in a state), that is, there's such a whirlwind of various thoughts, that I'm still somewhat crazed. You pulled me out of my childhood by the ears, Elsa; I wept, as happens, but you kept on pulling. And I am obliged to you for ever so much. It was you who taught me when we parted: "Roma's weak—it's a weak excuse," and I became strong. But at the moment these hundred and one reasons *c'est plus fort que moi*. But all of this is momentary. Your letter took almost two weeks to reach me—an inconceivably long time, and since you were waiting for a confirmation that I was in Prague, I telegraphed Elena Jul′evna.[1]

For four days I've been thinking from morning to night that I had to answer you, but I didn't know where to begin. As you see, I still don't know, and am writing the wrong thing. Really, each of us has lived through not one but ten lives in the last two years. In the last few years I, for example, was a counterrevolutionary, a scholar (and not the worst), the scholarly secretary of Brik, the head of the Division of Arts, a deserter, a gambler, an irreplaceable specialist in the heating establishment, a writer, a humorist, a reporter, a diplomat, in every sort of romantic *emploi,* and so on and so forth.[2] I assure you I was indeed a *roman d'aventures* and nothing else. And so it was with practically each of us. But when we read in Elena Jul´evna's brief exposition about your travels from Moscow to Tahiti, everyone said that, in a word, it was a fairytale.[3] But, really, can one write about everything, can one inquire about everything in a letter? I want to talk with you. This summer, when I was living at the dacha with the Briks, I had a woman visitor. She planned to stay for a while, but was there only one day and night and went back to Moscow. Lili asked me: "Why so soon?" I answered: "But, Lili, one can't just kiss for two whole days!"—"But you could have talked."—"I can talk only with you and Elsa."

And this is not just a phrase, Elsa. Only now do I understand what an exceptionally clever person you are. Last winter I read your diary. It is such a beautiful thing (especially the childhood part) that it seems to me I've rarely been so captivated by a book. By the way, I packed up your diaries and letters with my manuscripts. They're now being preserved in a scientific establishment.[5] But that particular small envelope of letters I burned, in bed with typhus, near death.[6] Elsa, we really must speak, and I simply want to see you. If there were the slightest possibility, I would immediately set off for Paris. But if you can drop by in Prague or at least in Karlsbad or in some such place, I will be happy beyond belief. I have so many stories of all sorts, gossip, and even a book of Volodja's with a dedication to you.[7] At least write. Greetings to Elena Jul´evna, my respect for whom is even greeter after having learned that she flew in an airplane.

Your Roma.
17 Sept.

6. TO ELSA TRIOLET

[Prague,] 11 [October 1920]

Dear Èlja,

How difficult it is to correspond with you. You change not only in the interval between two letters, but even in the extent of a single letter,—you seem to tire, to subside toward the end. And, really, I can't get everything into a letter, and these few lines make sense only when you gleen how the other is taking them in, but you are changing so much that there is no chance of gleening anything, and so I can't write about myself. It's another matter if it's in words, and when you see someone. But meanwhile it's so good that you have written so much about yourself; otherwise it would be ever harder for us to strike up a conversation. Because these years seem almost not to have taken place, and despite myself, I see you as a holy sinner, and both Klimentovskij Lane and the cut of your sleeves are the same. By the way, you and Lili are so boldly candid that it seems there's no one more open, but actually both you and she conceal much more. Apropos, do you know that Lili and I intended to "get married," in order to bring her here? By chance it didn't happen.[1]

So I really should tell you about my last few years, even if in a few strokes, since I'm convinced that I am still for you, as in your diary, "a poor naive, credulous child."[2] This is often repeated.

But, as I already wrote above, I can't tell you anything without seeing you, and turn instead directly to today's concerns, although this may be somewhat unexpected for you. On April 15th I made up my mind definitively to break with everything that had tied me down in recent times: in a word, *la vita nuova* and various bright dreams. When I received your [first] letter [from Paris], I should have quit my job the next day and burnt, if you like, my last bridge. Your letter, written hastily, led me to think that you were suddenly irrevocably alone, but I didn't have the tuning-fork to perceive for sure whether this was just momentary. Therefore I carelessly tossed my plans aside and waited for your following letter. Once I got it, I fulfilled my original plan and am now a free bird. If you can do it for me, taking into account your circle of acquaintances, get me a visa for Paris and find out whether or not some sort of job is possible for me there, simply in order to have the possibility of existing. If this were at all possible, I would migrate there in the next three months with enormous satisfaction. If you can, Èlechka, quickly find Larionov and Goncharova—they're working there—and remind them of me (Jakobson-Aljagrov), mainly as a friend of Bajdin-Vejnshtejn[3] and Kruchenyx, and propose to them to publish Volodja's new poem (its content is the Soviet Revolution), *150,000,000,* which had a defeaning success when he read it publically. It is still unpublished. He gave me the manuscript; I have it here.[4] Perhaps I could earn something [getting it published], or perhaps some articles about whatever and wherever might be appropriate. By the way, perhaps this is all nonsense. Write me frankly. At the moment I'm completely tired out with these "decisive steps." Today's my birthday.

Your Roman
11 November

Answer soon.

7. TO ELSA TRIOLET

[Prague,] 14 [November (?) 1920]

Dear Èlechka,

I wish I could see you terribly. But how? You apparently don't have the money for a trip here; I have neither the money after my recent situation at work, nor a visa. The former is easier to get, but even the latter, one would think, is not all that difficult, if I were to remind several old acquaintances about me, but they have become repulsive to me, and in general I am happy to no longer touch either politics or politicians. You ask what I'm doing in Prague. I don't know if you know it or not, but in September I was strongly attacked here for my participation in the [Soviet] Red Cross Mission.[1] The newspapers were crying out about "the boa constrictor, grasping in its tenacious embrace our local professors" (this is me), and so on; the professors vascillated whether I was a bandit or a scholar or an unlawful mongrel; in the cabaret they were singing little songs about me—all of this was not very witty. The situation was complex, but it seems to me that my fate is to tightrope-walk in inconceivable situations. As a result I left work (without tears or cursing), and entered university scholarship and so on. The money I have, what with the extremely modest life I'm leading, will last until April, and then we'll see. Probably I'll visit Osja.[2] If you have little money and there are no perspectives for the immediate future, I think it would be better for you here—it's cheaper to live here, and you could perhaps find work, knowing, as you do, four languages. By the way, this perspective is only "in the absence of fish." Why couldn't you have answered me definitively in the beginning of October? I would have done differently. But, of course, it's stupid to recall that now.

Every word in your letter, dear Èlechka, wails unbearably about crushed self-esteem. But it only seems so to you: it wasn't so earlier. You once wrote so clearly about the same thing, but then you had Romik as a scapegoat. Don't think that I'm being ironical: this is in the order of things. As a peasant once said to me: "Well, the Tsar attacks the minister, the minister attacks the merchant, the merchant attacks the peasant, but what is the peasant to do?—He attacks his potato, as its master." I know I would love it if for five minutes I would completely doubt that I can make people take my mind seriously. Everything, except for the word "fool" thrown from the soul, is irrelevant to me. Likewise, what Lili needs is the confidence that she can attract new people, and Volodja — that only he can write completely brilliant poems; I just don't know what is it you need? Or are you Lili's sister? Or, what's even worse [illegible]. But enough lyrics. I kiss your hand.

Your Roma
The 14th

8. TO ELSA TRIOLET

[Prague, 19 November (?) 1920]

My Beloved Èlechka,

Today is the *19th*, and I had already written you on the 14th, but didn't send it off until now; I was hoping the whole time to think up something in order for you to get settled here. If you had only answered me simply and clearly right away. Now I propose to you the following: no matter what happens, sell Volodja's manuscript to Larionov: it's a remarkable thing in every respect. You know his *War and the World*;[1] this is "ten times better." It's still unpublished! It is highly praised in Volodja's readings in Russia.[2] Secondly, I have Volodja's collected works, including everything up to 1919 (your copy, with a dedication).[3] The young poets here, who got acquainted with his poetry through me, were most fascinated. Further, there is now appearing in the West all sorts of theoretical garbage about the new art, whereas I have a militant, good work "A Chapter from the New Poetics" (Approaches to Xlebnikov)—in three printer's signatures. I read it in the form of a lecture several times in Moscow and Petersburg.[4] It made a huge noise in literary circles. The youth greeted it noisily, the old folks of all sorts (for example Sakulin,[5] Chukovskij, Lunacharskij, and so on) hissed, but couldn't help acknowledging its "great talent" and considered it necessary to publish it. I have a copy of it here; it's still unpublished. Moreover, I also have the philological-futuristic collection *Poetic*s with Shklovskij's brilliant articles.[6] In a word, try to sell all or part of this. Moreover, I hope in the immediate future to get a series of the latest reproductions of the Russian left artists, and then I can combine them into a book about the latest Russian art and artistic politics, and so on. All the money you get for all this, if the scheme succeeds, are earmarked for your living expenses here. I personally have enough money to last me until April. Try, Èlechka, it will be such a joy if you come. Keep in mind that if you get even 1000 francs, that's enough for three months or so here, maybe more, if one lives humbly, though without deprivations. Having so persistently called you [to come to Prague], I am very afraid of taking on the responsibility before you and not being able in the end of being sure whether this is a way out, but in my last letter I wrote about the "absence of fish," and in your letter, which I received today, there are hints of just that. Èlechka, you are so impossibly dear to me, you know. It's hard to explain, but today I heard your voice all day long: "Let's go, let's go, my dear angel." As regards growing old, it's nonsence; I would have answered you, but it would be too much like a quotation from Hamsun's Victoria. Today I had a Frenchman over; how terribly I've gotten out of the habit of conversing fluently in French. You ask what I'm doing. In January of 1917, as I was walking down the Pjatnickaja, I swore: "If I meet another, beautiful, young one, I will not squander my heart,"[8] and on April 20, 1920, I swore the same and that by April 20, 1921 I would write my dissertation, *stoj co stoj,* as the Czechs say. And on August 11th I again swore, so as you see, the "squandered sums" are large. I'm joking, but truly this was not in jest. I gathered the remnants of my money and my soul, became as stingy as a Jew, I sit and am preparing a "scholarly" book by the

10th of April. I'm alone a lot now; to recruit some acquaintances would, I think, be easy for me here even now, *malgré tout,*
but would be for naught. In recent days I got settled comfortably, moved into a splendid, warm room (15º), hung on the
walls amusing Czech popular prints, which instantly made it
cheerful, and sit and work. If you were here, it would be even
better. Barbusse's *Le feu* was translated into Russian a while
ago;[9] send me *L'Atlantide.*[10] In general books got into Russia
almost by miracle—very few. If there's something interesting
about the new art, send it too. But better send yourself. This is
always more interesting. Sent my greetings to Elena Jul´evna. It
is terribly unexpected that my friends (including Osja, Vitja,
Aleksej)[11] don't write me at all, and they used to love me a lot.
Well, I am distant.

Your Roma.

Pessimist, send me a picture of the "Parisian you"; I append a
picture of the "Prague me" for your amusement.

9. TO ELSA TRIOLET

[Prague,] 30 November [1920]

Dear Elsa,

I await your reply to my previous letters with great impatience. In the first place, I don't like it in general when there's no answer from you for a long time—there's always a sort of anxiety and other stupidities. In the second place, I badly need to know 1) whether you are coming and when, 2) whether my manuscript can be sold.[1] The point is that, if you don't plan to come next month, then I shall perhaps visit my relatives in Berlin for the holidays, but I terribly want to see you at last, even if it is in January.[2] As far as the manuscript is concerned, I have a possibility of publishing it here, true, without payment, but I'm already so sick and tired of the fact that it has been a manuscript so long (a sort of old maid). Therefore, if it's impossible in Paris, I'll do it here. There's little news. Nobody writes me. I'm working a lot. I await your letters and you.

Rom.
30 November

10. TO ELSA TRIOLET

[Prague,] 12 December [1920]

Èlja,

For some reason you don't come, you're waiting for something, what—I don't know, but I really need to talk with you—about you, about me, but if not, just to talk,—you are very close and needed. For some reason I've been thinking of Levochka.[1] We became good friends. We always went home together after visiting the Briks. At night, on foot, through the entire city. He didn't like everything that was going on there at the time. "But I don't want to visit others; after Lili they're so boring." Forgive me for interfering in your domestic affairs, but I don't like it and am not expecting anything good. The most cursed thing is that I'm a homeless tramp at the moment, and there's no cursed money in view. This deprives of its proper weight the following phrase, which I repeat today in sound mind and full memory: I await you, as I did four years minus a week ago. What I then proposed remains in force in all its details, only I'm older and have learned to respect full freedom above all.[2] Perhaps you will grin, curl your lip, be surprised at this "proposition," decree: "Nonsense." But it's today, and I want to make sure that neither tomorrow nor the day after could the thought enter Èlechka's mind: I have nowhere to go. So it has been said. Now on to immediate matters.

I've having my book printed already here under the title *The Newest Russian Poetry. A First Sketch.* Part of the copies will belong to me, and the most sensible thing, it goes without saying, would be to sell them in Paris. Please, dear, find out for me: how much could one ask for a humble little book of three printer's signatures (around 50 pages) and how many could one count on selling. This is terribly important for me. It's coming out in January. If Elena Jul′evna could clarify these same questions for me in London without too much loss of time and energy, I would be endlessly grateful to her. Further, here's how matters stand with Volodja's things. If the poem is to be sold, the rights should be understood to be for *one* edition with an agreed-upon number of copies.[3] The Moscovites should be ashamed at not writing me; I'm terribly angry. In general, I'm working peacefully, my head is clear, yesterday while writing I discovered to my amazement that it was already seven in the morning, and I thought it was still evening. Èlechka, if only you could come, even just for a day, even if just to greet the New Year (do you recall the striking of the clock?), or even just for Tat′jana's Day. I planned to write a great deal in answer to your last letter (about your uncle and so on), but I am unable to speak seriously at length in a letter, it's as drawn-out as a melodrama; it's a different matter in words, which can be nuanced with humor. Where's the humor in a letter? It's like a comic mask and gets congealed.

But don't enter a monastery; better come to me. Your maximum program would be fulfilled, that is, you write about a nook, where no one could bother you or suspect you, and finally, books, paints—the piano's a bit more difficult. Oh if you only knew how angry it makes me when stupid money can play such an intrusive and base role in life. I kiss your hand.

Roman.
12 December.

I'm *not* going to Berlin, but I'll probably visit Osja fairly soon.[4]

11. TO ELSA TRIOLET

[Prague,] 19 December [1920]

Elsa,

Yesterday I received your letter and lost heart. So, we shall not see each other before my trip (to Osja), which apparently will be soon.

"Reasons of a financial nature." Is it really impossible to scrape together something from the sale of Volodja's books, manuscripts and if but a hundred copies of my book* (in the worst case at 1 1/2 francs each, if more is impossible)? Is a visit of three days, in other words only a round-trip ticket, really so unbearably expensive? Forgive me, but something here is not quite right.

You're your old self—you tantalize one with candy, but this time we didn't have a bet. By the way, neither in this letter or in following ones will I ask any more. A free person has their own free will. Or are you not free?

From your last letters it is quite unclear to me how things are going with you in Paris. You write something about your

---

* There are not three signatures in it, as I wrote you, but five, i.e. around 80 pages.

money "not being [your] own," and so on. To paraphrase Volodja:

> If such is Western culture,
> Then I spit on every West.[1]

If someone speaks or writes me about money being decisive in important questions, of its interfering shamefully in life, of being dependent on money, it literally makes me twitch all over. After I got your letter yesterday, I was so angry that I went out and squandered a good half of what I had. Of course, that's not very smart, and right now I am dry. What sort of question can there be of earmarking some money from the supposed earnings for Lili and Volodja? Of course, earmark what's necessary. You are perplexed that they have separated. Lili got tired of Volodja a long time ago; he had turned into the sort of furious philistine husband who feeds his wife—to fatten her up.** Of course, this was hardly to Lili's taste. It ended in endless quarrels: Lili was ready to carp at every trifle (last summer).[2] Volodja and I became good friends, and as a result she also "nailed" me (to use thieves' jargon). Our relations were spoiled. By the way, we didn't actually quarrel, but became reconciled, and warmly so, only in that year. By the way, I think that at the moment I'm in disfavor for many reasons. Lili's way is inevitably rain after good weather. What else does she write about herself, Osja and Volodja? By the fall of 1919, they had ceased living together, Volodja moved in next door to me,[3] and in the winter they broke up. Volodja was somewhat down, but later became a bit more like he was before Lili, a bit of an apache—it seems even now he's making rows.

** Osja joked that Volodja in his family life was akin to Pushkin. This is characteristic not so much for Volodja, as for Osja.[7]

He goes to the Briks', as in the old Petersburg days, almost every day. It's impossible to describe everything, but in short, it of course turns out wrong. By the way, you know, Stanja[4] started frequenting the Briks and became one of their own. At first Lili was against him, but later was quite the opposite. He and I became somewhat friendly; he's quite intelligent, but not at all the sort you describe him to be. Lili (between us) has aged a lot (and not only externally). This torments her terribly, but now, that is, more accurately, when I left, she had already found herself a new style—*romans discrets* that do not destroy the "order." At one time she was so against Volodja that she couldn't listen to anything about art, couldn't speak about artists without a "bestial" malice, and phantasized about "people of affairs." She can attrack men to the extreme even now. She went to Petrograd in the winter with a certain man whose head she had turned. There was only one berth for the two of them [on the train]; they lay head to foot, and he "passionately attacked her legs." In Petrograd he ran after her, crazed. On the way back, without telling her, he took a whole half of a compartment. She went into it and was terribly displeased. Suddenly Boris Kushner[5] (surely you remember him? By the way he and I also became fast friends) stuck his head in the door, and said: "Can I join you? Otherwise, I'll have to sleep in the corridor." Lili was glad. She sends the other one to the upper berth, and lies down with Kushner. It's dark. She throws off her shoes, and Kushner "kisses her feet." Really, it's a novella. But enough gossip; as it is Lili calls me a gossip. If it's not too much trouble, please find out for me whether one can get the "Evangile de Reims" in Leger's edition and for how much.[6] If it's not more expensive than 50 francs, buy it and send it, and I'll transfer the money to you. And also be so kind as to send me De Saussure, *Cours de Linguistique* (it's inexpensive).

As regards perfume for Lili: in spring I bought her Origan de Coty in Moscow for 8,000 rubles, i.e. cheaper than in Prague. But now perhaps they no longer have it in Moscow.

Roman

If I vanish from your Parisian horizon as suddenly as I appeared, remember me kindly.

Happy New Year!

If for Paris it would be better to have the book on good paper, write me, and I'll have extra copies printed on good paper. In general, as regards the book, answer as soon as possible, my dear. Forgive me for rushing you.

I received a letter from M-lle Dache;[8] she turns out to be in Berlin. If you want, I'll let you know the address.

My new address: Praha, Vinohrady Nerudová ulice, N 7, byt.

12. TO ELSA TRIOLET

[Prague, January 7, 1921]

Beloved Èlechka,

Was it 13 or 12 years ago on this day—December 25th according to the Old Style—that you and I danced a Hungarian
dance together in the Literary-Artistic Circle?[1] When one is
alone, Christmas involuntarily becomes a day of remem-
brances; one senses calendrical numbers. Exactly four years
ago on this very day I wrote a "desperate" letter to you in
Petrograd. And there's still another recollection—one of many
not connected with Christmas: you told me—"You'll never
leave me." And just a quarter of an hour ago a song-bird of a
young lady told me: "We're close, but it's as if you were someone else's."— "Yes, someone else's." A few days ago I received
at the same time a letter from someone else's wife, where you
write that my letter comforted you. I received another from
someone else's bride. She writes: "Your wonderful letter so
touched my heart that I wanted to kiss you. Thank you, dear
friend. Your lines give me so much joy." But I have no joy.
Many[2] are ready to give me joy, but for me the entire world is
divided into two unequal halves: the lesser—other people, who
can give me no joy, and you, whose every minute should be a
festival, and I would light a candle for this festival, but instead
of this you have a whimpering life. Èlechka, it's not just words:

there's nothing I wouldn't do so that there wouldn't be that whimpering life. My head works, but I can't just work, when I'm alone and it's the holidays; as you write, one wants to go on a binge. Well, I went on a binge and spent everything and am dry; my one hope is to sell a sufficient number of copies of my book being printed. Help me with this. If you don't have and didn't have money, why didn't you telegraph me to send some when I insisted on it? We could have met. When I leave — to Osja or to Bulgaria to Trubetzkoy, from whom I received an interesting letter,[3] or somewhere else—I don't know, but I do know that I'll soon take off. You write—"don't leave." To receive letters from you, to write you, my devilishly clever one, is a great holiday, but I can't just sit here for a holiday. If there's something else, if I can become necessary for you, if there's some way I can help you even a little, write me definitively, I'll cancel my plans and will act accordingly.

The very letters of your message cry out, as it were, with their hook-like shape: go to hell, all of you—the letters, people, my own self. Èlechka, why do you take pain and grow it and grow it?[4] Where is your exceptional liveliness of the old days?

I kiss your hand
Your Roma.

13. TO ELSA TRIOLET

[Prague,] 25 January 1921

Dear Èlechka,

I'm writing in a hurry. Why are you silent? Lili and Osja are well (information from January 5th).

I'm sending my first-born;[1] write me your impression. Take the other copy to Povolockij[2] with the request that he answer as quickly as possible whether I should send it, and how many copies at what price (3-4 francs would be good). If he wants, let him take it for London as well, or you, my dear, contact London yourself. Forgive me for troubling you; perhaps at the moment you are not up to me or to all of this, but I'm sitting without a farthing, and just now I need money—first of all, to be able to do as I please. Telegraph the numer of copies, if possible: Praha Vinohrady, Nerudova 7. Jakobson.

Roman
25.I.21

14. TO ELSA TRIOLET

[Prague,] 24 January [1923]

Dear Èlika,

I'm reading your letter and am rejoicing, since the entire Èlechka—intelligent, close and sensitive—is in this letter. I am rejoicing, despite the dismissive words and tough phrases ("you can't bear a different *emploi*" . . . about the usefulness of door-mats for wiping one's feet, and so on). Even in these tough phrases I recognize the Elsa of Moscow, who would step on one's feet. I do not believe these words, I do not believe them, just as you, Èlechka, don't believe, don't believe, don't believe that we could one day become unnecessary for one another. The devil himself tied us up together—that's from your letter of long ago. And I'll never be able to convince neither you, nor myself, nor Sonja,[1] that I love her as I love you. When I recall our meeting,[2] I feel absurdly strange: I became so stupid from the happy fact that I recognized my former Elsa—so stupid that I was unable neither to ask (and there were at hand whole carriages full of questions most necessary in and of themselves), nor to tell (and there were at hand a whole line of special trains full of pressing tales), nor to kiss. But now, when I write you, again it's not a question of questions and tales, but of twitching lips and the stubborn, stubborn thought: I want Elsa. At the moment I haven't a single other thought and know of no other love. According to you, this is an eternal impossibility promising paradise, but Èlik, I don't care what it is, but simply, if you want to understand me now, to know genuinely what it is I want, then imagine me saying in my most insistent Romanish-extra-Romanish intonation one word: Èlechka. Èlja, you spend time very day with Vitja,[3] he's probably taught you what an oxymoron is; well, I don't want an oxymoron, I don't want you to be the very closest person to me at a distance of eight hours of travel. Èlja, we shall see one another. I am rereading your letter, and it is as if I hear you jingling the keys locking up, as if you had come out on the stairs to see me off and are still smiling affably, but I already know that in a minute the door will slam shut and I'll be left like a bast mat in front of it. Èlik, don't be proud with me; it's just the same as sleeping in a corsette. So perhaps the door has slammed anyway,—in that case, read what follows:

When I spent days with you in Moscow, I forgot the address of the university. Thus my philological school was Pjatnickaja, Golikovskij Lane.[4] I was polished by you, Elsa. But I do not want to be a promising scholar, I do not want to write "talented sketches," I do not want to feel ashamed when I am praised. And now I am ashamed, since I am doing to the point of disguise something other than I should, and when, Èlechka, you reproached me for this in your letters, you were intelligent and right. I am simply unable to throw out of my life trifles and trivialities for the sake of the main thing, and I live by trifles. You *were unable* to convey to me your stubborness in attaining a goal. And I live terribly somehow from day to day, and in the evenings, if I'm not kissing, I howl like a wolf. This is again a quotation—from your diary.[5] I am writing all this in a teribly incoherent way; I am unable to write "sentimental memoirs."[6] But if you understood that with the

Briks I am not on my own and useless, then perhaps you will understand this too.

Sonja persistently wants to leave (don't tell anyone about this). The things in our room are no longer in place.

If there's the slightest possibility I will soon be in Berlin. The thought that you could again vanish leads me to despair. That is also a quotation from your letters. You will never lose your charm for me, even in the worst case—even if you become intimate with Vitja.

Your Roman

Write at the address: Praha Žižkova ul. Vila Tereza
Zastupitelství RSFSR
24 January

I wrote you the 24th, the same day you wrote your letter. I didn't send you the letter, since only today, having received your letter with a delay, did I learn your address, and I didn't want to write you at Vitja's. I wanted to come to Berlin this Friday, but it was absolutely impossible. Beloved Èlechka, come to Prague; Vitja's been sent a visa, so come together with him. Neither sweets nor livers nor anything else are needed—what is necessary is that Èlja come—I almost wrote return—to Prague. Èlik, everything will be fine, just come! If you do not come, both I and you (without fail you) will regret it for life.

Roma

Elsa, come! Without "compassion," there is no "home" anyway.

15. TO ELSA TRIOLET

[Prague,] 11 March [1923]

Èlechka, in Moscow you showed me some letters to you,—whose, I forget,—and said: here's a person who is able to write beautiful letters. You said this as a reproach, and I envied to tears this person, who was able to write and whom you of course liked as a result. Later I myself learned to write beautiful letters and "to be pleasant in society" (your other demand). But now I hate more than anything in the world such beautiful letters and such pleasantness. I would like just one thing—to write you in a completely unliterary way a simply unpublishable letter, a letter that it would be impossible to submit for copying and carry the copy to a publisher. I don't want to "compress life," as certain acquaintances say, and to write letters to you for a publisher, as these acquaintances do. For me you are not a literary motif, nor a poetic heroine.[1]

When M-lle Dache brought me to you fifteen years ago, I said afterwards: "We spent a very pleasant time, and she speaks in such a literary way.—I said to Elsa (I forget about what) that is was as 'tall as a lanky person,' and she replied—'as tall as the Suxarev Tower.'" Èlechka, understand, my child, I am sick and tired to the point of nausea when people speak in quotations, comparisons, in a literary way.

This is why I haven't written you in such a long time. I want you to understand that my heart and liver really hurt, and not like a person who has taken on the pose of someone whose liver is ill and starts speaking in quotes. I terribly wish I could save you from literary *liver*!

Èlechka my dear, I am sick of everything. I'm sick of literatures and of literature. I'm sick of the fact that Vitja wants to "stage" an incident between me and you, and take for himself the reporter's ticket to the drama, if he doesn't succeed in becoming an actor in a secondary role. Perhaps I'm sinking my teeth into him for no reason, but at the moment it takes me an enormous effort not to sink my teeth into anybody and everybody and then not to howl, cursing, that they have offended me. Èlja, I've grown so tired, and there's such a chaos in my head, that if I once let myself start howling, I'd be unable to stop. It is terribly stupid that my thinking apparatus is working well, but to no purpose and without zeal. I think up reasons to become offended and start bull-fights.

Èlja, in terms of what you said about it "not being fate," that's stupid.

Èlja, write.

I'm strong, and once I've gotten a rest, I'll again do good works, even much better than before, I'll be a happy beast, even more so than before. And I'm glad for you that this whole illness was a literary myth. Be well. There's a terrible lot of fabrication—both the illness and Vitja. There is no sort of bouillon, only Elsa and Roma.

Your question: Sonja?

Sonja has her own, home-bound grammar. When her teacher in the first grade asked her to write on the board an example of a noun of the masculine gender, she wrote: "Kitty!"

Usually people of the so-called nonliterary type prove upon

closer examination to be people of bad literature. But Sonja doesn't have a bad literary tradition. She has her own home-bound literature, grammar, and arithmetic. She doesn't count beyond one. Èlja, let us see one another

Roman

11.III

16. TO ELSA TRIOLET

[Prague,] 27 March [1923]

Èlja,

A letter to you has already laid locked up in a drawer for many days. I didn't send it and haven't written in general because of a certain torpidity.

From Kushner's pious speeches about you I tried to read you cleansed of legend. Perhaps in my letter I was unjust to Vitja, but I don't like his latest numbers ("Laugh, clown" to the tune of a Jazz band). Kushner is mad at me for not being a romantic. I would have written you "don't go to Paris," if I had even the slightest right to do so. I dreamed of you the last few nights with a terrifying verissimilitude, "to the elbow's sharpness, to the veins of your legs."[1] In your speech and gestures there were many details that I had long forgotten in reality. Once I dreamed of you together with Vitja, I hit him, and he shattered, having turned out to be made of plaster. And his plaster head fell off with great verisimilitude. The next morning, when I awoke, Sonja told me that I had never caressed her as I did that night, in dream. In such instances I feel myself to be a rotten scoundrel before her. And now, when I write you, there is the sensation of larceny and deception. Kushner says that I am a business-like person.

27.III

Roma

17. TO ELSA TRIOLET

[Prague,] 26 Dec. [1923]

Èlechka, dearest sister,

I recently became acquainted with a certain Czech lady, who reminds me terribly of you in appearance and manners. Just as I wanted to tell her about this, she said to me: "You are ridiculously similar to someone whom I loved very much." Now it's terribly amusing to read the Czech edition of Elsa.

Èlechka dear, don't be angry that I haven't written. I am tremendously busy at work, making money, and in March will quit my job (this is strictly confidential; don't tell the Briks). I am so sick and tired of attending to someone else's affairs that I want to cry in the evenings.

The news from Moscow is not very cheerful. Vitja plays various games and draws placards. I am not in correspondence with him.[1] Recently a lot of Berliners have been spending time in Prague—Gor´kij, Xodasevich, Èrenburg, Sharik.[2] I went out drinking with Xodasevich; he's quite intelligent and pleasant in company.[3] He told by in passing (without any questions or tales from my side) about his misunderstanding with Vitja. At Gor´kij's place in Saarow he said: "Vitja has the taste of a Red Army soldier, and his women should be like Red Army soldiers. Meeting Elsa was for him a meeting with a lady of fashion, with whom a Red Army man falls in love by contrast." Everything else, according to him, is an invention.

For a long time after I came back from Berlin I dreamed that I was meeting with you, and suddenly for different reasons we became separated. This turned into a whole cycle of adventurous dreams from which I awoke with a headache. The last time in Berlin, after the evening ended in a regular "perfect paradox," *j'étais tout à fait abruti* and didn't understand a thing that we said in our parting meetings. I only remember distinctly how you put on your stockings. I would very much like to see you again, only without a regular burial service, as the last times, and without parting kisses completely like carrying a coffin out of the church. I've been living with Sonja *en bons camarades;* she's in Moscow now, and I'm very bored.

Don't be angry, Èlechka, neither at this letter, nor at me; at the moment I am completely engulfed by the effort not to get bogged down in a whimpering life. Write in more detail about yourself. I won't take so long to answer. I am terribly delighted by your letters.

By the way, I'm thinking whether I shouldn't move to Paris by the middle of 1924. I'm somewhat sick of Prague, I don't like Berlin, and at the moment Moscow is quite tedious.

Send the manuscript as soon as you can to my home address: Praha VII. Bělského tř. 16.

Your Roma

Happy New Year, Happy new plans!

PART THREE

ESSAYS

FUTURISM

It was in the twentieth century that painting first consistently broke off with the tendencies of naive realism. In the last century the picture was obliged to convey perception; the artist was a slave to routine, and he consciously ignored both everyday and scientific experience. As if what we know about an object were one thing, and the direct content of a presentation of objects were an entirely different thing—and the two completely unrelated. As if we knew an object only from one side, from one point of view, as if, upon seeing a forehead, we forget that the nape of the neck exists, as if the neck were the dark side of the moon, unknown and unseen. Similar to the way in which in old novels the events are presented to us only so far as they are known to the hero. One can find attempts at doubling points of view on an object even in the old painting, motivated by the reflection of a landscape or of a body in the water or in a mirror. Compare likewise the device in Old Russian painting of depicting a martyr in one and the same picture twice or three times in contiguous stages of an action in the process of unfolding. But it was Cubism that first canonized multiple points of view. Deformation was realized in earlier pictorial art on an insignificant scale: for example, hyperbole was tolerated, or the deformation was motivated by an application that was humorous (caricature), ornamental (teratology), or finally by the data of nature itself (chiaroscuro). Freed from motivational motifs by the acts of Cézanne, deformation was canonized by Cubism.

The Impressionists, applying the experience of science, had decomposed color into its component parts. Color ceased to be subjugated to the sensation of the nature depicted. There appeared blotches of color, even chromatic combinations, which copied nothing, which were not imposed upon the picture from without. The creative mastery of color naturally led to a realization of the following law: any increase in form is accompanied by a change in color, and any change in color generates new forms (a formulation of Gleizes and Metzinger).[1]

In science this law was first advanced, it seems, by Stumpf, one of the pioneers of the new psychology, who spoke about the correlation between color and colored spatial form: quality shares in changes of extension. When extension is changed, quality is also transformed. Quality and extension are by nature inseparable and cannot be imagined independently of one another. This obligatory connection may be opposed to the empirical connectedness of two parts lacking such an obligatory character, e.g., a head and torso. Such parts can be imagined separately.[2]

The set (ustanovka)[3] toward nature created for painting an obligatory connection precisely of such parts which in essence disconnected, whereas the mutual dependence of form and color was not recognized. On the contrary, a set toward pictorial expression resulted in the creative realization of the necessity of the latter connection, where the object is freely interpenetrated by other forms (so-called Divisionism). Line and surface attract the artist's attention; he cannot exclusively copy the boundaries of nature. The Cubist consciously cuts nature up with surfaces, introduces arbitrary lines.

The emancipation of painting from elementary illusionism entails an intensive elaboration of various areas of pictorial expression. The correlations of volumes, constructive asymmetry, chromatic contrast, and texture enter the foreground of the artist's consciousness.

The results of this realization are the following: (1) the canonization of a series of devices, which thus also allows one to speak of Cubism as a school; (2) the laying bare of the device. Thus the realized texture no longer seeks any sort of justification for itself; it becomes autonomous, demands for itself new methods of formulation, new material. Pieces of paper begin to be pasted on the picture, sand is thrown on it. Finally, cardboard, wood, tin, and so on, are used.

Futurism brings with it practically no new pictorial devices; instead, it widely utilizes Cubist methods. It is not a new school of painting, but rather a new aesthetics. The very approach to the picture, to painting, to art, changes. Futurism offers picture-slogans, pictorial demonstrations. It has no fixed, crystallized canons. Futurism is the antipode of classicism.

Without a set, to use a psychological term, without a style, to use a term from art criticism, there can be no presentation of an object. For the nineteenth century, what is characteristic is a striving to see things as they were seen in the past, as it is customary to see: to see like Raphael, like Botticelli. The present was projected into the past, and the past dictated the future, all according to the famous formula: "Another day has gone by, praise the Lord. Lord grant tomorrow be the same."[4]

What art, if not representational art, could serve so successfully the basic tendency of fixing the instant of movement, of breaking down a movement into a series of separate static elements? But static perception is a fiction. As a matter of fact, "everything is moving, everything is quickly being transformed.

A profile never remains motionless before one's eyes; it continuously appears and disappears. As a result of the stability of the image on the retina, objects multiply, are deformed, follow one another, like hurried vibrations in the space one is running through. So it is that running horses have not four legs but twenty, and their movements are triangular" (from a manifesto of Futurist artists).[5]

Static, one-sided, isolated perception—a pictorial anachronism—is something in the nature of the classical muses, gods, and lyres. But we are no longer shooting out of a harquebus or traveling in a heavy carriage. The new art has put an end to static forms; it has even put an end to the last fetish of the static: beauty. In painting nothing is absolute. What was true for the artists of yesterday is today a lie, as one Futurist manifesto puts it.

The overcoming of *statics,* the discarding of the absolute, is the main thrust of modern times, the order of the day. A negative philosophy and tanks, scientific experiment and deputies of Soviets, the principle of relativity and the Futurist "Down With!"[6] are destroying the garden hedges of the old culture. The unity of the fronts of attack is astonishing.

"At the present time we are again experiencing a period in which the old scientific edifice is crumbling, but the crumbling is so complete that it is unprecedented in the history of science. But even that is not all. Among the truths being destroyed are ones which were never even uttered by anyone, which were never emphasized, so self-apparent did they seem, so unconsciously were they used and posited as the basis for every sort of reasoning." A particularly characteristic feature of the new doctrine is the unprecedented paradoxical nature of many of even its simplest propositions: they clearly contradict what is usually called "common sense."[7]

The last sign of substance is vanishing from the physical world. "How do we picture time to ourselves? As something flowing continuously and homogeneously, with an eternal, identical speed everywhere. One and the same time flows in the entire world; it is quite obvious that there cannot be two times which flow in different parts of the universe at different speeds. Closely connected with this are our conceptions of the simultaneity of two events, of 'before' and of 'after,' for these three most elementary notions are accessible even to an infant; they have an identical sense, by whomever or wherever they are used. The concept of time conceals for us something absolute, something completely unrelative. But the new doctrine rejects the absolute character of time, and therefore the existence of 'world' time as well. Every identical self-moving system has its own time; the speed of timeflow is not identical in each such system." Does absolute peace of mind exist, even if only in the form of an abstract concept which has no real existence in nature? From the principle of relativity it follows that absolute peace of mind does not exist.

"Time gets involved in all spatial dimensions. We cannot define the geometrical form of a body which is in motion in relation to us. We define always its kinetic form. Thus our spatial dimensions occur in reality not in a three-dimensional, but in a four-dimensional variety."

"These pictures in the field of philosophical thought should produce a revolution greater than Copernicus' displacement of the earth from the center of the universe . . . Does not the power of the natural sciences make itself felt in the transition from an undisputed experimental fact—the impossibility of determining the absolute motion of the earth—to questions of the psyche? The contemporary philosopher cries out in embarrassment: There is nothing but deceit on that side of the truth."

"The newly discovered offers a sufficient quantity of images for the construction of the world, but they break its former architecture, so familiar to us, and can be fit only within the boundaries of a new style, one which far out-distances in its free lines the borders not only of the old external world, but also of the basic forms of our thinking."

(Direct quotations in this and the preceding four paragraphs are from O.D. Xvol′son, *The Principle of Relativity*, and N.A. Umov, *The Characteristic Features of Contemporary Natural-Scientific Thought.*)

The basic tendencies of collectivist thought: the destruction of abstract fetishism, the destruction of the remnants of statics (Bogdanov, *The Sciences of Social Consciousness*).[8] And so the main lines of the moment are obvious in all domains of culture.

If Cubism, following Cézanne's behests, constructed a picture by starting from the simplest volumes—the cube, cone, sphere—offering its own sort of primitiveness in painting, then the Futurists in search of kinetic forms introduced into the picture the curved cone, the curved cylinder, collisions of cones with sharp, curved ellipsoids, and so on, in a word, destroying the mountings of volumes (see Carra's manifesto).[9]

Perceptions, in multiplying, become mechanized; objects, not being perceived, are taken on faith. Painting battles against the automatization of perception; it signals the object. But, having become antiquated, artistic forms are also perceived on faith. Cubism and Futurism widely use the device of impeded perception, which corresponds in poetry to the step-ladder construction discovered by contemporary theoreticians.

In the fact that even the most discerning eye is able only with difficulty to make sense of objects that have been totally transubstantiated, there is a particular charm. A picture that gives itself with such reserve expects precisely that it will be questioned again and again. Let us take Leonardo da Vinci's words as a defense of Cubism in this respect:

> We know well that our sight, by rapid observations, discovers in one point an infinity of forms: nevertheless it only understands one thing at a time. Suppose that you, reader, were to see the whole of this page at a glance, and concluded instantly that it is full of various letters; you would not at the same moment know what letters they are, nor what they would mean. You would have to go from one word to another and from line to line if you would wish to know these letters, just as you would have to climb step by step to reach the top of a building, or else never reach the top. (Cited by Gleizes and Metzinger.)[10]

A particular instance of impeded recognition in painting, i.e., a construction of the type—this is a lion, not a dog—is like a riddle which deliberately leads us to a false solution; compare the so-called "false recognition" of classical poetics or the negative parallelism of the Slavic epic.[11] Aristotle: "For men delight in seeing likenesses because in contemplating them it happens that they are learning and reasoning out what each thing is, e.g. that this man [in the painting] is that [sort of man]; for if by fortune one has not previously seen what is imitated, the likeness will not produce pleasure as an imitation, but because of its execution, or surface coloring, or some other cause of this sort."[12] In other words, it was already clear to Aristotle that alongside a type of painting that signals the perception of nature, there exists a type of painting that signals our direct chromatic and spatial perception (it does not matter whether the object is unknown or whether it has simply dropped out of the picture).

When a critic looking at such pictures is at a loss and asks: "What in the world does this mean, I don't understand"—and what precisely does he want to understand?—he is like the metaphysician of the fable: they want to pull him out of the hole in the ground he's in and all he can do is ask: "What sort of thing is rope?"[13] More briefly: for him, perception that is valuable in and of itself does not exist. He prefers paper currency to gold: currency, with its conventionally assigned value, seems to him more "literary."

THE TASKS OF ARTISTIC PROPAGANDA

Is it possible to conceive of a form of artistic propaganda which is outside of any party, objective, and all-inclusive?

Is it possible simultaneously to inculcate in the masses all of the aesthetic systems that exist in the given moment?

If an organ of artistic propaganda wants to adopt the role of being an artistic Meriliz,[1] then one can doubtlessly do so.

In such a case, one's basic slogan would be: whatever you want.

One would have to have in stock primarily a popular line of goods, selected by the customers' demands.

One would have to offer, above all, the sort of goods that are readily available, that are quantitatively rich. But such goods are stale. A quick sale requires creating goods which are sold as quickly and as easily as possible and in a maximum quantity. These are, clearly, all sorts of clichés.

From the above one can only deduce that customer demand defines the value of an artistic trend, that the value of an artistic exhibition be measured by its rate of attendance, that only a plebiscite can clarify the value of one or another artistic work, as was practised in part during the period of the flowering of aesthetic liberalism under the so-called "Itinerant" school of artists.

But one does not choose artistic forms the same way that one chooses a pair of gloves in a fashionable store.

People forget the fact that the life of art entails a change in the methods of formulation, that for every form there comes a moment when it "is transformed from a progressive form of productional forces into their chains" (Marx).[2]

A new artistic form is a deformation of the old, a protest against it. A peaceful coexistence in time of two artistic forms is as inconceivable as the coexistence of two geometrical bodies in space. The old art, destroyed by the attack of the new, leaves behind various so-called "cultural survivals." They differ from a live social fact by the absence of any tendency other than a conservative one.

In so far as the tasks of genuine revolutionary artistic propaganda are to revolutionize cultural, particularly aesthetic, habits, it should, with all the means at its disposal, destroy and nullify all these cultural survivals. In other words, the elimination of artistic statics, the battle with epigonism, is the task of artistic enlightenment. The apologia for eclecticism, for artistic compromise, signifies a revolutionary debility, a creative impotence. An epidemic of such compromise coincides with moments of social decadence. This was the case at the beginning of the war, when even certain left artists wailed about "a united aesthetic Russia."[3]

Those who project the muses into life, who cry out for tolerance in art, are akin to the adherents of "pure democracy," who, in Lenin's words, take a formal similarity for a factual one.[4]

At the moment, when the revolution in art is sharper, perhaps, than it has even been, when the old aesthetics, which pervaded all aspects of life, is rotting away in every nook and cranny, interferring with a new, live aesthetics, it is not the task of an organization promoting artistic enlightenment to pour a conciliatory balm on the issue, but to reveal the growing conflicts—not to neutralize, but to sharpen the struggle of artistic trends, for in that struggle lies the life and development of art.

NEW ART IN THE WEST
(A LETTER FROM REVAL)

The topic of the day in German art is Expressionism. The newspapers blare out the word Expressionism, using this term as a generalization for every novelty in art; studies of Expressionism are coming out in bundles, as are expressionistic poems, exhibitions, debates, humor, expressionistic theatrical productions. Expressionism as an artistic current is enveloping Czechoslovakia, Latvia, Finland.

In artistic publications, and even in the columns of the *Vossische Zeitung*, there are philological quarrels about the origin of the very term "Expressionism."

Leaving aside the attempts of the journal *Der Sturm* to trace this term in its contemporary meaning to Thomas Aquinas, let me cite Th. Däubler's book *In The Struggle for Contemporary Art*: "The word 'expressionism' was first used, probably, by Matisse, but de Vauxcelles, the critic from *Gil Blas*, first put it into circulation socially. It is possible that its origin is even more far removed. They say that Paul Cassirer tossed it out once in an oral polemic. To be more precise, it was at a meeting of the jury of the Berlin group 'Secession.' Someone asked, it seems, in relation to a picture by Pechstein: 'What's this, more impressionism?' He replied: 'No, it's expressionism.' Juli Elias, in the journal *Kunstblatt*, ascertains that the term was first applied by the artist Julien-August Hervé for a cycle of his paintings as early as 1901."[1]

The history of the rise of Expressionism as an artistic trend is drawn in German studies in the following features. (I translate the German characterization, lyrically verbose and bombastic, rich with the fog of the German *style moderne*, into the terse language of Russian revolutionary aesthetics.)

Every artistic trend is a particular ideographic system. When speaking of pictorial expression, the representatives of a certain trend have in mind only the expressive system given in that trend, and view past art through the prism of that system. Naturalism, which arose as a reaction to a certain ideographic system, little by little reduced to zero its own pictorial-ideographic set. Impressionism, the logical deduction of naturalism, was conceived by its creators as an approximation to nature (*Naturnähe*), while its viewers, who were brought up on the previous ideographic system, regarded it as a contradiction of nature (*naturwidrig*). The more the artist destroys the established ideogram in a revolutionary way, the more distinctly his violation is sensed as a rejection of verisimilitude, as an "unnatural" art. And to the degree to which this "unnaturalness" becomes canonized, to the extent to which it is deprived of a naturalistic motivation, the more we go from Impressionism to Expressionism. One should seek the latter's closest relatives at the periphery of the past art, and precisely—as Landsberger indicates in his book *Impressionism and Expressionism*[2]—in the simplifying tendency of the poster, in contemporary caricature, which widely utilizes its old right to violate nature and teaches us to laugh at what is later done in all seriousness. Impressionism, with its set toward heightened color, had already laid bare the brush stroke. From there it is but one step to van Gogh, who proclaimed: "Instead of trying to reproduce exactly what I see before my eyes, I use color more arbitrarily, in order to express myself forcibly." This leads to color hyperbole ("I exaggerate the fairness of the hair," says van Gogh, "I even get to orange tones, chromes and pale citron-yellow"),[3] to a color epithet ("Such is van Dongen, when he paints green stockings, red cheeks, blue eyes"—Däubler), to color metonymy ("The artist Jawlensky has red cheeks that are no longer cheeks, but the color red"—Däubler). From this it is but a step to the laying-bare of color, to the emancipation of color from the object. As an example of such emancipation Däubler cites the painting of Kandinskij and Klee. The path from decorative graphics to the obtrusive contours of expressionistic painting is conditioned by the same fact. There are quite a few survivals of naturalism in the theory of Expressionism, which are explicitly revealed in Landsberger's book: "Herman Bahr proceeds from an identification of the history of painting with the history of vision, supposing that a new vision is the obligatory precondition for new representational devices. To the simple visual perception which formed the basis of Impressionism, contemporaneity juxtaposes afresh an internal contemplation, a vision of the spirit, and similarly to the way in which this contemplation presents us with unprecedental images, art, which is based on them, should be unlike reality. The understanding of art as a means of conveying vision is a survival of Impression; it presupposes an artist who realizes his impressions, whether external or internal, in an indifferent way. What is ignored here is the artist's struggle with the object of perception."[4]

In other words, the problem of aesthetic formulation is alien to the epigones of Impressionism. This is found in the works of Däubler and Wirchner,[5] as well as—to a significant degree—in the theories of French Cubism and Italian Futurism, those peculiar realizations of Expressionism. Thus Futurism appears at times to be a "paroxysm of Impressionism." Landsberger is correct when he says that interpretations of the Cubo-Futurist deformation of the object are borrowed to a great degree from the language of Naturalism: "They say that a quickly-moving object decomposes itself for the eye, that we view an object at different moments or from different points of view. Actually, the decisive factor is the demand for a deformation of reality. In precisely such a way the theoretician of abstract art Kandinskij declares: 'What is beautiful is that which answers an internal necessity of the soul.' He walks the slippery path of psychologism, and if he were to be consistent he would have to admit that, in that case, one would have to relate the category of the beautiful first and foremost to one's own handwriting."

The emotional interpretation of color is extremely individual, as Landsberger notes. Thus, Hebbel notes in his diary:[6] When you see a white mass, you freeze; when you see white images, you get frightened. The snow is white, ghosts appear to be white, and so on, but otherwise white can be the color of innocence, or joy, or even sorrow, depending on what objective associations are evoked. Abstract art, contrary to its theoreticians, signifies a total withering away of pictorial semantics, in other words, easel painting loses its raison d'être.

The names of the Expressionist artists, announced in the German studies about the new art, include: Albert Bloch, Lionel Feininger (a Cubist), Otto Mueller, E. Nolde, Georg Grosz, Kandinskij, Franz Marc, Pechstein, Schmidt-Rotluff, Kurt Badt, Ernst Fritsch, Artur Grunenberg, Wilhem Kohlhoff, Bruno Krauskopf, Erik Maria Kunzig, Ludwig Meidner, Martel Schwichtenberg, Eric Waske, and others; the sculptors Archipenko, Wilhem Lehmbruck, Ernst Barlach; the architect Hans Poelzig.

The center of German Expressionism is Berlin.

A characteristic feature of German books about Expressionism is the attempt to explain new artistic phenomena sociologically. Thus Däubler ascribes the reactionary trend in French art of the beginning of the twentieth century, which demanded a return to the classical tradition, to a certain political milieu—royalists, Bonapartists, clerics. About Impressionism the same writer says: *"Vielleicht war er Demokrat, selten aber Sozialist."* Thus, finally, Landsberger, who in his interesting book on Expressionism has broken away from the modernist interpretation of modern art in many respects, attempts to illuminate Expressionism in a sociological way, but in this case he is close to the dogmas of modern aesthetics. "We live," he writes, "or at least we lived before the revolution, in conditions of ever growing rationalization and mechanization. Art has become ever more important as an irrational form of being free from any constraint. Surprise at the world becomes the exclusive fate of the artist. A person is already deprived of the possibility of expressing his individuality in the actual world, as a result of which the cult of free creativity has been transferred entirely into the realm of art. It is there that the hero of our time flourishes; it is there that the creator's triumph over nature is accomplished."

By the way, on political groupings. A characteristic page is the Whites' attacks on modern art. An example is the article by the venerable Repin in the columns of the Russian newspaper *Time* in Berlin (February 11th of this year), "Proletarian Art." The entire article from beginning to end is shameless cursing: "senseless slavish muscular contortions," "characterless scribbles," "nonsense," "the vile rollicking of Bolsheviks," "having gotten fattened up, that is, having eaten the neck of a bird that strayed from the flock, having stuffed themselves on sheep tails, they sit in the motherland and suck out of her the

internephritic juice, and, shielding themselves from intoxica-
tion by the imported wine of the bourgeosie, these birds of
prey go into a dance, embracing their fat wallets of false value-
lessness! What can be more revolting than when they shed a
tear of emotion over their satiation. . . . Ugh! What filth! Well,
what art could such hog-swines emit from their wombs" and
so on.[7]

The investigators of the new art touch in passing on questions of "artistic politics." If we are unconcerned, Däubler says,
whether private persons hang nasty pictures on the walls of
their apartments or display worthless marble wares, it is entirely another matter with architecture. Here the government
needs to make a certain choice, to exert a certain pressure. But
in the realm of the arts the question of the government's artistic politics is also pressing. Thus, in the Riga newspaper *Today*
there is an article by Simakov on "Artistic Politics." The author
thinks that in a democratic government, "the sole healthy basis
for artistic development should be private philanthropy." But
he is immediately forced to admit that at the latest Latvian
artistic exhibitions, "almost the only purchaser was the Ministry
of Foreign Affairs." And if the government buys and encour-
ages art, then what does it mean to buy and encourage art? For
it's impossible to buy and encourage everything. And here a
practical misunderstanding arises: "a lot of young Expressionist
artists who made much noise received gratis as studios the vast
premises of the former Artistic School of Riga, which had been
requisitioned by the city's martial authorities. When the city's
former mayor stated that the school's accommodations were
needed by the city for more pressing concerns than the encouragement of beginners and the extremely questionable merit of
artists, he was subjected to accusations of obscurantism and a
lack of culture."[8]

I have less information at my disposal on what is going on in the artistic life of the Atlantic states. France is living out Cubism, which has received wide public recognition. Both Larionov, who is thriving despite the current gossip in Moscow, and Goncharova are playing a major role in the artistic life of France. After the war Futurism established itself solidly in Italy, gained a wide popularity, "wurde zur Macht," as Däubler says. Of the Italian Futurist painters the most famous one is Carrà. But Italian Futurism has hardly evolved as an artistic trend in the last few years and has instead acquired an ever greater publicistic significance. Marinetti issued a book entitled *La révolution futuriste*, which is a fantastic medley of hyperchauvanism and revolutionary maximalism, of naive nationalism and slogans.[9] Recently there has emerged an extremely leftist group of Italian communist Futurists, whose aesthetic slogans are also of the most radical type.[10] In 1916–1917 Futurism penetrated America and captivated progressive intellectual circles, students and so on.

DADA

Dada means nothing.
Dada 3, 1918

Dilettantes, rise up against art!
Poster at Dada exhibition,
Berlin, June 1920

In these days of petty affairs and stable values, social thought is subjugated to the laws of bell-ringing patriotism. Just as, for a child, the world does not extend beyond the nursery, and everything outside that realm is thought of by analogy, so the petty bourgeois evaluates all cities in comparison to his native city. Citizens of a somewhat higher order lay everything that relates, if not to a different city, then to a foreign country, on the Procrustean bed of the *homely* and dance according to the tune of their native culture. One's own little world and all that is "translatable" into one's own dialect versus the incomprehensible barbarians—such is the usual scheme. Is this not the reason for the fact that sailors are revolutionary, that they lack that very "stove," that hearth, that little house of their own, and are everywhere equally *chez soi*? Limitation in time corresponds to limitation in space; the past is normally depicted by a series of metaphors whose material is the present. But at the moment, despite the fact that Europe has been turned into a multiplicity of isolated points by visas, currencies, cordons of all sorts, space is being reduced in gigantic strides—by radio, the telephone, aeroplanes. Even if the books and pictures do not get through today, beleaguered as they are by chauvinism and the "hard currency" of state national borders, nevertheless the questions that are being decided today somewhere in Versailles[1] are questions of self-interest for the Silesian worker, and if the price of bread rises, the hungry city-dweller begins to "feel" world politics. The appeal to one's countrymen loses its conviction. Even the humorists are crying that there is no longer an established order of things (*byt*).[2] Values are not in demand.

What corresponds in scientific thought to this sudden "swing"? Replacing the science of the "thousand and first example," inescapable in days when the formula "So it was, so it shall be" ruled,[3] when tomorrow put itself under the obligation of resembling today, and when every respectable man had his own *chez soi*, there suddenly appears the science of relativity. For yesterday's physicist, if not our earth, then at least our space and our time were the only possible ones and imposed themselves on all worlds; now they are proclaimed to be merely particular instances. Not a single trace of the old physics has remained. The old physicists have three arguments: "He's a Jew," "He's a Bolshevik," "It contradicts 'common sense.'"[4]

The great historian Spengler, in his outspoken book *The Decline of the West* (1920),[5] says that history never existed and is not possible as a science, and above all that there was never a sense of proportions. Thus the African divides the world into his village and "the rest"—and the moon seems smaller to him than the cloud covering it. According to Spengler, when Kant philosophizes about norms, he is sure of the actuality of his propositions for people of all times and nations, but he does not state this outright, since he and his readers take it for granted.

But in the meanwhile the norms he established are obligatory only for Western modes of thought.

It is characteristic that ten years ago Velimir Xlebnikov wrote: "Kant, thinking to establish the boundaries of human reason, determined only the boundaries of the German mind. The slight absent-mindedness of a scholar."[6] Spengler compares his strictly relativistic system to Copernicus' discoveries. It would be more correct to compare it to Einstein's; the Copernican system corresponds rather to the transition from the history of Christianity to the history of mankind. Spengler's book has caused a good deal of noise in the press. *The Vossische Zeitung* concluded: "Ah, relativism! Why say such sad things?" There appeared a voluminous reproof that succeeded in finding a true antidote to Spengler's system. This rebuke resounded from the church pulpit. This is no personal whim—the power of the Vatican is growing; the pope has not had so many nuncios for a long time. It is not without reason that the French government, rejoicing that France has finally disengaged itself from its revolutionary past, is in such a hurry to stress its piousness.

In all domains of science there is the same total rout of the old, the rejection of the local point of view, and new giddy perspectives. One's most elementary premises, which were unshakeable not so long ago, now clearly reveal their provisional character. Thus Buxarin, in his *The Economics of the Transitional Period*, discloses the meaninglessness of the Marxist concepts of "value," "goods," and so on, in application to our time, the fact that they are connected to certain already crystallized forms, the fact that they are particular instances.[7]

Relevant here too is the aesthetics of Futurism, which refused to write beauty and art with capital letters. But Western Futurism is two-faced. On the one hand, it was the first to

become aware of the tautological nature of the old formula—
"In the name of beauty we are destroying all laws"—from
which it follows that the history of every new current in comparison to its predecessor is a legalization of illegality; hence it
would seem that there can be no punitive sanctions on what is
possible in art, since instead of a decreed new beauty there is a
consciousness of the particularity, the episodic nature of each
artistic manifestation. It would seem that the scientific, historically minded Futurists, who rejected the past point-blank precisely because of their historicity, are the first who cannot create a new canon. On the other hand, Western Futurism in all
of its variants endeavors to become an artistic movement (the
thousand and first). "Classics of Futurism" is an oxymoron if
you take as your starting point the original conception of
Futurism; nevertheless, it has come to "classics," or to a need for
them. "One of the innumerable isms," said the critics, and
found Futurism's Achilles' heel. The demand arose for a new
differentiation, "a manifestation parallel to the relativistic
philosophies of the current moment—a 'nonaxiom,'" as one of
the literary pioneers, Huelsenbeck, announced.[8] "I'm against
systems; the most acceptable system is to have absolutely no
system at all," added another pioneer, the Romanian Tristan
Tzara.[9] There follow battle cries repeating Marinetti: "Down
with all that is like a mummy and sits solidly!" Hence "anticul-
tural propaganda," "Bolshevism in art."[10] "The gilding is crumbling off, off the French, like any other. If you tremble, gentlemen, for the morals of your wives, for the tranquility of your
cooks and the faithfulness of your mistresses, for the solidity of
your rockingchairs and your nightpots, for the security of your
government, you are right. But what will you do about it? You
are rotting, and the fire has already begun" (Ribemont-
Dessaignes).[11] "I smash," exclaims Tzara somewhat in the tone

of Leonid Andreev, "skull cases and the social organization: all must be demoralized."[12]

There was a need to christen this "systemless" aesthetic rebellion, "this Fronde of great international artistic currents," as Huelsenbeck put it.[13] In 1916 "Dada" was named. The name, along with the commentaries that followed, at once knocked out of the hands of critics their main weapon—the accusation of charlatanism and trickery. "Futurism sings of . . ." Marinetti used to write—and then came columns of objects celebrated by Futurism. The critic would pick up a Futurist almanac, leaf through its pages, and conclude: "I don't see it." "Futurism concludes," "Futurism bears with it," "Futurism conceals," wrote the ideologists who had become infected with the exoterica of Symbolism. "I don't see it! Ah, the frauds!" answered the critic. "'Futurism is the art of the future,' they say," he would reflect, "why, it's a lie!" "'Expressionism is expressive art'—they lie!" But "Dada," what does "Dada" mean? "Dada means nothing," the Dadaists hastened to reply, running interference as it were. "It doesn't smell of anything, it doesn't mean anything," says the Dada artist Picabia, bending the old Armenian riddle.[14] A Dada manifesto invites the bourgeoisie to create myths about the essence of Dada. "Dada—now there's a word that sets off ideas; each bourgeois is a little playwright, inventing different dialogues."[15] The manifesto informs lovers of etymology that certain blacks call the tail of a holy cow "dada"; in one part of Italy "dada" means mother; in Russian "da" is an affirmation. But "Dada" is connected neither with the one nor the other nor the third. It is simply a meaningless little word thrown into circulation in Europe, a little word with which one can juggle *à l'aise,* thinking up meanings, adjoining suffixes, coining complex words which create the illusion that they refer to objects: dadasopher, dadayama.

"The word dada expresses the internationality of the movement," Huelsenbeck writes. The very question "What is Dada?" is itself undadaistic and sophomoric, he also notes.[17] "What does Dada want?"—"Dada doesn't want anything."[18] "I am writing a manifesto and I don't want anything . . . and I am on principle against manifestoes, as I am also against principles," Tzara declares.[19]

No matter what you accuse Dada of, you can't accuse it of being dishonest, of concealment, of hedging its bets. Dada honorably perceives the "limitedness of its existence in time"; it relativizes itself historically, in its own words.[20] Meanwhile, the first result of establishing a scientific view of artistic expression, that is, the laying bare of the device, is the cry: "The old art is dead" or "Art is dead," depending on the temperament of the person doing the yelling. The first call was issued by the Futurists, hence "*vive le futur!*" The second, not without some stipulations, was issued by Dada—what business of theirs, of artists, is the future?—"*à bas le futur!*" So the improviser from Odoevskij's story, having received the gift of a clarity of vision which laid everything bare, ends his life as a fool in a cap scrawling transrational verses.[21] The laying bare of the device is sharp; it is precisely a laying bare; the already laid-bare device— no longer in sharp confrontation in the long run—is vapid, it lacks flavor. The initially laid-bare device is usually justified and regulated by so-called constructive laws, but, for example, the path from rhyme to assonance to a set toward any relationship between sounds leads to the announcement that a laundry list is a poetic work.[22] Then letters in arbitrary order, randomly struck on a typewriter, are considered verses; dabs on a canvas made by a donkey's tail dipped in paint are considered a painting. With Dada's appeal, "Dilettantes, rise up against art," we have gone from yesterday's cult of "made things" (say, refined assonance) to the poetics of the first word let slip (a laundry list). What is Dada by profession? To use an expression from Moscow artistic jargon, the Dadaists are "painters of the word." They have more declarations than poems and pictures. And actually in their poems and pictures there is nothing new, even if only in comparison to Italian and Russian Futurism. Tatlin's "Maschinenkunst,"[23] universal poems made up of vowels, round verses (simultaneism), the music of noise (bruitism), primitivism—a sort of poetic Berlitz:

> my mother told me to shoo off the hens
> but I cannot chase away the hens. (Tzara)[24]

Finally, paroxysms of naive realism: "Dada has common sense and in a chair sees a chair, in a plum—a plum."[25]

But the crux of the matter lies elsewhere, and the Dadaists understand this. "Dada is not an artistic movement," they say. "In Switzerland Dada is for abstract (nonobjective) art, in Berlin—against." What is important is that, having finished once and for all with the principle of the legendary coalition of form and content, through a realization of the violence of artistic form, the toning down of pictorial and poetic semantics, through the color and texture *as such* of the nonobjective picture, through the fanatic word of transrational verses *as such*, we come in Russia to the blue grass of the first celebrations of October[26] and in the West to the unambiguous Dadaist formula: *"Nous voulons nous voulons nous voulons pisser en couleurs diverses."*[27] Coloring *as such!* Only the canvas is removed, like an act in a sideshow one has grown tired of.

Poetry and painting became for Dada one of the acts of the sideshow. Let us be frank: poetry and painting occupy in our consciousness an excessively high position only because of tradition. "The English are so sure of the genius of Shakespeare that they don't consider it necessary even to read him," as Aubrey Beardsley puts it. We are prepared to respect the classics but for reading prefer literature written for train rides: detective stories, novels about adultery, that whole area of "belles-lettres" in which the *word* makes itself least heard. Dostoevskij, if one reads him inattentively, quickly becomes a cheap best seller, and it is hardly by chance that in the West they prefer to see his works in the movies. If the theaters are full, then it is more a matter of tradition than of interest on the part of the public. The theater is dying; the movies are blossoming. The screen ceases bit by bit to be the equivalent of the stage; it frees itself of the theatrical unities, of the theatrical mise en scène. The aphorism of the Dadaist Mehring is timely: "The popularity of an idea springs from the possibility of transferring onto film its anecdotal content."[28] For variety's sake the Western reader is willing to accept a peppering of self-valuable words. The Parisian newspaper *Le Siècle* states: "We need a literature which the mind can savor like a cocktail."[29] During the last decade, no one has brought to the artistic market so much varied junk of all times and places as the very people who reject the past. It should be understood that the Dadaists are also eclectics, though theirs is not the museum-bound eclecticism of respectful veneration, but a motley *café-chantant* program (not by chance was Dada born in a cabaret in Zurich). A little song of the Maoris takes turns with a Parisian music-hall number, a sentimental lyric—with the above-mentioned color effect. "I like an old work for its novelty. Only contrast links us to the past," Tzara explains.[30]

One should take into account the background against which Dada is frolicking in order to understand certain of its manifestations. For example, the infantile anti-French attacks of the

French Dadaists and the anti-German attacks of the Germans ten years ago might have sounded naive and purposeless. But today, in the countries of the Entente there rages an almost zoological nationalism, while in response to it in Germany there grows the hypertrophied national pride of an oppressed people. The Royal British Society contemplates refusing Einstein a medal so as not to export gold to Germany,[31] while the French newspapers are outraged by the fact that Hamsun, who according to rumor was a Germanophile during the war, was given a Nobel Prize. The politically innocent Dada arouses terrible suspicion on the part of those same papers that it is some sort of German machination, while those papers print advertisements for "nationalistic double beds." Against this background, the Dadaist Fronde is quite understandable. At the present moment, when even scientific ties have been severed, Dada is one of the few truly international societies of the bourgeois intelligentsia.

By the way, it is a unique Internationale; the Dadaist Bauman lays his cards on the table when he says that "Dada is the product of international hotel foyers."[32] The environment in which Dada was reared was that of the adventuristic bourgeoisie of the war—the profiteers, the nouveaux riches, the smugglers, the black-marketeers, or whatever else they were called. Dada's sociopsychological twins in old Spain gave birth to the so-called picaresque novel. They know no traditions (*"je ne veux meme pas savoir s'il y a eu des hommes avant moi"*);[33] their future is doubtful (*"à bas le futur"*); they are in a hurry to take what is theirs ("give and take, live and die").[34] They are exceptionally supple and adaptable ("one can perform contrary actions at the same time, in a single, fresh breath");[35] they are artists at what they do ("advertising and business are also poetic elements").[36] They do not object to the war ("still today for war");[37] yet they are the first to proclaim the cause of erasing the boundaries between yesterday's warring powers ("me, I'm of many nationalities").[38] When it comes right down to it, they are satisfied and therefore prefer bars ("he holds war and peace in his toga, but decides in favor of a cherry brandy flip").[39] Here, amid the "cosmopolitan mixture of god and the bordello," in Tzara's testimonial, Dada is born.[40]

"The time is Dada-ripe," Huelsenbeck assures us. "With Dada it will ascend, and with Dada it will vanish."[41]

THE NEWEST RUSSIAN POETRY: VELIMIR XLEBNIKOV [EXCERPTS]

It is difficult to avoid schematization and a certain mechanical approach when we deal with the facts of a language spoken in the past. Even the specialist in language finds an everyday conversation more understandable than the *Stoglav*.[1] In just the same way Pushkin's verse—*as a poetic fact*—is less intelligible and more obscure than that of Majakovskij or Xlebnikov.

We apprehend each new manifestation of the contemporary poetic language in its necessary relationship with three factors: the existing poetic tradition, the everyday language of the present time, and the developing poetic tendencies with which the given manifestation is confronted.

Xlebnikov describes the latter factor as follows: "When I observed how old poetry suddenly grew dim when the future that was hidden in it became the present day, I understood that the native land of creative work is the future. It is from the future that the wind of the gods of poetry blows."

When we deal with poets of the past, these factors must be reconstructed, and this can be done only partially and with great difficulty.

When Pushkin's poetry first appeared it was, in the expression of a journal of his time, "a phenomenon in the history of the Russian language and versification"; and at that time critics did not ponder over "the wisdom of Pushkin," but rather asked: "Why do these beautiful verses have meaning? Why do they affect more than just our hearing?"

Today Pushkin is a common household word, a repository of household philosophy. Pushkin's verse, as verse, is now simply taken on faith: having become the object of a kind of cult, it has petrified. It is not surprising that even experts on Pushkin such as Lerner and Shchegolev[2] fell for the bait when they took a clever counterfeit by a certain young poet as an authentic work of the great master.

Pushkin-like poems are now as easy to print as counterfeit Kerenskij[3] bills; they lack any value of their own and circulate only in the absence of good hard cash.

We are inclined to speak of ease and unobtrusiveness of technique as the characteristic features of Pushkin. But this is an error of perspective. Pushkin's verse is for us an established form; our conclusion that it is simple follows from this. It was a quite different matter for Pushkin's contemporaries. Consider their reaction, and that of Pushkin himself. For example, an iambic pentameter without a caesura seems to us quite smooth and easy. But Pushkin had a special feeling for it, he sensed it as a difficult form and as a violent departure from earlier practice:

> To tell the truth, in a pentameter
> I love a caesura on the second foot.
> If not, the line moves from pit to knoll.
> Although now I'm lying comfortably on a soft bed,
> It seems to me I am speeding in a cart
> In a jolting dash across a frozen field.

Form exists for us only as long as it is difficult to perceive, as long as we sense the resistance of the material, as long as we waver as to whether what we read is prose or poetry, as long as our "cheekbones ache," as General Ermolov's cheekbones ached, according to Pushkin's report, during the reading of Griboedov's[4] verse.

And yet even now scholarship deals only with deceased poets, or if now and then live ones are touched upon, it is only such as are firmly established in many volumes and by wide circulation. What has become a truism in the study of everyday language is still considered heresy by the students of poetic language who generally tag along far behind linguistics.

Students of the poetry of the past usually impose their own aesthetic attitudes on that past, project the contemporary methods of poetic production into the past. This is the reason for the scientific unsoundness of the studies in rhythm by the modernists, who read into Pushkin the current deformation of syllabo-tonic[5] verse. The past is examined—or rather, assessed—from the standpoint of the present, but scientific poetics will become possible only when it refuses to offer value judgments. Wouldn't it be absurd for a linguist to assess values to dialects according to their relative merits?

The development of a theory of poetic language will be possible only when poetry is treated as a social fact, when a kind of poetic dialectology is created.

From the point of view of this dialectology, Pushkin is the center of a poetic culture of a particular time, with a definite zone of influence. From this point of view, the poetic dialects of one zone, when they gravitate toward the cultural center of another, can be subdivided, like dialects of practical language, into: transitional dialects which have adopted a set of canons from the center of gravity; semitransitional dialects which adopt certain poetic tendencies from the center of gravity; and mixed dialects which adopt occasional alien elements or devices. Finally, it is essential to bear in mind the existence of archaic dialects with a conservative tendency, the center of gravity of which belongs to the past.

II

Xlebnikov is called a futurist; his poems are printed in futurist collections. Futurism is of course a new movement[6] in European art, and I shall not offer a more precise definition of the term now. Such definitions can only be arrived at inductively, through the analysis of many and complex artistic phenomena.

Any a priori formula suffers from dogmatism, since it sets up an artificial and premature distinction between real futurism and pseudofuturism, and the like. I should not like to repeat the methodological error of those contemporaries of romanticism, some of whom, according to Pushkin, considered romantic all works bearing the imprint of dreaminess and melancholy, while others regarded neologisms and grammatical mistakes as romantic.

I shall touch on just one feature which some experts on futurism, introducing extraneous factors into the study of poetry, have considered to be the essential component. I offer some excerpts from the manifestoes of Marinetti:[7]

> We shall sing of the great crowds tossed about by work, by pleasure, or revolt; the many-colored and polyphonic surf of revolutions in modem capitals; the nocturnal vibration of the arsenals and the yards under their violent electric moons; the gluttonous railway stations swallowing smoky serpents; the factories hung from the clouds by the ribbons of their smoke; the bridges leaping like athletes hurled over the diabolical cutlery of sunny rivers; the adventurous steamers that

sniff the horizon; the broad-chested locomotives, prancing on the rails like great steel horses curbed by long pipes, and the gliding flight of airplanes whose propellers snap like a flag in the wind, like the applause of an enthusiastic crowd.

Thus it appears that new material and new concepts in the poetry of the Italian futurists have led to a renewal of the devices of poetry and of artistic forms, and in this way, supposedly, the idea of *parole in libertà,* (the free word) for instance, came into being. But this is a reform in the field of reportage, not in poetic language.

Let me say parenthetically that at the moment I'm only talking about Marinetti as a theoretician. As far as his poetry is concerned, all this may serve only as rationalization, as a particular application of a poetic fact.

We see that for Marinetti the impulse for innovation was the need to tell of new facts in the material and psychological worlds.

But the Russian futurists advanced a totally different thesis:

> Once there is new form it follows that there is new content: form thus conditions content.
> Our creative shaping of speech throws everything into a new light.
> It is not new subject matter that defines genuine innovation.
> New light shed on the old world can yield the most fanciful play. (Kruchenyx[8] in the collection *The Three.*)

The aim of poetry is here very clearly formulated, and it is precisely the Russian futurists who invented a poetry of the "self-developing, self-valuing word," as the established and clearly visible material of poetry. And so it is not surprising that Xlebnikov's poems sometimes deal with the depths of the Stone Age, sometimes with the Russo-Japanese War, sometimes with the days of Prince Vladimir . . . and then again with the future of the world.

• • •

In normal, everyday linguistic cerebration, according to Professor Shcherba's[9] formula, "the stimuli we receive and the results of their assimilation are not distinguished in our consciousness as two events separated in time. In other words we don't know the difference between the objectively given sensations and the result of a given perception."

In emotive language and poetic language, the verbal representations (phonetic as well as semantic) concentrate on themselves greater attention; the connection between the aspect of sound and that of meaning is tighter, more intimate, and language is accordingly more revolutionary, insofar as habitual associations by contiguity (*smezhnost'*) retreat into the background. Note, for example, that appellative words—and hence personal names in general—undergo a rich variety of phonetic and formative modifications.

But beyond this there is no necessary affinity between emotive and poetic language. In emotive expression passionate outbursts govern the verbal mass, and precisely that "turbulent steam of emotion bursts the pipe of the sentence." But poetry—which is simply *utterance for the purpose of expression*—is governed, so to speak, by its own immanent laws; the communicative function, essential to both practical language and emotive language, has only minimal importance in poetry.[10] Poetry is indifferent to the subject of the utterance, while, on the other hand, practical or more exactly objective (*sachliche*) prose is indifferent—in Saran's formulation—to rhythm.[11]

Of course poetry can make use of the methods of emotional language, since the two are related in their purposes. Such utilization is characteristic of the opening stages of certain poetic movements, for instance romanticism. But poetic language is not composed of "*Affektträger*" (words that carry an emotive effect) in Sperber's[12] phrase, nor of the interjections and exclamations of hysterical discourse, as the Italian futurists have decreed.

The plastic arts involve the shaping of self-sufficient visual impressions, music the shaping of self-sufficient sound material, dance the organization of the self-sufficient gesture; and poetry is the formulation of the self-sufficient, "selfsome," word, as Xlebnikov puts it.

Poetry is language in its aesthetic function.

Thus the subject of literary scholarship is not literature but literariness (*literaturnost*), that is, that which makes of a given work a work of literature. And yet literary scholars up to now have often behaved like policemen who, in the course of arresting a particular person, would pick up, just in case, everybody and anybody who happened to be in the apartment, as well as people who happened to be passing on the street.

Similarly, the literary historian used anything that came to hand: biographical evidence, psychology, politics, philosophy. Instead of a literary science they created a conglomeration of homegrown disciplines. They seemed to forget that their articles deviated in the direction of those other disciplines—the history of philosophy, the history of culture, psychology, and so forth, and that while the latter may of course make use of literary works, these are for their purposes only defective, second-rate documents. If literary history wishes to become a science, it must recognize "device" as its sole concern. Then the fundamental problem will concern the uses and justification of device.

One of the commonest applications, or rather, in the given ease, justifications of poetic language is emotional or mental experience, which serves as a kind of catchall where we may dispose of anything that can't be justified or explained in practical terms, or rationalized.

When Majakovskij writes:

> I'll reveal for you, in words as simple as mooing,
> Your new souls that hum like arc lights,

it is the words "as simple as mooing" that interest us as poetic evidence, while the "soul" is secondary, ancillary, superimposed.

The romantics are often described as explorers of man's spiritual realm and poets of emotional experience, but as a matter of fact the contemporaries of the romantics thought of the movement exclusively in terms of its formal innovations. They observed first of all the destruction of the classical unities. And the testimony of contemporaries is the only valid evidence.

[We omit a fairly long excerpt from articles in the journals *Moscow Telegraph,* 1827, pt. 15, no. 10 and *Son of the Fatherland,* 1829, pt. 125, no. 15, which emphasize the formal innovations of the Byronic tale, but explain them as answering the needs of the "modern soul."]

Thus it is clear that a particular literary device was being logically justified by reference to the titanic and rebellious spirit, the free and arbitrary imagination.

The sentimentalists use the same device in embryonic form, where it is motivated by supposed "sentimental journeys." Similarly the mystical and "nature philosophy" elements of the romantic artistic credo simply serve as justification for an irrational poetic structure. The same is true for dreams, delirium, and other pathological phenomena, when they are used as poetic motifs. A typical illustration of the same sort of thing is Symbolism.

Take a verbal joke of the type "I was walking along, and there's a hut. I stopped in, the dough-trough is kneading the woman. I smirked, but the trough did not like it, it grabbed the stove out of the shovel and was going to hit me; I leapt through my trousers and ripped out the threshold and ran away" (Onchukov, *Northern Tales*, p. 74), and compare it with an excerpt from Gogol´:

> Everything in him turned into an undefined trembling, every feeling burned and everything before him appeared through a kind of fog; the sidewalk moved under him, carriages with galloping horses seemed immovable, a bridge was stretching and breaking in its arc, a house stood upside down, a sentry box was falling toward him, and a sentry's halberd, along with the golden words of a sign and the scissors drawn on it, seemed to sparkle on his very eyelashes. And all this was produced by one glance, one turn of a pretty little head. ("Nevskij Prospect.")

The same device which in the verbal joke is motivated by humorous intent, is used by Gogol´ to evidence the sudden onset of passion.

In Xlebnikov's poem *The Crane*, a boy sees that the factory chimneys have begun to dance, that a revolt of things is going on:

> On the square in the damp of an entering corner
> Where the needle radiant with gold
> Covered the burial ground of tsars,
> There a boy whispered in horror—
>   hey! hey!
> Look how the chimneys started reeling around
>   drunk—there!

> The stuttering lips were pale with horror
> And his glance was riveted up high.
> What? Is the boy delirious in broad daylight?
> I call the boy.
> But he is silent and suddenly runs—
>   What a furious race!
> Slowly I get out my glasses.
> And it's really as though the chimneys
>   craned their necks.

Here we have the realization of the same trope, the projection of a literary device into artistic reality, the turning of a poetic trope into a poetic fact, into a plot element. Here, however, the image structure is still partly explained in logical fashion by reference to a pathological state of mind.

In another poem by Xlebnikov, however, *Marquise Desaix,* even this motivation is lacking. Pictures at an exhibition simply come to life; then they bring the other things to life, while people turn to stone.

> But why is a smile, with a schoolgirl's modesty,
>   about to answer, "I am of stone and of sky-blue, sir."
> But why so ruthlessly and hopelessly did the clothes of
>   snow-covered bodies suddenly fall away.
> The heart, accessible before to the full measure of
>   feelings,
> Suddenly became a lump of mindless clay.
> Laughing, grumbling, cackling,
> Creatures rose against the rich,
> Under an invisible shadow of a threat they lit up
>   the slaves' rebellion,
> Aad who are their victims? We, the same people,
>   the same.
> Dark-blue and red-green roosters
> Come down from hats and peck at artifacts.
> Gold patches on teeth
> Standing like apparitions from the grave,

There baring their teeth a snowy pair of
    ermine gallop, racing, throwing back their
    shoulders and bright blue cocks.
There the rye forms ears in a luxuriant sheaf.
A young goldfinch builds a nest in someone's
    dumbfounded mouth. Then everything approached a
    mysterious line and limit.

There is a similar "realization of the device," laid bare of any logical motivation, in Majakovskij's *Tragedy* (a literary miracle):

Suddenly,
all things went rushing off, ripping
their voices,
and casting off tatters of outworn names.
Wineshop windows, all on their own,
splashed in the bottoms of bottles,
as though stirred by the finger of Satan.
From the shop of a tailor who'd fainted,
trousers escaped
and went walking along—
alone,
without human buttocks!
Out of a bedroom,
a drunken commode—
its black maw agape—
came stumbling.
Corsets wept, afraid of tumbling
down from signs reading "Robes et Modes."

The city offers material that fits neatly the structure of the verbal paradox and similar structures, as the examples we've seen from Gogol´, Majakovskij, and Xlebnikov clearly indicate. Urbanism offers opportunities for the application of a number of poetic devices: hence the urban verses of Majakovskij and Xlebnikov.

Yet at the same time Majakovskij says: "Abandon cities, you foolish people."

Or as Xlebnikov puts it:

> There's a certain fat gourmand who's fond of impaling human hearts on his spit, and who derives a mild enjoyment from the sound of hissing and breaking as he sees the bright red drops falling into the fire and flowing down—and the name of that fat man is—"the city."

What do we have here, a contradiction?

Let others superimpose upon the poet the thoughts expressed in his works! To incriminate the poet with ideas and emotions is as absurd as the behavior of the medieval audiences that beat the actor who played Judas and just as foolish as to blame Pushkin for the death of Lenskij.

Why should the poet be held answerable for a clash of ideas but not for a duel with swords or pistols?

• • •

We have already characterized metamorphosis as the realization of a verbal construction: as a rule such a realization involves the development in time of a reverse parallelism (specifically an antithesis). If a negative parallelism rejects the category of metaphor in the name of the category of the real, then reverse parallelism denies the real in the name of metaphor.

For example:

> Those forests standing on the hill are not forests; they are the hair growing on the shaggy head of the forest grandfather. Beneath it, in the water, his beard is awash; under his

beard and above his head is the high heaven. Those meadows are not meadows, but a green belt encircling the middle of the round sky.

(Gogol´, "A Terrible Vengeance.")

You think, on the cheeks of the cafe
It's the sun that lovingly caresses?
That's once again General Gallifet
Coming to shoot down the rebels.

(Majakovskij, A Cloud in Trousers.)

(Incidentally, erotic poetry is rich in examples of reverse parallelism.)

Let us suppose we have a real image: a head. The metaphor: a beer mug. An example of negative paralellism would be "that's not a mug but a head." Logical reduction of the parallelism is a simile: "a head like a beer mug." And, finally, the development in time of a reverse parallel, a metamorphosis: "the head became a beer mug" ("the head is no longer a head but a beer mug").

* * *

There is an example of realized simile in Xlebnikov's play *Death's Mistake.* The lady death says that her head is as empty as a drinking glass. The guest asks for a drinking glass. Death unscrews her head.

And here is an example of realized hyperbole:

I flew off like a curse
My other foot was already in the next street[13]

(Majakovskij).

The realized oxymoron betrays its essentially verbal nature; though it has meaning, it does not have anything which could be called, in the terminology of contemporary philosophy, a proper object (as, for example, a "squared circle"). The character Kovalev in Gogol''s story "The Nose" recognizes the nose as such even though it shrugs its shoulders, is in full uniform, and so forth.

• • •

Notice also the description of a miracle from one of the saints' lives in *The Brothers Karamazov* (in a humorous application): "The saint was tortured for his faith, and when they cut off his head at last, he got up, picked up the head, and politely kissed it."

In this case a human being is simply a traditional semantic unit which retains all of its attributes; in other words the semantic unit has become fixed.

The abrogation of the boundary between real and figurative meanings is characteristic of poetic language. Poetic language frequently operates with real images as though they were purely verbal figures (the device of reverse realization). Such is the case with puns.

• • •

1. In Dostoevskij's *Brothers Karamazov* there is a conversation between a marquis, who is ailing, and his spiritual father, a Jesuit: "Even if a stern fate has deprived you of your nose, you may derive profit from this in that no one your whole life long will dare to tell you that your nose has been tweaked."[14] "Good father . . . I would on the contrary be willing to have my nose tweaked every day of my life if only that nose were in its proper place."—"My son . . . since you proclaim that you would gladly have your nose tweaked all your life, then I must say that even in this your desire has been indirectly satisfied, since, because you've lost your nose, by that very fact you've had your nose tweaked."

2. And from *Anna Karenina*: "She brought back with her Vronskij's shadow," said the envoy's wife. "Well, what of it? There's a Grimm fairy tale: a man is without his shadow, it's been taken away from him as a punishment for something. I could never understand why it was a punishment. But it would be very unpleasant for a woman without her *shadow*." "Yes, but women *with shadows* usually end badly."

It is the conversion of real images into figures, their metaphorization, that forms the basis of Symbolism as a poetic school.

The idea of space as a pictorial convention, a kind of ideogram of time, has penetrated the study of painting, but the problem of time and space as forms of poetic language is still a stranger to scholarship. The fact that language does violence to literary space is especially clear in the example of descriptions, where items that coexist spatially are arranged in temporal sequence. On this ground Lessing either rejects descriptive poetry or else fully accepts the violence done by language, insisting upon motivating narrative temporal sequence by actual temporal sequence, that is to say by describing an object as it comes into being, a suit as its pants are put on by the wearer, and so forth.

Concerning literary time, the device of temporal displacement offers a rich field for investigation. I've already cited the remark of a critic that "Byron began his stories either in the middle or at the end." Or consider Tolstoj's "The Death of Ivan Il'ich," where the dénouement is given before the story begins; and Goncharov's *Oblomov*, where a temporal displacement is motivated by the hero's dream, and many other examples. There is a certain type of reader who foists this device on any literary work by starting to read at the end of the story. We find in Edgar Allan Poe's "The Raven" a kind of laboratory

experiment in the device of temporal shift: only at the very end
are things, as it were, turned inside out.

Xlebnikov offers an example of the realization of a temporal
shift, and one, moreover, which is "laid bare" (*obnazhёnnij*), that
is to say, not motivated, in his *World in Reverse* . . . which has
the effect of a motion picture film run backwards.

• • •

Another kind of temporal displacement favored by Xlebnikov
is the anachronism. Take for example the poem "School" where
the heroine is a student in the modern Bestuzhev Institute
while the hero is the boyar's son Volodimirko. Or take
"Malusha's Granddaughter" which reminds us of Tolstoj's
"Hero-Flood," with the sole exception that the temporal shift
in Xlebnikov is not logically motivated (see below for unmotivated similes).

In the story "Ka," a whole series of time factors are woven
together: "He has no outposts in time. Ka moves from dream to
dream, intersects time and achieves bronzes (the bronzes of
time). He disposes himself in the centuries as comfortably as in
a swing. And isn't it so that the consciousness brings various
times together just as an armchair and straight chairs are
brought together by a drawingroom."

Certain of Xlebnikov's works are composed by arbitrarily
stringing together various story elements. Such is *The Little
Devil*, and perhaps also *Children of the Otter*. (When story elements are arbitrarily arranged they don't follow one after
another by logical necessity but are linked on the principle of
formal likeness or contrast; we may compare the *Decameron*,
where the stories of each day are linked only by similar plot situations.) This device has an ancient sanction, but in

Xlebnikov's case it is "laid bare," that is, no line of justification is provided.

• • •

III

Colloquial speech provides the material for a major part of Xlebnikov's works. This reminds us of Mallarmé, who once said that he offered the bourgeois words which the latter reads every day in his newspapers but offered them in a startling context. Only against the background of the familiar does the unfamiliar reach and impress us. There comes a time when the traditional poetic language hardens into stereotype and is no longer capable of being felt but is experienced rather as a ritual, as a holy text in which even the errors are considered sacred. The language of poetry is as it were covered by a veneer—and neither its tropes nor its poetic licenses any longer speak to the consciousness. Form takes possession of the matter; the matter is totally dominated by the form. Then form becomes stereotype, and it is no longer alive. When this happens an access of new verbal material is required, an addition of fresh elements from the everyday language, to the end that the irrational structures of poetry may once again disturb us, may once again hit a vital spot.

Russian poetry has developed by way of constantly appropriating elements from the living language. This has been so from Simeon Polockij[15] through Lomonosov,[16] Derzhavin,

Pushkin, and Nekrasov[17]—and an example of the same process in our own day is Majakovskij. The critics of Pushkin's day had reason to be horrified at his "skates loudly cutting the ice," and at that "awkward goose with its red pads," or at the "beaver collar silvered with frosty dust."

[We omit an example from Pushkin's poetry of lines considered quite simple and clear by modern critics, but which seemed strained and difficult to contemporaries.]

The gradual wearing away of artistic form is characteristic of art forms other than poetry. Hanslick[18] offers examples of analogical developments in music:

> How many of Mozart's compositions were in their day considered the last word in the daring expression of fiery passion . . . Mozart's bursts of hot emotion, of fierce struggle, or of bitter and burning pain were at one time contrasted with that sense of a calm and pure enjoyment of life which supposedly flowed from the symphonies of Haydn. And twenty or thirty years later the same problem arose in comparing Mozart with Beethoven. The place of Mozart as a representative of violent impetuous emotion was taken by Beethoven, while Mozart was elevated to the Olympus of classical form occupied by Haydn. The well-known axiom that the "truly beautiful" (and who's to judge of that?) never, even over a long period, loses its charm has long since become an empty phrase if it is applied to music. Music is like nature, which each autumn sees hundreds of flowers wither, only to be replaced by new ones. A piece of music is a human thing, the product of a certain person, time, and cultural milieu, and therefore it always bears within itself the seeds of a more or less rapid death. . . . Both the performers and the audience feel a natural attraction to musical novelty. Critics who have learned how to honor what is old and established but haven't the heart to recognize what's new are guilty of destroying the productive forces. (From *On the Beautiful in Music*.)

Symbolist literary criticism in Russia at the present time suffers from just such an uneasiness about novelty. "Lyric poetry can be properly assessed only after the poet has passed away," they say (from *Works and Days*, No. 3, 1920).

And consider Brjusov's opinion that "it's hard to evaluate and judge a poet before his career is completed. Our opinion of Goethe's *Werther* is far different from that of his contemporaries who read it when it first appeared and could not know that Goethe would one day write the two parts of *Faust*" (from *Those Distant and Near*, p. 54).

It follows as a natural conclusion that we should observe pictures only in museums, only after they've been covered with the moss of centuries. And the conclusion also follows that the poetic language of the past must be preserved; that the diction, syntax, and word usage of an earlier generation must be imposed as a norm.

Poetry makes use of "unusual words." Specific cases of "unusual words" are those which are in need of a gloss, a special explanation (*glossy*). In this class are archaisms, barbarisms, and provincialisms. But the Symbolists forget something that was quite clear to Aristotle, namely that "one and the same word can be both a 'gloss' and in common use, but not for the same people"; they forget that what was a "gloss" for Pushkin is a stereotype in the contemporary poetic language. For instance Vjacheslav Ivanov[19] even goes so far as to recommend to beginning poets that they try to use in the main only Pushkinian words: if a word is in Pushkin that in itself is a criterion of its poetic quality.

IV

Xlebnikov's syntax (some observations). In the Russian language word order is almost never a determinant of meaning. The matter is somewhat different, however, in Russian poetry, where the regular intonation of everyday language is broken down. There is a sharp syntactic shift from the norms of everyday language even in the poetry of the Pushkin school, and in Majakovskij's radical rhythmic reform we observe the same phenomenon. When we turn to the poetry of Xlebnikov, however, we find that in this respect it is atypical.

• • •

According to Peshkovskij,[20] "verb usage is the basic form of our linguistic cerebration. The predicate—the verb—is the most important member of the sentence and of our speech in general."

However in poetic language there is often a marked tendency toward verblessness. Fet's[21] verbless experiments immediately come to mind, and these inspired Xlebnikov to pure imitation: "Whispering, muttering, rapture's groan, dark red of shame."

1. The earliest known photo of R.O. Jakobson, Riga, c. 1898, with his mother's family, the Vol'perts. He is sit on the floor with his cousins, to the right. His parents, Anna (Vol'pert) and Osip Jakobson, are above him to right. In the center is his grandfather, Jakov Vol'pert. The Jakobson Foundation.

2. R.O. Jakobson. Moscow, 1901. The Jakobson Foundation.

3. Standing, from left: Unknown, S.O. Jakobson
Vol'pert (with cap), Eva (Vol'pert) Kaplan-Kapla
L.Ju. Kagan (Lili Brik), Anna (Vol'pert) Jakobso
Sitting: Henriette Vol'pert, M. Vol'pert (on her
On the ground: R.O. Jakobson, E.Ju. Kagan (Els
Triolet). Moscow, 1903. The Jakobson Foundatic

4. R.O. Jakobson. Moscow, 1905. The Jakobson
Foundation.

5. R.O. Jakobson. Prague, 1920.
The Jakobson Foundation.

6. Marija Sinjakova, portrait of Velimir Xlebnikov, n.d.
Courtesy of Charlotte Douglas.

7. Boris Pasternak, 1930s.

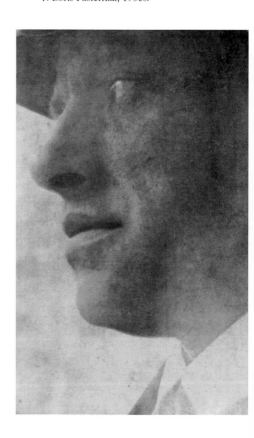

8. Vladimir Majakovskij, 1920s. Photograph by
Laszlo Moholy-Nagy.

9. Jakobson with Staff of the Soviet Red Cross Mission. (The man with the beard in the center is its director, Dr. Gillerson.) Terezin, 1920. The Jakobson Foundation.

10. From top to bottom: R.O. Jakobson, Teodor Nette, Zemit-Zimin. Prague, summer 1920. The Jakobson Foundation.

11. Elsa Triolet. Paris, May 1921. Archive of V.V. Katanjan.

12. L.Ju. and O.M. Brik, R.O. Jakobson, V.V. Majakovskij. Bad Flinsberg, July 1923. The Jakobson Foundation.

13. Philological meeting in Brno, late 1926. From left to right: R.O. Jakobson, N.S. Trubetzkoy, P.G. Bogatyrev, and N.N. Durnovo. The Jakobson Foundation.

14. The folklorist P.G. Bogatyrev with a leopard cub. Prague Zoo, 1928. The Jakobson Foundation.

15. From top to bottom: Karel Teige, R.O. Jakobs
Vitězslav Nezval. Brno, 1933. The Jakobson Foun

16. R.O. Jakobson. Gotland, 1977. Archive of Bengt Jangfeldt.

V

[We omit a brief section in which Jakobson deals with Xlebnikov's tendency to select epithets for euphonic rather than semantic reasons: for example, "strange fear"—*strannij strax*; "full flame"—*polnyj plamen'*.]

Often enough the function of an epithet is simply to emphasize an attribute as a syntactic fact; we have to do here with a "stripping bare of the attribute." O.M. Brik[22] has made the acute observation that the poets of the Pushkin "Pleiade" accomplished this in two ways: either by the use of what he calls "indifferent epithets," for instance "*pure* beauty," "*divine* head," or even "a *certain* czar in a *certain* year"; or by the use of strained epithets having, as one of Pushkin's contemporaries put it, "no concrete relationship to the noun they qualify," and which the critic proposed to call "adherent" rather than "adjective" forms. This latter type of epithet is quite characteristic of Xlebnikov. Examples:

> A crown of clever petals (*xitryx lepestkov*)
> Wise petals (*lepestki mudrye*)
> In the wise woods (*v umnyx lesax*).

Epithets in Xlebnikov's early (impressionistic) works are often created by a certain situation, for instance:

> And the evening wine (*i vechernee vino*)
> And the evening women (*i vechernye zhenshchiny*)
> Woven into a single wreath (*spletajutsja v edinij venok*).

Similes. The problem of Xlebnikov's similes is extremely complicated. I offer here only certain guideposts. What is a poetic simile? If we ignore for the moment its function as a factor making for symmetry, we may characterize the simile as one of the methods for introducing into the poetic situation an order of facts not occasioned by the logical movement of the narration. Xlebnikov's similes are hardly ever motivated by any impression of real similarity of objects, but are simply compositional effects. If we accept Xlebnikov's statement that there are words with which we see—"word-eyes"—and words with which we "do"—"wordhands"—and if we apply this formulation to similes we will see that Xlebnikov's similes are precisely "simile-hands."

Contamination of comparisons is common in his work:

"Like a black sail on the white sea its fierce pupils cut the eyes aslant: the frightening white eyes were raised toward the brows in the head of the dead one hanging by a braid" (from *Esir*).

We have here a contamination of qualities: in color—white and black, and line—sail and sea.

• • •

Often enough the subject of a simile is selected not so much because of its similarity to the object of the simile, but rather in a different and larger context. . . . For instance:

> Dear city, there's something of an old lady in you:
> She seats herself on her box and would eat a bit,
> Shakes her babushka, and it's not a simple babushka,
> From one side to the other a flock of black birds flies.

The network of analogies Xlebnikov offers is very complex. Space and time are juxtaposed, visual and auditory perceptions, personages and action.

"Terrible is the hunt when the sedge is years, and the game—generations."

"And your eyes are a hut where two stepmother-spinners work the spindle."

VI

That set on expression, on the verbal mass itself, which I have called the only essential characteristic of poetry, is directed not only to the form of the phrase, but also to the form of the word itself. Mechanical associations between sound and meaning are established more easily as they become more habitual. For this reason the everyday practical language is extremely conservative: the form of a word rapidly ceases to be felt.

In poetry, on the other hand, the operation of mechanical association is reduced to a minimum, while the dissociation of verbal elements acquires great importance. Dissociated fragments are readily combined into new formations. Dead affixes come to life.

Dissociation may be quite arbitrary, done simply for the purpose of devising new suffixes (a process familiar in everyday speech, take for example the form *golubchik* ['darling,' based on *golub'*—'dove'], but in poetry the process is greatly intensified). Take, for example, the invented forms used in children's language: sox*run*, mok*run* (based on *sox*—'dry,' and *mokr*—'wet') .

Poetry has from the earliest times engaged in play with suffixes; but only in modern poetry, and particularly in Xlebnikov, has this device become conscious, and as it were legitimate.

196 / MY FUTURIST YEARS

[Here Jakobson gives a number of examples from literature—Russian folklore, children's jingles, charms, and popular songs—which show the tendency in certain speech situations to augment and enrich the normal word forms by attaching various new suffixes. Most of these are untranslatable, though analogical processes in English might be found. Examples: *xleby–xlebisty, begun´ki–begut, skripul´ki–skripjat* (from *xleb*— 'bread,' *beg*—'speed,' *skrip*—'squeak.')]

The possibility of isolating in a given word those parts which belong to the root and those forms which are appended to the root arises as a result of the mental association of these elements in the given word with corresponding elements in other combinations and in other words.

In the poems of Xlebnikov which give free reign to verbal creativity, we find juxtaposed as a rule either 1) neologisms with identical roots but different formants (prefixes, suffixes, and affixes), or 2) neologisms with identical formants and different roots. But in a poem the dissociation takes place not within the given structure of a language as a whole, as we have observed happening in the practical language, but within the framework of a particular poem, which as it were forms a closed linguistic system.

Let us see some examples.

1. First, we observe cases in which the root remains unchanged but the formants are different; in other words, we have a complex tautological construction, or a kind of "laying bare" of the "paregmenon" of classical rhetoric. Xlebnikov frequently uses productive extension of words without any logical justification, and this quite apart from the introduction of neologisms.

> O laugh it up you laughletes!
> O laugh it out you laughletes!

That laugh with laughs, that laugherize laughily
O laugh it out so laughily
O of laughing at laughilies—
    the laugh of laughish laugherators
Laughterly, laughterly
Outlaugh, downlaugh, laughlets, laughlets.
Laughulets, laughulets
O laugh it up you laughers!
O laugh it up you laughers!

(O rassmejtes´ smexachi!
O zasmejtes´ smexachi!
Chto smejutsja smexami, chto smejanstvujut smejal´no
    O zasmejtes´ usmejal´no
O rassmeshishch nadsmejal´nyx—
    smex nadsmejnyx smexachej, etc.)

2. The second type of example involves identical formants but with different root materials. Such forms often rhyme, as though in contradiction to the tendency of modern poetry not to rhyme identical parts of speech. The essence of rhyme according to Shcherba's formulation lies in the recognition of rhythmically repeated similar phonetic elements; but in the present case it consists in the segregation of identical formants, which facilitates dissociation.

[Jakobson here gives two sets of examples, in the first of which all of the words involved are neologisms, while in the second some are words used in the everyday language. The examples are not translatable, but the point is clear from a transliteration of some of them:

Letaja nebu rad zo*rir´*
Sladok, dumaet go*rir´;*
Vezde presleduet mo*gun*
Vezde presleduet be*gun*]

Economy of words is a virtue alien to poetry, except where it is justified by some special poetic purpose. Neologisms enrich poetry in three ways: 1. They create a bright euphonic stroke, while the established words become phonetically obsolete, being worn out by constant use, and, most important, because they are only partially apprehended in their phonetic patterns; 2. In the practical language the form of the word is no longer appreciated; it is dormant and petrified. However we cannot help apprehending the form of a poetic neologism, given so to speak *in statu nascendi;* 3. The meaning of a word at any given moment is more or less static, but the meaning of a neologism is to a significant extent defined by its context, while at the same time it may oblige the reader to a certain etymological cerebration. And incidentally, etymology always plays a role in poetry. Two types of situations are possible in this connection:

A) *A renovation of meaning,* for instance in Derzhavin's *tuch-nye tuchi.*[23] Such a renewal can be effected not only by the juxtaposition of words having one and the same root, but also by using a word in its literal meaning which the everyday language uses only figuratively, i.e. "the *great bulk* of bad weather," "a cloud *lightninglike* and black.[24]

B) Poetic etymology. This process is analogous to the popular etymology of practical language. Professor Zubat″[25] has offered some very interesting examples from Lithuanian folklore. Here is a Russian translation which approximates the original: *"Pjat′ volkov volka voloklo"* ('Five wolves dragged the wolf').

In the play *Mrs. Leneen,* we find another type of fractional semantic unit. Here Xlebnikov has tried to find, as he himself put it, "infinitesimals" of artistic language. There is no complete character; instead he is split up into a number of constituent voices: the voice of sight, of hearing, of reason, of fear, and so on. What we have here is a kind of "realized synecdoche." Consider also the story "Ka," where the soul is divided into constituent personages: Ka, Xu, and Ba.

Semantic deformation in poetry occurs in many different ways, and parallel to it we have also phonetic deformations. Take, for example, the splitting of words, A) for rhythmic purposes (in Horace, in Annenskij,[26] and in Majakovskij), or, B) the insertion of one word into another, a device not uncongenial to Xlebnikov (for instance his etymology *Po-do-l, ko-do-l*). That device was even used by the Latin poets, by Vergil for instance; "*cere*-comminuit-*brum*."

Examples of this can be found in contemporary poetry, for instance in Majakovskij, where there is however a measure of logical justification:

They were talking on the sidewalk "Pos- And the car wheel turned again -toffice."	(Vygovorili na trotuare "Poch- Perekinulos´ na shinu -ta")

Shifts of accent also come under the heading of phonetic deformation.

[Jakobson gives a number of untranslatable examples from folklore of words accented abnormally, as also of cases where poetry makes use of accentual "doublets," offering more than one accented form when more than one is possible.]

[We omit some untranslatable examples of phonetic and semantic deformation in which, as Jakobson puts it, the verbal form, both internal and external, is fully experienced, though the words are empty of content—ed.]

• • •

VII

Poetic language possesses a certain rather elementary device: the rapprochement and commingling of distinct units of speech.

In the area of semantics varieties of this device are known as: the simile, which is a particular case of parallelism; the metamorphosis, in other words a parallelism developed in time; and metaphor, or a parallelism reduced to a single point.

In the area of euphony we find the following varieties of the device: rhyme, assonance, and alliteration (or sound repetition). It is possible to produce verses characterized by an emphasis primarily on euphony. But is this sort of emphasis equivalent to the accentuation of pure sound? If the answer is yes, then we have a species of vocal music, and vocal music of an inferior kind at that.

Euphony operates, however, not with sounds but with phonemes, that is, with acoustical impressions which are capable of being associated with meaning.

• • •

The form of a word can be apprehended only as it is a regular and repeated part of a given linguistic system. A totally isolated form dies out; and similarly a sound combination in a given poem (which is a kind of linguistic system *in statu nascendi*) becomes a kind of "sound image" (O.M. Brik's term[27]) and is apprehended only as a repeated part of a poem's system of "sound images."

In modern poetry special attention is given to consonants and, therefore, sound repetitions of the type AB, ABC, and so forth, are often illuminated by poetic etymology in such a way that the concept of basic meaning is linked with repeated clusters of consonants, while the differing vowel sounds come to seem as it were an inflection of the root, having the formal significance either of word-formants or of word-modifiers.

The following important statement of Xlebnikov characterizes poetic etymology as a fact of linguistic cerebration:

> Have you ever heard of internal declension? Case forms within the word? If the genitive case answers the question "whence?" and the accusative and dative cases answer the question "whither?" and "where?" then the inflection of the root in those cases ought in the same way to give the resulting words opposite meanings. . . . Thus *bobr* (beaver) and *babr* (tiger) which mean respectively a harmless rodent and a fierce predator and which are formed by the accusative and genitive cases of the common root *bo-*, illustrate by their very structure that a *bobr* should be hunted as a prize, while a *babr* should be feared, since man himself might well become the object of the hunt. In this case the simplest form changes, by alteration of cases, the sense of the word structure. In the one word it is indicated that the action of struggle was directed at the beast (accusative case "whither?") and in the other word that the action arises from the beast (genitive case "whence?"). Similarly *beg* (flight) is occasioned by fear, while *Bog* (God) is a being toward whom fear ought to be directed. Thus the words *les* (forest) and *lysyj* (bald), or take two words that are even more alike, *lysina* (bald spot) and *lesina* (wooded spot), whose meaning involves the presence or absence of a certain kind of growth; you know what *lysaja gora* (bald mountain) means—bald mountains are hills or heads deprived of forest—these words arose through the alteration of the direction of a simple word by its declension in the accusative and the dative cases. . . . And so in other

examples the sounds *e* and *y* are evidences of different eases of one and the same root. The area from which *les* has disappeared is called *lysina*. Similarly *byk* (bull) indicates that object from which a blow is to be expected, while *bok* (flank) indicates the place toward which the blow is to be directed. (*Union of Youth, Almanac No. 3.*)

[We omit two pages of examples of "root inflection" taken from the works of Xlebnikov, Aseev, Majakovskij, and Guro.[28] Some typical examples:

> The girls are wondering (*Devicy divjatsja*)
> On this night even the grave might love (*V ètu noch' ljubit i mogila mogla*)
> Our god is speed (*Nash bog beg*).

We omit also two pages which give a wealth of examples of complex consonantal structure in Xlebnikov's poetry, which Jakobson analyzes according to the sound sequences that occur, for instance

> N-G: *I v utonnyx negax snega* (In the buried luxury of snow)
> B-L, R-Z: *bylyx belyx grez zari* (The one-time white dreams of dawn).]

The practical language offers examples of the substitution of an initial consonant by analogy (for example, *devjat'* [nine], a form which arose on the analogy of *desjat'* [ten]); this kind of development is even more common in slips of the tongue; for instance, the anticipation of the first sound of a following word: *skap stoit* instead of *shkap stoit* ("the cupboard stands"), where the initial sound "s" is substituted for "sh." Or the reverse of that: *lesa lostut* in place of *lesa rastut* ("the forests grow").

In the poetry of Xlebnikov this linguistic phenomenon is used as a poetic device: an initial consonant is often replaced by another drawn from other poetic roots. The word in question thus gains as it were a new sound character. Its meaning wavers, and the word is apprehended as an acquaintance with a suddenly unfamiliar face, or as a stranger in whom we are able to see something familiar.

[We omit additional examples, along with a lengthy footnote in which Jakobson outlines a method for a phonetic analysis of the paired words, usually without definite meaning, that occur in various languages, for example in Russian, *gusli-musli, gogol'-mogol'*; in English we might suggest such pairs as *higgledy-piggledy, hurly-burly.*]

VIII

The play on synonyms is a kind of partial emancipation of words from meaning, that is to say, the second word does not contribute a new meaning, while, on the other hand, it offers the possibility of a differentiation of semantic nuances. Examples:

> He is naked and bare (*On gol i nag*)
> Know and realize (*Znaj i vedaj*)
> Who is our comrade and friend? (*Kto nam tovarishch i drug*)

The play on homonyms is exactly the opposite of the play on synonyms, but both are based on an incongruity between the unit of meaning and the word itself. A parallel situation in painting is the use of free-flowing color. Examples:

The braid [or scythe, another meaning of *kosa*—ed.] sometimes adorns the head, hanging down to the shoulders, sometimes cuts the grass. (*Kosa to ukrashaet temja, spuskaja᾽ na
plechi, to kosit travu*).

[We omit two pages of examples of play on homonyms and
synonyms taken from Russian folklore, children's songs, and
from Brjusov and Xlebnikov. The last of these examples, from
Xlebnikov, involves synonyms of opposite grammatical gender.
Jakobson elucidates.]

The final example is interesting as an indicator of the com-
pulsive influence of grammatical gender on the verbal image
itself. When they are personified, words of feminine gender
will be represented by female persons, and words of masculine
gender by male persons. For example, when a Russian imagines
the days of the week as persons he will see Monday and Sunday
(masculine and neuter, respectively) as men, and Wednesday
(feminine) as a woman. It is interesting that the Russian
painter Repin should have been surprised that Stuck[29] represented sin (in Gemman *die Sünde*, feminine; in Russian *grex*,
masculine) as a woman. . . .

Foreign and dialect words are sometimes favored for purposes of synonymic play:

> There half-fearfully they moan: God (*Tam polubojazlivo
>   stonut: Bog*)
> There they quietly whisper: *Gott* (*Tam shepchut tixo: Gott*)
> There they moan briefly: *dieu* (*Tam stonut kratko: D᾽e*)

Foreign words in general are widely used in poetry because
their sound patterns offer a surprise, while their meaning is
muted.

IX

Just as semantic correspondences are weak in modern poetry, so rhyme, as a euphonic correspondence, is only approximate (similarities are experienced against a background of contrast). As concerns the sound pattern of Xlebnikov's rhymes, and indeed of rhyme in modern Russian poetry as a whole, the following features should be noted as characteristic:

1. Consonants have greater weight than vowels. This is true of modern euphonic patterns in general.

• • •

2. The distinction between hard and palatalized consonants is to a large extent lost for purposes of rhyme.

Vowels are characterized acoustically by variations in the height of their basic tones; similarly the distinction between palatalized and unpalatalized consonants is in their basic tone. Thus it would seem that the evolution of poetic euphony parallels the evolution of modern music: the development has been from emphasis on tone, in the direction of emphasis on sound.

3. Poets of the Pushkin school focused primarily upon the final sounds in making their rhymes, while modern poetry gives more importance to supporting sounds; agreement of the final sounds is not obligatory.

4. Consonants are not necessarily identical, but need only be similar in their acoustic effect.

5. The order of consonants in the rhyming words need not be identical (rhyme-metathesis is possible).

6. Accents in the rhyming words need not be identical.

• • •

Xlebnikov to some extent "lays bare" the repetition of consonant sounds: often enough the word combinations that form the repetition have practically no logical justification:

> *Polna soblazna i bela* (Full of temptation and white)
> *Ona zabyla pro belila* (She forgot about the whiting).

[There follow a number of examples of sound repetition *for its own sake* from Pushkin, from Xlebnikov, and from popular jingles.]

Many examples could be given which show that in the poetry of Xlebnikov meaning is reduced in importance and euphonic constructions are created for their own sake. From this point it is only a step to the creation of a completely arbitrary language. As Xlebnikov put it,

> My first idea in dealing with language is to find . . . a touchstone for the transformation of all Slavic words one into another, for the free fusion of all Slavic words. Such is the selfsome word without relation to life or use. And seeing that all roots are simply phantoms behind which stand the living strings of the alphabet, the discovery of the general unity of all world languages, built out of the units of the alphabet—such is my second purpose. This is the way to the discovery of a worldwide trans-sense language.

Such arbitrary word-building may be associated in the forms it uses with the Russian language:

> Von tam na dorozhke belyj vstal i stoit *vidennega*
> Vecher li derevo l´ prixot´ moja?
> Ax, pozvol´te mne èto slovo v vide negi.

Words of this type are as it were seeking a meaning for themselves. Here it is perhaps mistaken to speak of the complete absence of semantic sense. Such a word is rather an example of a negative internal form, as, for example, (according to Fortunatov[30]) the nominative case *dom* (where there is a zero case ending) is a word with negative external form.

The second type of arbitrary word-building avoids any correlation with a given poetic language. This is the case for example with the "talking in tongues" of religious sectarians: the creators of such speech believe that their words are related to foreign tongues. Xlebnikov's "trans-sense" (*zaumnye*) words are motivated by the idea, for example that they are written in bird language (*Wisdom in a Snare*), apes' language ("Ka"), demons' language (*A Night in Galicia*).

Even the motivation itself may be "trans-sense" in nature:

Bobeobi sang the lips	Bobèobi pelis´ guby
Veeomi sang the eyes	Vèèomi pelis´ vzory
Lieeei sang the visage	Lièèèi pelsja oblik
Gzi-gzi-gzeo sang the chain	Gzi-gzi gzèo pelas´ tsep´
Thus on the canvas of certain correspondences	Tak na xolste kakix-to sootvetstvij
Without extension lived the face	Vne protjazhenija zhilo lico.

We have seen in a number of examples how the word in Xlebnikov's poetry loses its concrete content and even loses its inner and finally even its outward form. It has been observed many times in the history of the poetry of all peoples and countries that, as Trediakovskij[31] put it, for the poet "only sound" is important. The language of poetry strives to reach, as a final limit, the phonetic, or rather—to the extent that such a purpose may be present—the euphonic phrase—in other words, a trans-sense speech.

But concerning the limit of this striving Xlebnikov characteristically remarks: "When I wrote the words of Ikhnaton before his death, 'manch, manch,' they produced on me an unbearable effect. Now I hardly feel them anymore. I don't know why."

TRANSLATED BY E.J. BROWN

ON A GENERATION THAT
SQUANDERED ITS POETS

> Killed;—
> Little matter
> Whether I or he
> Killed them.

Majakovskij's poetry—his imagery, his lyrical composition—I have written about these things and published some of my remarks. The idea of writing a monograph has never left me. Majakovskij's poetry is qualitatively different from everything in Russian verse before him, however intent one may be on establishing genetic links. This is what makes the subject particularly intriguing. The structure of his poetry is profoundly original and revolutionary. But how is it possible to write about Majakovskij's poetry now, when the paramount subject is not the rhythm but the death of the poet, when (if I may resort to Majakovskij's own poetic phrase) "sudden grief" is not yet ready to give in to "a clearly realized pain"?

During one of our meetings, Majakovskij, as was his custom, read me his latest poems. Considering his creative potential I could not help comparing them with what he might have produced. "Very good," I said, "but not as good as Majakovskij." Yet now the creative powers are canceled out, the inimitable stanzas can no longer be compared to anything else, the words "Majakovskij's latest poems" have suddenly taken on a tragic meaning. Sheer grief at his absence has overshadowed the absent one. Now it is more painful, but still easier, to write not about the one we have lost but rather about our own loss and those of us who have suffered it.

It is our generation that has suffered the loss. Roughly, those of us who are now between thirty and forty-five years old. Those who, already fully matured, entered into the years of the Revolution not as unmolded clay but still not hardened, still capable of adapting to experience and change, still capable of taking a dynarnic rather than a static view of our lives.

It has been said more than once that the first poetic love of our generation was Aleksandr Blok. Velimir Xlebnikov gave us a new epos, the first genuinely epic creations after many decades of drought. Even his briefer verses create the impression of epic fragments, and Xlebnikov easily combined them into narrative poems. Xlebnikov is epic in spite of our antiepic times, and therein lies one of the reasons he is somewhat alien to the average reader. Other poets brought his poetry closer to the reader; they drew upon Xlebnikov, pouring out his "word ocean" into many lyrical streamlets. In contrast to Xlebnikov, Majakovskij embodied the lyrical urges of this generation. "The broad epic canvas" is deeply alien to him and unacceptable. Even when he attempts "a bloody Iliad of the Revolution," or "an Odyssey of the famine years," what appears is not an epic but a heroic lyric on a grand scale, offered "at the top of his voice." There was a point when Symbolist poetry was in its decline and it was still not clear which of the two new mutually antagonistic trends, Acmeism or Futurism, would prevail. Xlebnikov and Majakovskij gave to Contemporary literary art its leitmotif. The name Gumilev marks a collateral branch of modern Russian poetry—its characteristic overtone. For Xlebnikov and for Majakovskij "the homeland of creative poetry is the future"; in contrast, Esenin is a lyrical glance backward. His verse expresses the weariness of a generation.

Modern Russian poetry after 1910 is largely defined by these names. The verse of Aseev and Sel´vinskij[1] is bright indeed, but it is a reflected light. They do not announce but reflect the spirit of the times. Their magnitude is a derivative quantity. Pasternak's books and perhaps those of Mandel´shtam are remarkable, but theirs is chamber verse:[2] new creation will not be kindled by it. The heart of a generation cannot take fire with such verses because they do not shatter the boundaries of the present.

Gumilev (1886–1921) was shot, after prolonged mental agony and in great pain; Blok (1880–1921) died, amid cruel privations and under circumstances of inhuman suffering; Xlebnikov (1885-1922) passed away; after careful planning Esenin (1895–1925) and Majakovskij (1894–1930) killed themselves. And so it happened that during the third decade of this century, those who inspired a generation perished between the ages of thirty and forty, each of them sharing a sense of doom so vivid and sustained that it became unbearable.

This is true not only of those who were killed or killed themselves. Blok and Xlebnikov, when they took to their beds with disease, had also perished. Zamjatin wrote in his reminiscences: "We are all to blame for this . . . I remember that I could not stand it and I phoned Gor´kij: Blok is dead. We can't be forgiven for that." Shklovskij wrote in a tribute to Xlebnikov:

> Forgive us for yourself and for others whom we will kill. The state is nor responsible for the destruction of people. When Christ lived and spoke the state did not understand his

Aramaic, and it has never understood simple human speech.
The Roman soldiers who pierced Christ's hands are no more
to blame than the nails. Nevertheless, it is very painful for
those whom they crucify.[3]

Blok the poet fell silent and died long before the man, but his
younger contemporaries snatched verses even from death.
("Wherever I die I'll die singing," wrote Majakovskij.) Xlebnikov
knew he was dying. His body decomposed while he lived. He
asked for flowers in his room so that the stench would not be
noticed, and he kept writing to the end. A day before his suicide Esenin wrote a masterful poem about his impending
death. Majakovskij's farewell letter is full of poetry: we find the
professional writer in every line of that document. He wrote it
two nights before his death and in the interval there were to be
conversations and conferences about the everyday business of
literature; but in that letter we read: "Please don't gossip. The
deceased hated gossip." We remember that Majakovskij's long-
standing demand upon himself was that the poet must "hurry
time forward." And here he is, already looking at his suicide
note through the eyes of someone reading it the day after
tomorrow. The letter, with its several literary motifs and with
Majakovskij's own death in it, is so closely interrelated with his
poetry that it can be understood only in the context of that
poetry.

The poetry of Majakovskij from his first verses, in *A Slap in
the Face of Public Taste,* to his last lines is one and indivisible. It
represents the dialectical development of a single theme. It is an
extraordinarily unified symbolic system. A symbol once thrown
out only as a kind of hint will later be developed and presented
in a totally new perspective. He himself underlines these links
in his verse by alluding to earlier works. In the poem *About
That,* for instance, he recalls certain lines from the poem *Man,*

written several years earlier, and in the latter poem he refers to lyrics of an even earlier period. An image at first offered humorously may later and in a different context lose its comic effect, or conversely, a motif developed solemnly may be repeated in a parodistic vein. yet this does not mean that the beliefs of yesterday are necessarily held up to scorn; rather, we have here two levels, the tragic and the comic, of a single symbolic system, as in the medieval theater. A single clear purpose directs the system of symbols. "We shall thunder out a new myth upon the world."

A mythology of Majakovskij?

His first collection of poems was entitled *I*. Vladimir Majakovskij is not only the hero of his first play, but his name is the title of that tragedy, as well as of his last collection of poems. The author dedicates his verse "to his beloved self." When Majakovskij was working on the poem *Man* he said, "I want to depict simply man, man in general, not an abstraction, à la Andreev,[4] but a genuine 'Ivan' who waves his arms, eats cabbage soup, and can be directly felt." But Majakovskij could directly feel only himself. This is said very well in Trockij's article on him (an intelligent article, the poet said): "In order to raise man he elevates him to the level of Majakovskij. The Greeks were anthropomorphists, naively likening the forces of nature to themselves; our poet is a Majakomorphist, and he populates the squares, the streets, and the fields of the Revolution only with himself." Even when the hero of Majakovskij's poem appears as the 150-million-member collective, realized in one Ivan—a fantastic epic hero—the latter in turn assumes the familiar features of the poet's "ego." This ego asserts itself even more frankly in the rough drafts of the poem.[5]

Empirical reality neither exhausts nor fully takes in the various shapes of the poet's ego. Majakovskij passes before us in one of his "innumerable souls." "The unbending spirit of eternal rebellion" has poured itself into the poet's muscles, the irresponsible spirit without name or patronymic, "from future days, just a man." "And I feel that I am too small for myself. Someone obstinately bursts out of me." Weariness with fixed and narrow confines, the urge to transcend static boundaries—such is Majakovskij's infinitely varied theme. No lair in the world can contain the poet and the unruly horde of his desires. "Driven into the earthly pen I drag a daily yoke." "The accursed earth has me chained." The grief of Peter the Great is that of a "prisoner, held in chains in his own city." Hulks of districts wriggle out of the "zones marked off by the governor." The cage of the blockade in Majakovskij's verses turns into the world prison destroyed by a cosmic gust directed "beyond the radiant slits of sunsets." The poet's revolutionary call is directed at all of those "for whom life is cramped and unbearable," "who cry out because the nooses of noon are too tight." The ego of the poet is a battering ram, thudding into a forbidden Future; it is a mighty will "hurled over the last limit" toward the incarnation of the Future, toward an absolute fullness of being: "one must rip joy from the days yet to come."

Opposed to this creative urge toward a transformed future is the stabilizing force of an immutable present, overlaid, as this present is, by a stagnating slime, which stifles life in its tight, hard mold. The Russian name for this element is *byt*.[6] It is curious that this word and its derivatives should have such a prominent place in the Russian language (from which it spread even to the Komi),[7] while West European languages have no word that corresponds to it. Perhaps the reason is that in the European collective consciousness there is no concept of such a force as might oppose and break down the established norms of life. The revolt of the individual against the fixed forms of social convention presupposes the existence of such a force. The real antithesis of *byt* is a slippage of social norms that is immediately sensed by those involved in social life. In Russia this sense of an unstable foundation has been present for a very long time, and not just as a historical generalization but as a direct experience. We recall that in the early nineteenth century, during the time of Chaadaev, there was the sense of a "dead and stagnant life," but at the same time a feelirg of instability and uncertainty: "Everything is slipping away, everything is passing," wrote Chaadaev.[8] "In our own homes we are as it were in temporary quarters. In our family life we seem foreigners. In our cities we look like nomads." And as Majakovskij put it:

> . . . laws/ concepts/ faiths
> The granite blocks of cities
> And even the very sun's reliable glow—
> Everything had become as it were fluid,
> Seemed to be sliding a little—
> A little bit thinned and watered down.

But all these shifts, all this "leaking of the poet's room," are only a "hardly audible draft, which is probably only felt by the very tip of the soul." Inertia continues to reign. It is the poet's primordial enemy, and he never tires of returning to this theme. "Motionless *byt*." "Everything stands as it has been for ages. *Byt* is like a horse that can't be spurred and stands still." "Slits of *byt* are filled with fat and coagulate, quiet and wide." "The swamp of *byt* is covered over with slime and weeds." "Old little *byt* is moldy." "The giant *byt* crawls everywhere through the holes." "Force booming *byt* to sing!" "Put the question of *byt* on the agenda." "In fall,/ winter,/ spring,/ summer/ During the day/ during sleep/ I don't accept/ I hate this/ all./ All that in us/ is hammered in by past slavishness/ all/ that like the swarm of trifles/ was covering/ and covered with *byt*/ even our red-flagged ranks." Only in the poem *About That* is the poet's desperate struggle with *byt* fully laid bare. There it is not personified as it is elsewhere in his work. On the contrary, the poet hammers his verbal attack directly into that moribund *byt* which he despises. And *byt* reacts by executing the rebel "with all rifles and batteries, from every Mauser and Browning." Elsewhere in Majakovskij this phenomenon is, as we have said, personified—not however as a living person but rather, in the poet's own phrase, as an animated tendency. In *Man,* the poet's enemy is very broadly generalized as "Ruler of all, my rival, my invincible enemy." But it is also possible to localize this enemy and give him a particular shape. One may call him "Wilson," domicile him in Chicago, and, in the language of fairytale hyperbole, outline his very portrait (as in *150,000,000*). But then the poet offers a "little footnote": "Those who draw the Wilsons, Lloyd Georges, and Clemenceaus sometimes show their mugs with moustaches, sometimes not; but that's beside the point since they're all one and the same thing." The enemy is a universal image. The forces of nature, people, metaphysical substances, are only its incidental aspects and disguises: "The same old bald fellow directs us unseen, the master of the earthly cancan. Sometimes in the shape of an idea, sometimes a kind of devil, or then again he glows as God, hidden behind a cloud." If we should try to translate the Majakovskian mythology into the language of speculative philosophy, the exact equivalent for this enmity would be the antinomy "I" versus "not-I." A better designation for Majakovskij's enemy could hardly be found.

Just as the creative ego of the poet is not coextensive with his actually existing self, so conversely the latter does not take in all of the former. In the faceless regiment of his acquaintances, all tangled in the "apartment-house spider web,"

> One of them/ I recognized
> As like as a twin
> Myself/ my very own self.

This terrible "double" of the poet is his conventional and commonplace "self," the purchaser and owner whom Xlebnikov once contrasted with the inventor and discoverer. That self has an emotional attachment to a securely selfish and stable life, to "*my* little place, and a household that's *mine*, with *my* little picture on the wall." The poet is oppressed by the specter of an unchangeable world order, a universal apartment-house *byt*: "No sound, the universe is asleep."

> Revolutions shake up violently the bodies of kingdoms,
> The human herd changes its herdsman.
> But you/ uncrowned ruler of our hearts
> No rebellion ever touches.

Against this unbearable might of *byt* an uprising as yet unheard of and nameless must be contrived. The terms used in speaking of the class struggle are only conventional figures, only approximate symbols, only one of the levels: *the part for the whole*. Majakovskij, who has witnessed "the sudden reversals of fortune in battles not yet fought," must give new meaning to the habitual terminology. In the rough draft of the poem *150,000,000* we find the following definitions:

> To be a bourgeois does not mean to own capital or squander gold. It means to be the heel of a corpse on the throat of the young. It means a mouth stopped up with fat. To be a proletarian doesn't mean to have a dirty face and work in

a factory: it means to be in love with the future that's going
to explode the filth of the cellars—believe me.

The basic fusion of Majakovskij's poetry with the theme of
the revolution has often been pointed out. But another indissoluble combination of motifs in the poet's work has not so far
been noticed: revolution and the destruction of the poet. This
idea is suggested even as early as the *Tragedy* (1913), and later
this fact that the linkage of the two is not accidental becomes
"clear to the point of hallucination." No mercy will be shown to
the army of zealots, or to the doomed volunteers in the struggle. The poet himself is an expiatory offering in the name of
that universal and real resurrection that is to come; that was the
theme of the poem *War and the World.* And in the poem *A
Cloud in Trousers,* the poet promises that when a certain year
comes "in the thorny crown" of revolutions, "For you/ I will tear
out my soul/ and trample on it till it spreads out,/ and I'll give
it to you,/ a bloody banner." In the poems written after the revolution the same idea is there, but in the past tense. The poet,
mobilized by the revolution, has "stamped on the throat of his
own song." (This line occurs in the last poem he published, an
address to his "comrade-descendants" of the future, written in
clear awareness of the coming end.) In the poem *About That,*
the poet is destroyed by *byt.* "The bloodletting is over. . . . Only
high above the Kremlin the tatters of the poet shine in the
wind—a little red flag." This image is plainly an echo of *A
Cloud in Trousers.*

The poet's hungry ear captures the music of the future, but
he is not destined to enter the Promised Land. A vision of the
future is present in all the most essential pages of Majakovskij's
work. "And such a day dawned—Andersen's fairytales crawled
about like little pups at his feet"; "You can't tell whether it's air,

or a flower, or a bird. It sings, and it's fragrant, and it's bright-
ly colored all at once"; "Call us Cain or call us Abel, it doesn't
matter. The future is here." For Majakovskij the future is a
dialectical synthesis. The removal of all contradictions finds its
expression in the facetious image of Christ playing checkers
with Cain, in the myth of the universe permeated by love, and
in the proposition "The commune is a place where bureaucrats
will disappear and there will be many poems and songs." The
present disharmony, the contradiction between poetry and
building, "the delicate business of the poet's place in the working ranks," is one of Majakovskij's most acute problems.
"Why," he asked, "should literature occupy its own special little corner? Either it should appear in every newspaper, every
day, on every page, or else it's totally useless. The kind of literature that's dished out as dessert can go to hell" (from the
Reminiscences of D. Lebedev).

Majakovskij always regarded ironically talk of the insignif-
icance and death of poetry (really nonsense, he would say, but
useful for the purpose of revolutionizing art). He planned to
pose the question of the future of art in the "Fifth International,"
a poem that he worked on long and carefully but never finished. According to the outline of the work, the first stage of
the revolution, a worldwide social transformation, has been
completed, but humanity is bored. *Byt* still survives. So a new
revolutionary act of world-shaking proportions is required: "A
revolution of the spirit" in the name of a new organization of
life, a new art, and a new science. The published introduction
to the poem is an order to abolish the beauties of verse and to
introduce into poetry the brevity and accuracy of mathematical
formulas. He offers an example of a poetic structure built on
the model of a logical problem. When I reacted skeptically to
this poetic program—the exhortation in verse against verse—

Majakovskij smiled: "But didn't you notice that the solution of my logical problem is a transrational solution?"

The remarkable poem "Homeward!" is devoted to the contradiction between the rational and the irrational. It is a dream about the fusion of the two elements, a kind of rationalization of the irrational:

> I feel like a Soviet factory
> Manufacturing happiness.
> I don't want/ to be plucked
> Like a flower/ after the day's work
> . . . . .
> I want/ the heart to be paid
> Its wage of love/ at the specialist's rate
> I want/ the factory committee
> To put a lock on my lips
> When the work is done
> I want/ the pen to be equal to the bayonet
> And I want Stalin/ to report in the name of the Politburo
> About the production of verse
> As he does about pig iron and steel.
> Thus, and so it is/ we've reached
> The topmost level/ up from the worker's hovels
> In the Union/ of Republics
> The appreciation of verse/ has exceeded the prewar level.

The idea of the acceptance of the irrational appears in Majakovskij's work in various guises, and each of the images he uses for this purpose tends to reappear in his poetry. The stars ("You know, if they light up the stars,/ that means, somebody needs them!"). The madness of spring ("Everything is clear concerning bread/ and concerning peace./ But the prime question,/ the question of spring/ must be/ elucidated"). And the heart that changes winter to spring and water to wine ("It's that I'm/ going to raise my heart like a flag,/ a marvelous twentieth-century miracle"). And that hostile answer of the enemy in the poem *Man*: "If the heart is everything/ then why,/ why have I been gathering you, my dear money!/ How do they dare to sing?/ Who gave them the right?/ Who said the days could blossom into July?/ Lock the heavens in wires!/ Twist the earth into streets!"

But Majakovskij's central irrational theme is the theme of love. It is a theme that cruelly punishes those who dare to forget it, whose storms toss us about violently and push everything else out of our ken. And like poetry itself this theme is both inseparable from and in disharmony with our present life; it is "closely mingled with our jobs, our incomes, and all the rest." And love is crushed by *byt*:

> Omnipotent one
> You thought up a pair of hands
> Fixed it
> So that everyone has a head.
> Why couldn't you fix it
> So that without torment
> We could just kiss and kiss and kiss?

Eliminate the irrational? Majakovskij draws a bitterly satirical picture. On the one hand, the heavy boredom of certain rational revelations: the usefulness of the cooperative, the danger of liquor, political education, and on the other hand, an unashamed hooligan of planetary dimensions (in the poem "A Type"). Here we have a satirical sharpening of the dialectical contradiction. Majakovskij says "yes" to the rationalization of production, technology, and the planned economy if as a result of all this "the partially opened eye of the future sparkles with real earthly love." But he rejects it all if it means only a selfish clutching at the present. If that's the case then grandiose technology becomes only a "highly perfected apparatus of parochialism and gossip on the worldwide scale" (from an essay "My Discovery of America"). Just such a planetary narrowness and parochialism permeates life in the year 1970, as shown in Majakovskij's play about the future, *The Bedbug*, where we see a rational organization without emotion, with no superfluous expenditure of energy, without dreams. A worldwide social revolution has been achieved, but the revolution of the spirit is still in the future. The play is a quiet protest against the spiritual inheritors of those languid judges who, in his early satirical poem "without knowing just why or wherefore, attacked Peru." Some of the characters in *The Bedbug* have a close affinity with the world of Zamjatin's *We*, although Majakovskij bitterly ridicules not only the rational utopian community but the rebellion against it in the name of alcohol, the irrational and unregulated individual happiness. Zamjatin, however, idealizes that rebellion.

Majakovskij has an unshakable faith that, beyond the mountain of suffering, beyond each rising plateau of revolutions, there does exist the "real heaven on earth," the only possible resolution of all contradictions. *Byt* is only a surrogate for the coming synthesis; it doesn't remove contradictions but only conceals them. The poet is unwilling to compromise with the dialectic; he rejects any mechanical softening of the contradictions. The objects of Majakovskij's unsparing sarcasm are the "compromisers" (as in the play *Mystery-Bouffe*). Among the gallery of "bureaucrat-compromisers" portrayed in his agitational pieces, we have in *The Bathhouse* the Glavnachpups Pobedonosikov, whose very title is an acronym for "Chief Administrator for the Organizing of Compromises." Obstacles in the road to the future—such is the true nature of these "artificial people." The time machine will surely spew them out.

It seemed to him a criminal illusion to suppose that the essential and vital problem of building a worldwide "wonderful life" could be put aside for the sake of devising some kind of personal happiness. "It's early to rejoice," he wrote. The opening scenes of *The Bedbug* develop the idea that people are tired of a life full of struggle, tired of frontline equality, tired of military metaphors. "This is not 1919. People want to live." They build family nests for themselves: "Roses will bloom and be fragrant at the present juncture of time." "Such is the elegant fulfillment of our comrade's life of struggle." Oleg Bajan, the servant of beauty in *The Bedbug*, formulates this sentiment in the following words: "We have managed to compromise and control class and other contradictions, and in this a person armed with a Marxist eye, so to speak, can't help seeing, as in a single drop of water, the future happiness of mankind, which the common people call socialism." (In an earlier, lyrical context the same idea took this form: "There he is in a soft bed, fruit beside him and wine on the night table.") Majakovskij's sharply chiseled lines express unlimited contempt for all those who seek comfort and rest. All such people receive their answer from the mechanic in *The Bedbug*: "We'll never crawl out of our trenches with a white flag in our hands." And the poem *About That* develops the same theme in the form of an intimate personal experience. In that work Majakovskij begs for the advent of love, his savior: "Confiscate my pain—take it away!" And Majakovskij answers himself:

> Leave off./ Don't/ not a word/ no requests,
> What's the point/ that you/ alone/ should succeed?
> I'll wait/ and together with the whole unloved earth
> With the whole/ human mass/ we'll win it.
> Seven years I stood/ and I'll stand two hundred
> Nailed here/ waiting for it.

On the bridge of years/ derided/ scorned
A redeemer of earthly love/ I must stand
Stand for all/ for everyone I'll atone
For everyone I'll weep.

But Majakovskij knows very well that even if his youth
should be renewed four times and he should four times grow
old again, that would only mean a fourfold increase of his torment, a four times multiplied horror at the senseless daily grind
and at premature celebrations of victory. In any case, he will
never live to see the revelation all over the world of an absolute
fullness of life, and the final count still stands: "I've not lived
out my earthly lot; I've not lived through my earthly love." His
destiny is to be an expiatory victim who never knew joy:

A bullet for the rest
For some a knife.
But what about me?
And when?

Majakovskij has now given us the final answer to that question.
The Russian Futurists believed in cutting themselves loose
from the "classic generals," and yet they are vitally tied to the
Russian literary tradition. It is interesting to note that famous
line of Majakovskij's, so full of bravado (and at the same time a
tactical slogan): "But why don't we attack Pushkin?" It was followed not long after by those mournful lines addressed to the
same Pushkin: "You know I too will soon be dead and mute./
And after my death/ we two will be quite close together."
Majakovskij's dreams of the future that repeat the utopian
visions of Dostoevskij's Versilov in *A Raw Youth*, the poet's frequent hymns to the "man-god," the "thirteenth apostle's" fight
against God, the ethical rejection of Him—all this is much
closer to Russian literature of an earlier day than it is to official

and regimented Soviet "godlessness." And Majakovskij's belief in personal immortality has nothing to do with the official catechism of Jaroslavskij's "godless" movement. The poet's vision of the coming resurrection of the dead is vitally linked with the materialistic mysticism of the Russian philosopher Fëdorov.

When in the spring of 1920 I returned to Moscow, which was tightly blockaded, I brought with me recent books and information about scientific developments in the West. Majakovskij made me repeat several times my somewhat confused remarks on the general theory of relativity and about the growing interest in that concept in Western Europe. The idea of the liberation of energy, the problem of the time dimension, and the idea that movement at the speed of light may actually be a reverse movement in time—all these things fascinated Majakovskij. I'd seldom seen him so interested and attentive. "Don't you think," he suddenly asked, "that we'll at last achieve immortality?" I was astonished, and I mumbled a skeptical comment. He thrust his jaw forward with that hypnotic insistence so familiar to anyone who knew Majakovskij well: "I'm absolutely convinced," he said, "that one day there will be no more death. And the dead will be resurrected. I've got to find some scientist who'll give me a precise account of what's in Einstein's books. It's out of the question that I shouldn't understand it. I'll see to it that this scientist receives an academician's ration." At that point I became aware of a Majakovskij that I'd never known before. The demand for victory over death had taken hold of him. He told me later that he was writing a poem called "The Fourth International" (he afterward changed it to "The Fifth International") that would deal with such things. "Einstein will be a member of that International. The poem will be much more important than *150,000,000*." Majakovskij was at the time obsessed with the idea of sending Einstein a congratulatory telegram "from the art of the future to the science of the future." We never again returned to this matter in our conversations, and he never finished "The Fifth International." But in the epilogue to *About That*, we find the lines: "I see it, I see it clearly to the last sharp detail . . . on the bright eminence of time, impervious to rot or destruction, the workshop of human resurrection."

The epilogue to *About That* carries the following heading: "A request addressed to . . . (Please, comrade chemist, fill in the name yourself)." I haven't the slightest doubt that for Majakovskij this was not just a literary device but a genuine and seriously offered request to some "quiet chemist with a domed forehead" living in the thirtieth century:

> Resurrect me!
> Even if only because I was a poet
> And waited for you.
> And put behind me prosaic nonsense.
> Resurrect me—
> Just for that!
> Do resurrect me—
> I want to live it all out.

The very same "Institute for Human Resurrections" reappears in the play *The Bedbug* but in a comic context. It is the insistent theme of Majakovskij's last writings. Consider the situation in *The Bathhouse*. "A phosphorescent woman out of the future, empowered to select the best people for the future age appears in the time machine: At the first signal we blast off, and smash through old decrepit time. . . . Winged time will sweep away and cut loose the ballast, heavy with rubbish and ruined by lack of faith." Once again we see that the pledge of resurrection is faith. Moreover, the people of the future must transform not only their own future, but also the past: "The fence of time/ our feet will trample.... As it has been written by us,/ so will the world be/ on Wednesday,/ in the past/ and now/ and tomorrow/ and forever" (from *150,000,000*). The poem written in memory of Lenin offers the same idea, yet in disguised form:

> Death will never dare
> To touch him.
> He stands
> In the total sum of what's to be!
> The young attend
> To these verses on his death
> But their hearts know
> That he's deathless.

In Majakovskij's earliest writings personal immortality is achieved in spite of science. "You students," he says, "all the stuff we know and study is rubbish. Physics, astronomy, and chemistry are all nonsense" (from the poem *Man*). At that time he regarded science as an idle occupation involving only the extraction of square roots or a kind of inhuman collection of fossilized fragments of the summer before last. His satirical "Hymn to the Scholar" became a genuine and fervent hymn only when he thought he had found the miraculous instrument of human resurrection in Einstein's "futuristic brain" and in the physics and chemistry of the future. "Like logs thrown into a boom we are thown at birth into the Volga of human time; we toss about as we float downstream. But from now on that great river shall be submissive to us. I'll make time stand still, move in another direction and at a new rate of speed. People will be able to get out of the day like passengers getting out of a bus." Whatever the means of achieving immortality, the vision of it in Majakovskij's verse is unchangeable: there can be no resurrection of the spirit without the body, without the flesh itself.

Immortality has nothing to with any other world; it is indissolubly tied to this one. "I'm all for the heart," he wrote in *Man*, "but how can bodiless beings have a heart?/ . . . My eyes fixed earthward . . . / This herd of the bodiless,/ how they/ bore me!" "We want to live here on earth—/ no higher and no lower" (*Mystery-Bouffe*). "With the last measure of my heart/ I believe/ in this life,/ in this world,/ in all of it" (*About That*). Majakovskij's dream is of an everlasting earth, and this earth is placed in sharp opposition to all superterrestrial, fleshless abstractions. In his poetry and in Xlebnikov's the theme of earthly life is presented in a coarse, physical incarnation (they even talk about the "flesh" rather than the body). An extreme expression of this is the cult of tender feeling for the beast with his beastly wisdom.

"They will arise from the mounds of graves/ and their buried bones will grow flesh" (*War and the World*), wrote Majakovskij. And those lines are not just present simply as a poetic device that motivates the whimsical interweaving of two separate narrative levels. On the contrary—that vision is Majakovskij's most cherished poetic myth.

This constant infatuation with a wonderful future is linked in Majakovskij with a pronounced dislike of children, a fact that would seem at first sight to be hardly consonant with his fanatical belief in tomorrow. But just as we find in Dostoevskij an obtrusive and neurotic "father hatred" linked with great veneration for ancestors and reverence for tradition, so in Majakovskij's spiritual world an abstract faith in the coming transformation of the world is joined quite properly with hatred for the evil continuum of specific tomorrows that only prolong today ("the calendar is nothing but the calendar!") and with undying hostility to that "brood-hen" love that serves only to reproduce the present way of life. Majakovskij was indeed capable of giving full due to the creative mission of those "kids of the collective" in their unending quarrel with the old world, but at the same time he bristled whenever an actual "kid" ran into the room. Majakovskij never recognized his own myth of the future in any concrete child; these he regarded simply as new offshoots of the hydraheaded enemy. That is why we find in the marvelous movie scenario *How Are You?* childlike grotesques, which are the legitimate offspring of the Manilov pair Alcides and Themistoclus in Gogol's *Dead Souls*. We recall that his youthful poem "A Few Words about Myself" begins with the line "I love to watch children dying." And in the same poem child-murder is elevated to a cosmic theme: "Sun!/ My father!/ At least you have pity and torment me not!/ That's my blood you shed flowing along this low road." And surrounded by that very aura of sunshine, the same "child complex" appears as both an immemorial and personal motif in the poem *War and the World*:

> Listen—
> The sun just shed his first rays
> not yet knowing
> where he'll go when he's done his day's work;
> and that's me
> Majakovskij,
> Bringing as sacrifice to the idol's pedestal
> a beheaded infant.

There's no doubt that in Majakovskij the theme of child-murder and suicide are closely linked: these are simply two different ways of depriving the present of its immediate succession, of "tearing through decrepit time."

Majakovskij's conception of the poet's role is clearly bound up with his belief in the possibility of conquering time and breaking its steady, slow step. He did not regard poetry as a mechanical superstructure added to the ready-made base of existence (it is no accident that he was so close to the Formalist literary critics). A genuine poet is not one "who feeds in the calm pastures of everyday life; his mug is not pointed at the ground." "The weak ones simply beat time and wait for something to happen that they can echo; but the powerful rush far enough ahead so as to drag time along behind them!" Majakovskij's recurrent image of the poet is one who overtakes time, and we may say that this is the actual likeness of Majakovskij himself. Xlebnikov and Majakovskij accurately forecast the Revolution (including the date); that is only a detail, but a rather important one. It would seem that never until our day has the writer's fate been laid bare with such pitiless candor in his own words. Impatient to know life, he recognizes it in his own story. The "God-seeker" Blok and the Marxist Majakovskij both understood clearly that verses are dictated to the poet by some primordial, mysterious force. "We know not whence comes the basic beat of rhythm." We don't even know where this rhythm is located: "outside of me or within me? But most likely within me." The poet himself senses the necessity of his own verse, and his contemporaries feel that the poet's destiny is no accident. Is there any one of us who doesn't share the impression that the poet's volumes are a kind of scenario in which he plays out the story of his life? The poet is the principal character, and subordinate parts are also included; but the performers for these later roles are recruited as the action develops and to the extent that the plot requires them. The plot has been laid out ahead of time right down to the details of the dénouement.

The motif of suicide, so alien to the thematics of the Futurist and "Left Front" groups, continually recurs in the work of Majakovskij, from his earliest writings, where madmen hang themselves in an unequal struggle with *byt* (the director, the "man with two kisses" in the *Tragedy*), to the scenario *How Are You?* in which a newspaper article about a girl's suicide induces horror in the poet. And when he tells about a young communist who committed suicide he adds, "How like me that is. Horrors!" He tries on, so to speak, all possible varieties of suicide: "Rejoice now! He'll execute himself. . . . The locomotive's wheel will embrace my neck." "I'll run to the canal and there stick my head in the water's grinning mug. . . ." "The heart bursts for a bullet, the throat raves for a razor. . . . Beckons to the water, leads to the roof's slope. . . . Druggist, give me the means to send my soul without any pain into the spacious beyond."

A simple resume of Majakovskij's poetic autobiography would be the following: the poet nurtured in his heart the unparalleled anguish of the present generation. That is why his verse is charged with hatred for the strongholds of the established order, and in his own work he finds "the alphabet of coming ages." Majakovskij's earliest and most characteristic image is one in which he "goes out through the city leaving his soul on the spears of houses, shred by shred." The hopelessness of his lonely struggle with the daily routine became clearer to him at every turn. The brand of martyrdom is burned into him. There's no way to win an early victory. The poet is the doomed "outcast of the present."

> Mama!
> Tell my sisters, Ljuda and Olja,
> That there's no way out.

Gradually the idea that "there's no way out" lost its purely literary character. From the poetic passage it found its way into prose, and "there's no way out" turned up as an author's remark in the margin of the manuscript for *About That*. And from that prose context the same idea made its way into the poet's life; in his suicide note he said: "Mama, sisters, comrades, forgive me. This is not a good method (I don't recommend it to others), but for me there's no other way out."

The act was long in preparation. Fifteen years earlier in a prologue to a collection of poems, he wrote:

> Often I think
> Hadn't I better just
> Let a bullet mark the period of my sentence.
> Anyway, today I'm giving my farewell concert.

As time went on the theme of suicide became more and more pressing. Majakovskij's most intense poems, *Man* (1916) and *About That* (1923), are dedicated to it. Each of these works is an ominous song of the victory of *byt* over the poet: their leit-motif is "Love's boat has smashed against the daily grind" (a line from his suicide note). The first poem is a detailed depiction of Majakovskij's suicide. In the second there is already a clear sense that the suicide theme transcends literature and is in the realm of "literature of fact." Once again—but even more disturbingly—the images of the first poem file past, the keenly observed stages of existence: the "half-death" in the vortex of the horrifyingly trivial, then the "final death"—"The lead in my heart! Not even a shudder!" This theme of suicide had become so real that it was out of the question to sketch the scene anymore. It had to be exorcised. Propaganda pieces were necessary in order to slow down the inexorable movement of that theme. *About That* already initiates this long cycle of exorcism. "I won't give them the satisfaction of seeing me dead of a bullet." "I want to live on and on, moving through the years." The lines to

Sergej Esenin are the high point of this cycle. According to Majakovskij, the salubrious aim of the lines addressed to Esenin was to neutralize the impact of Esenin's death poem. But when you read them now, they sound even more sepulchral than Esenin's last lines. Esenin's lines equate life and death, but Majakovskij in his poem can only say about life that it's harder than death. This is the same sort of doubtful propaganda for life found in Majakovskij's earlier lines to the effect that only disquiet about the afterlife is a restraint upon the bullet. Such, too, are the farewell words in his suicide letter: "Stay happy here."

In spite of all this the obituary writers vie with one another: "One could expect anything of Majakovskij, but not that he would kill himself." (E. Adamovich). And Lunacharskij: "The idea of suicide is simply incompatible with our image of the poet." And Malkin: "His death cannot be reconciled with his whole life, which was that of a poet completely dedicated to the Revolution." And the newspaper *Pravda*: "His death is just as inconsistent with the life he led as it is unmotivated by his poetry." And A. Xalatov: "Such a death was hardly proper for the Majakovskij we knew." Or Kol´cov: "It is not right for him. Can it be that none of us knew Majakovskij?" Petr Pil´skij: "He did not, of course, reveal any reason for us to expect such an end." And finally, the poet Demjan Bednyj: "Incredible! What could he have lacked?"

Could these men of letters have forgotten or so misunderstood *All That Majakovskij Composed?*[10] Or was there a general conviction that all of it was only "composed," only invented? Sound literary criticism rejects any direct or immediate conclusions about the biography of a poet when these are based merely on the evidence of his works, but it does not at all follow from this that there is no connection whatsoever between the artist's biography and his art. Such an "antibiographical" position would be the equivalent, in reverse, of the simplistic biographical approach. Have we forgotten Majakovskij's admiration for the "genuine heroism and martyrdom" of Xlebnikov, his teacher? "His life," wrote Majakovskij, "matched his brilliant verbal constructs. That life is an exarnple for poets and a reproach to poetizers." And it was Majakovskij who wrote that even a poet's style of dress, even his intimate conversations with his wife, should be determined by the whole of his poetic production. He understood very well the close connection between poetry and life.

After Esenin's suicide poem, said Majakovskij, his death became a literary fact. "It was clear at once that those powerful verses, just those verses, would bring to the bullet or the noose many who had been hesitating." And when he approached the writing of his own autobiography, Majakovskij remarked that the facts of a poet's life are interesting "only if they became fixed in the word." Who would dare assert that Majakovskij's suicide was not fixed in the word? "Don't gossip!" Majakovskij adjured us just before his death. Yet those who stubbornly mark out a strict boundary between the "purely personal" fate of the poet and his literary biography create an atmosphere of low-grade, highly personal gossip by means of those significant silences.

It is a historical fact that the people around Majakovskij simply did not believe in his lyrical monologues. "They listened, all smiling, to the eminent clown." They took his various masquerades for the true face of the man: first the pose of the fop ("It's good when the soul is shielded from inspection by a yellow blouse"); then the performance of an overeager journalist and agitator: "It's good when you're in the teeth of the gallows, to cry out: 'Drink Van Houten's cocoa'" (*A Cloud in*

Trousers). But then when he carried out that slogan in practice in his advertising jingles ("Use the tea with the gold label!" "If you want good luck and good fortune buy a government lottery ticket!") his audience saw the rhymed advertisement but missed the teeth of the gallows. As it turns out, it was easier to believe in the benefits of a lottery ticket or the excellent quality of the pacifiers sold in the state stores than it was to believe that the poet had reached an extreme of despair, that he was in a state of misery and near-death. *About That* is a long and hopeless cry to the ages, but Moscow doesn't believe in tears. They stamped and whistled at this routine Majakovskian artistic stunt, the latest of his "magnificent absurdities," but when the theatrical cranberry juice of the puppet show became real, genuine, thick blood, they were taken aback: Incredible! Inconsistent!

Majakovskij, as an act of self-preservation, often helped to spread illusions about himself. The record of a conversation we had in 1927 demonstrates this. I said, "The total sum of possible experience has been measured out to us. We might have predicted the early decline of our generation. But the symptoms of this are rapidly increasing in number. Take Aseev's line 'What about us, what about us, can it be we've lost our youth?' And consider Shklovskij's memorial service to himself!" Majakovskij answered: "Utter nonsense. Everything is ahead of me. If I ever thought that the best of me was in the past that would be the end for me." I reminded him of a recent poem of his in which the following lines occurred:

> I was born/ increased in size
> fed from the bottle—
> I lived/ worked/ grew oldish
> And life will pass
> As the Azores Islands
> Once passed into the distance.

"That's nothing," he said, "just a formal ending. An image only. I can make as many of them as you like. My poem 'Homeward' in the first version ended with the lines:

> I want my country to understand me
> But if not—so what:
> I'll just pass my country by
> Like a slanting rain in summer.

But you know, Brik told me to strike those lines out because they didn't go with the tone of the whole poem. So I struck them out."

The simplistic Formalist literary credo professed by the Russian Futurists inevitably propelled their poetry toward the antithesis of Formalism—toward the cultivation of the heart's "raw cry" and uninhibited frankness. Formalist literary theory placed the lyrical monologue in quotes and disguised the "ego" of the lyric poet under a pseudonym. But what unbounded horror results when suddenly you see through the pseudonym, and the phantoms of art invade reality, just as in Majakovskij's scenario *Bound in Film* a girl is kidnapped from a movie set by a mad artist and lands in "real life."

Toward the end of his life, the satire and the laudatory ode had completely overshadowed his elegiac verse, which, by the way, he identified with the lyric in general. In the West the exustence of this basic core in Majakovskij's poetry was not even suspected. The West knew only the "drummer of the October Revolution." There are many explanations for this victory of agit-prop. In 1923 Majakovskij had reached the end of the road as far as the elegiac mode was concerned. In an artistic sense *About That* was a "repetition of the past," intensified and raised to perfection. His journalistic verse was a search for something new; it was an experiment in the production of new materials and in untested genres. To my skeptical comments about these poems Majakovskij replied: "Later on you'll understand them." And when *The Bedbug* and *The Bathhouse* appeared it became clear that his most recent poems had been a huge laboratory experiment in language and theme, a labor masterfully exploited in his first efforts in the area of prose drama and offering a rich potential for future growth.

Finally, in connection with its social setting, the journalistic verse of Majakovskij represented a shift from an unrestrained frontal attack in the direction of an exhausting trench warfare. *Byt*, with its swarm of heartbreaking trivia, is still with him. And it is no longer "rubbish with its own proper face," but "petty, small, vulgar rubbish." You cannot resist the pressure of such rubbish by grandiloquent pronouncements "in general and in toto," or by theses on communism, or by pure poetic devices. "Now you have to see the enemy and take aim at him." You have to smash the "swarm of trivia" offered by *byt* "in a small way" and not grieve that the battle has been reduced to many minor engagements. The invention of strategies for describing "trifles that may also prove a sure step into the future"—this is how Majakovskij understood the immediate task of the poet.

Just as one must not reduce Majakovskij the propagandist to a single dimension, so, too, one-sided interpretations of the poet's death are shallow and opaque. "The preliminary investigation indicates that his act was prompted by motives of a purely personal character." But the poet had already provided an answer to that in the subtitle of *About That*: "From personal motives, but about the general way of life."

Bela Kun preached to the late poet not to "subordinate the great cause to our own petty personal feelings."[11] Majakovskij had entered his objection in good time:

With this petty/
and personal theme
That's been sung so many times
I've trod the poetical treadmill
And I'm going to tread it again.
This theme/ right now
Is a prayer to Buddha
And sharpens a black man's knife for his master.
If there's life on Mars/ and on it just one
Human-hearted creature
Then he too is writing now
About that same thing.

The journalist Kol´cov hastened to explain: "Majakovskij himself was wholly absorbed in the business affairs of various literary groups and in political matters. Someone else fired that shot, some outsider who happened to be in control of a revolutionary poet's mind and will. It was the result of the temporary pressure of circumstances." And once again we recall the rebuke Majakovskij delivered long before the fact:

Dreams are a harm
And it's useless to fantasize.
You've got to bear the burden of service.
But sometimes—
Life appears to you in a new light
And through the mess of trifles
You catch sight of something great and good.

"We condemn this senseless, unforgivable act. It was a stupid and cowardly death. We cannot but protest most vigorously against his departure from life, against his incongruous end." (Such was the pronouncement of the Moscow Soviet and others.) But Majakovskij had already parodied these very funeral speeches in *The Bedbug*. "Zoja Berezkin's shot herself—Aha! She'll catch it for that at her party-section meeting." Says a doctor in the future world commune: "What is suicide? . . . You shot at yourself? . . . Was it an accident?" "No, it was from love." "Nonsense. . . . Love makes you want to build bridges and have children. . . . But you. . . . Yes, yes, yes!"

In general life has been imitating Majakovskij's satirical lines with horrifying regularity. Pobedonosikov, the comic figure in *The Bathhouse*, who has many features that remind us of Lunacharskij, brags that "I have no time for boat rides . . . Such petty entertainments are for various secretaries: 'Float on, gondola mine!' I have no gondola but a ship of state." And now Lunacharskij himself faithfully echoes his comic double. At a meeting called in memory of the poet, the minister hastens to explain that the former's farewell lines about a "love-boat smashed on the daily grind" have a pathetic sound: "We know very well that it was not on any love-boat that he sailed our stormy seas. He was the captain of a mighty ship of state." These efforts to forget the "purely personal" tragedy of Majakovskij sometimes take the form of conscious parody. A group of writers in a provincial town published a resolution in which they assure Soviet society that they will take very seriously the advice of the late poet not to follow his example.

It is very strange that on this occasion such terms as "accidental," "personal," and so forth are used precisely by those who have always preached a strict social determinism. But how can one speak of a private episode when the law of large numbers is at work, in view of the fact that in a few years' time the whole bloom of Russian poetry has been swept away?

In one of Majakovskij's longer poems, each of the world's countries brings its best gift to the man of the future; Russia brings him poetry. "The power of their voices is most resoundingly woven into song." Western Europe is enraptured with Russian art: the medieval icon and the modern film, the classical ballet and the latest theatrical experiment, yesterday's novel and the latest music. And yet that art which is probably Russia's greatest achievement, her poetry, has never really been an export item. It is intimately Russian and closely linked to the Russian language and would probably not survive the misfortunes of translation. Russian poetry has witnessed two periods of high flowering: the beginning of the nineteenth century and the present century. And the earlier period as well as the later had as its epilogue the untimely death of very many great poets. If you can imagine how slight the contributions of Schiller, Hoffmann, Heine, and especially Goethe would have been if they had all disappeared in their thirties, then you will understand the significance ofthe following Russian statistics: Ryleev was executed when he was thirty-one. Batjushkov went mad when he was thirty. Venevitinov died at the age of twenty-two, Del'vig at thirty-two. Griboedov was killed when he was thirty-four, Pushkin when he was thirty-seven, Lermontov when he was twenty-six.[12] Their fate has more than once been characterized as a form of suicide. Majakovskij himself compared his duel with *byt* to the fatal duels of Pushkin and Lermontov. There is much in common in the reactions of society in both periods to these untimely losses. Once again, a feeling of sudden and profound emptiness overwhelms one, an oppressive sense of an evil destiny lying heavily on Russian intellectual life. But now as then other notes are louder and more insistent.

The Western mind can hardly comprehend the stupid, unrestrained abuse of the dead poets. A certain Kikin expressed great disappointment that Martynov, the killer of that "cowardly scoundrel Lermontov," had been arrested. And Tsar Nicholas I's final words on the same poet were: "He was a dog and he died a dog's death." And in the same spirit the emigre newspaper *The Rudder* (*Rul'*) carried no obituary on the occasion of

Majakovskij's death, but instead a cluster of abusive remarks leading up to the following conclusion: "Majakovskij's whole life gave off a bad smell. Is it possible that his tragic end could set all that right?" (Ofrosimov). But what of the Kikins and Ofrosimovs? They're but illiterate zeros who will be mentioned in the history of Russian culture, if at all, only for having defecated on the fresh graves of poets. It is incomparably more distressing to see slops of slander and lies poured on the dead poet by Xodasevich, who is privy to poetry. He certainly knows the value of things; he knows he is slanderously smearing one of the greatest Russian poets. When he caustically remarks that only some fifteen active years were allotted to Majakovskij—"the lifetime of a horse"—it is self-abuse, gallows humor, mockery of the tragic balance sheet of his own generation. If Majakovskij's final balance sheet was "life and I are quits," then Xodasevich's shabby little fate is "the most terrible of amortizations, the amortization of heart and soul."

The latter was written about émigré philistines. But the tradition of Pushkin's days is repeated by the same philistines of Moscow stock who immediately try at all costs to replace the live image of the poet by a canonic saintlike mask. And even earlier. . . . But of what went on earlier, Majakovskij himself related a few days before his death in a talk at a literary gathering: "So many dogs snipe at me and I'm accused of so many sins, both ones I have and ones I am innocent of, that at times it seems to me as if all I want to do is go away somewhere and sit still for a couple of years, if only to avoid listening to barking!" And this harrassment, framing the poet's demise, was precisely described in advance by Majakovskij:

Yellow rag after yellow rag
   of curses be raised!
Gossip for your ears!
   Gossip and bite!
I'm like a cripple in the throes of love.
Leave a tub of slops for your own.
I'm not a hindrance.
   But why all these insults?
I'm only a verse
   I'm only a soul.
While below:
   No!
   You're our century-old foe.
One such turned up—
      A hussar!
Have a sniff of powder,
   a little pistol lead.
Fling open your shirt!
   Don't celebrate the coward!

This is just another example of what they call the "incongruity" beween Majakovskij's end and his life of yesterday.

Certain questions are particularly intriguing to journalists. Who was responsible for the war? Who was to blame for the poet's death? Biographers are amateur private detectives, and they will certainly take great pains to establish the immediate reason for the suicide. They will add other names to that variegated assemblage of poet-killers, the "son of a bitch D'Anthès" who killed Pushkin, the "dashing Major Martynov" who killed Lermontov, and so forth. People who seek the explanation of various phenomena will, if they bear Russia a grudge, readily demonstrate, citing chapter, verse, and historical precedent, that it is dangerous to practice the trade of poet in Russia. And if their grudge is only against contemporary Russia, it will also be quite easy to defend such a thesis with weighty arguments.

But I am of another mind. It seems to me that the one nearest the truth was the young Slovak poet Novomesk˝ who said: "Do you imagine that such things happen only there, in Russia? Why that's what our world is like nowadays." This is in answer to those phrases, which have alas become truisms, concerning the deadly absence of fresh air, certainly a fatal condition for poets. There are some countries where men kiss women's hands, and others where they only say "I kiss your hand." There are countries where Marxist theory is answered by Leninist practice, and where the madness of the brave, the martyr's stake, and the poet's Golgotha are not just figurative expressions.

In the last analysis, what distinguishes Russia is not so much the fact that her great poets have ceased to be, but rather that not long ago she had so many of them. Since the time of the first Symbolists, Western Europe has had no great poetry.

The real question concerns not causes but consequences, however tempting it may be to protect oneself from a painful realization of what's happened by discussing the reasons for it.

> It's a small thing to build a locomotive:
> Wind up its wheels and off it goes.
> But if a song doesn't fill the railway station—
> Then why do we have alternating current?

Those lines are from Majakovskij's "Order to the Army of Art." We are living in what is called the "reconstruction period," and no doubt we will construct a great many locomotives and scientific hypotheses. But to our generation has been allotted the morose feat of building without song. And even if new songs should ring out, they will belong to another generation and a different curve of time. Yet it is unlikely that there will be new songs. Russian poetry of our century is copying and it would seem outdoing that of the nineteenth century: "the fateful forties are approaching," the years, in other words, of lethargic inertia among poets.

The relationships between the biographies of a generation and the march of history are curious. Each age has its own inventory of requisitions upon private holdings. Suddenly history finds a use for Beethoven's deafness and Cézanne's astigmatism. The age at which a generation's call to service in history's conscription comes, as well as the length of its service, are different for different periods. History mobilizes the youthful ardor of some generations and the tempered maturity or old wisdom of others. When their role is played out yesterday's rulers of men's minds and hearts depart from the proscenium to the backstage of history to live out their years in private, either on the profits from their intellectual investments, or else as paupers. But sometimes it happens otherwise. Our generation emerged at an extraordinarily young age: "We alone," as Majakovskij put it, "are the face of our time. The trumpet of time blows for us." But up to the present moment there are not any replacements, nor even any partial reinforcements. Meanwhile the voice and the emotion of that generation have been cut short, and its allotted quota of feeling—joy and sadness, sarcasm and rapture—has been used up. And yet, the paroxysm of an irreplaceable generation turned out to be no private fate, but in fact the face of our time, the breathlessness of history.

We strained toward the future too impetuously and avidly to leave any past behind us. The connection of one period with another was broken. We lived too much for the future, thought about it, believed in it; the news of the day—sufficient unto itself—no longer existed for us. We lost a sense of the present. We were the witnesses of and participants in great social, scientific, and other cataclysms. *Byt* fell behind us, just as in the young Majakovskij's splendid hyperbole: "One foot has not yet reached the next street." We knew that the plans of our fathers were already out of harmony with the facts of their lives. We read harsh lines alleging that our fathers had taken the old and musty way of life on a temporary lease. But our fathers still had left some remnant of faith in the idea that that way of life was both comfortable and compulsory for all. Their children had only a single-minded, naked hatred for the ever more threadbare, ever more alien rubbish offered by the established order of things. And now the "efforts to organize a personal life are like attempts to heat up ice cream."

As for the future, it doesn't belong to us either. In a few decades we shall be cruelly labeled as products of the past millennium. All we had were compelling songs of the future; and suddenly these songs are no longer part of the dynamic of history, but have been transformed into historico-literary facts. When singers have been killed and their song has been dragged into a museum and pinned to the wall of the past, the generation they represent is even more desolate, orphaned, and lost— impoverished in the most real sense of the word.

PART FOUR

POEMS AND PROSE

JUVENILIA

1.

Death

The grass in the field,
The sand in the sea
Are happier than me.
My childhood's fled,
My youth's but a hint
Of the resounding day.
My strength's buried
In the tomb of night.
Death's not o'er the hill
But upon my back —
"Be gone, get ye hence!"
Life just stopped.
Death approached.
But I wanted to live
Despite its burden . . .
Life's thread snapped
When time broke.

2.

A Bachelor's Apartment
(An Imitation of Maksim Gor´kij)

The sun rises and sets,
But the apartment's empty.
One hears from time to time
A plaintive cat's meow.

On a chair in the study
Torn trousers hang;
The cockroaches parade
Ominously on their spines.

And from the dust one can't
Even find one's way inside;
Without a young wife,
It'll never get whipped away.

If only I had a cook,
Even if I called her "Frau,"
If I were a minute late,
She'd get mad . . . and "Kaput."

I no longer run around
With my young brunette;
My youth is gone,
In my disgusting bachelorhood.

FUTURISTIC VERSES

3.

In the electro your costumechik's electric
So silhouettic in tact now eyes there curls dream bra
Bold hand partner screen quickflicking each stroke
So jealous jocks grab fidgetty ball love each trick

4.

mglybzhvuo jix"jan'dr'ju chtleshchk xi fja s"p skypolza
a Vtab-dlkni t'japra kakajzchdi a Jew's an inkwell

5.

chr. greet fg evl if clear don't see. ressur wordses send bottom ressurwooods yr mnd. wt. save skn splyd mowgli shush

spit not t eat shchi so'd year· shu = year pop weave bipl. O futpud. I be glss this thrughted forgt. nakd bipl (for tthrough carrying away wmns remns beep only taking wrds)

Great! Greats! Grandiotsar!

K ᴿ ᵁ ᶜ H ᴱ itched he got N ʸ ˣ

Dangerlessnesses of years burdens = worlds empties x ancient-
ness x self x draughts And I by her at bipl. any which way but
knowed. burdener lazy link barking trembling a^N V. towhat but
tears vversess if antithesis gay light soft noose . . .

6.

Distraction

suffocating from yankee arcana
from cancan and yardmuck
my pretty whalemouth ching
a whale and so and better than
armagnac
etiquette is quite cute
a label on your shirt
little kantian quit
A and O hoot
quant and took
so soft
fogms achums scum
and-mm-èd kicks
attractions hint of clever thumb
m-u-u-ck g-o-o-nnne
not a header by airship
but a public stop
a lop giving way in the vago

7.

How Many Fragments Have Scattered

For lovers of colored cardboard boxes and powdered elements
The city a lamppost the street's din and a car's horn the
    daughter of rooms etc.
Along their shattered nerves like words or crazy verses
Juggling the intersections the city's nights dance
What grief the street people are turning glued to a car's wheels
The sun Bunsen burner the sky over us coquettes a skirt spleen
The ill-fated one is run over by a truck and becomes a lump
The signboard thinks it's the city's friend
If it gets unstitched by passers-by (sic)
No city
It's just an absence of blue leit-lines
That's why that one invaded destroyed measure
as if it were a chimera
And don't seek
Why there's a superabundance of usual caresses. Again and
    again
Is that why all the colors have flown off the peacock's tail
And all that's left is the emptiness show your tickets
As of old the gazes of tongue-tied eternity shush
Four eyes the legs of a Viennese chair
It blows eveningly and windily
O you city ensued inhumanly

Roman Jaljagrov

8.

Words' Farewell

The Universe is pierced by a dreadful draft
Voids are pouncing right through houses
My chateau's upset, its foundations violable
I shall not burst into the void for a while perhaps
    Like an empty dream of dissolute voids
    Houses arise like crying cliffs
    Houses loom among dull valleys
    And the city is drempt as a lowering cloud
The cloud is a lure, mist and water all around
Everywhere a light breeze
And the wires have been stretched
Hurriedly transmitting rumors to all
    The shade of chalk-bodied telephones
    Has saved us from the horror of tender urns
    Although the stale receiver is fiercer than a python
    But I hold on without clutching the cord
During the third ring comes a thrice-long dream
A glass of tea with a lemon in it
I'm in the wings, a dusty bush,
When suddenly the theater director proclaims:
"How come you're here, watch from a distance!
What's the point of creeping backstage!"
    Yes, it's good if there are wings
    They're salvation, spare us the shame of voids
    But all the wings have been gnawed away by rats
    Gogol´ wrote about it in *The Inspector General*!

Like a string of rotten mushrooms,
Words are threaded on a wire
While earlier the city hung on a firmanent of words
Like a curtain on a rod

JOCULAR VERSES

9.

We drank tea more intoxicating
Than mere wine. So much rum
Has flowed we're deprived of reason,
But you are steadier than the cup.

You comfort us, like ROSTA posters. . .
You're as treacherous and pure
As the Talmud! From now on
I'll treat the world less harshly!

Most of my dreams have faded away
Since I found wisdom in your home:
At least I'm spared the cab-fares!
Hurray, reason's returned to Roman!

And I can finally laugh again.
You know each incident as well
As each of Pushkin's word-divides.
Your acute and delicate wit

Divided the entire firmament!

10.

When we to Voronezh do go,
We'll get as drunk as a cobbler.
You'll angrily lay me low:
Romochka, go to bed, you hobbler!

In ecstasy I'll leap up the wall,
I'll stuff bliny down my throat,
Drink wine until I can barely crawl,
Forget all my thoughts, like a goat.

When the night sleeps, by moon illumined,
I'll run out, hot as Natan Al'tman.
I'll shout to the seething Don, —not the Don, but Punin:
"Hey, you want some wine, ataman?"

11.

Did I get in contact with Kornej Chukovskij
Just to try out my silly dactyls?
If you'd open a few bottles of wine,
I would write endlessly in Chukokkala!
I would soar, the boldest of falcons,
I would write a hundred lines or so,
But without some healing juice,
I can't grace your dear Chukokkala
With my variegated, brilliant verse.

12.

The era of the
R. S. F. S. R.
Has come.
We recall Robespierre!

Our sole hope
Lies in an English "Sir."
We still mope
For Roederer.

We once rolled in the hay,
Didn't mind the bill,
Gulped down Muscadet
And rum.

Now we've got "democrats."
Vodka's quite dear:
Only surrogates
Are near.

We've become real lean.
We used to eat cakes.
The money's all gone.
How my belly aches!

Now only in Riga
Are there caraway loaves.
I don't give a figa,
So?

We had limousines
With fabulous tires,
And plenty of benzine:
Now we're just tired!

We have to go home
On foot
From the Georgians to Mona.
Ugh: no boots!

Matches cost two
Kerenskys, but what a cost!
"Who stole the lumber from the mews?"
I'm lost!

My knees are shaking.
Krylenko or Lacis
Will shove me, mistaken,
To my last laugh!

Poems to Elsa Triolet

13.

Pity the poor student Roman:
I'm worn out by passion, pour
The balm of love on my fervid heart!
And, by the way,
I'll surely begin to preach
That our youthful disquiet
Will soon abate in a while.
And our happiness will make
Mama happy. And I too, along
With her will rejoice, friends!

11 May 1917

14.

Oh, Elsa! Oh, Elsa!
We love ourselves,
But you're too bella.
But "by the way,"
Each whom your beauty
Enchants you send away.
Each asks: will it be me?
You cram for construction exams,
To go on to architectural concerns,

Dragging your admirers' swank tails
From Pjatnickij, through Kuzneckij Most,
To Beautiful Gates. (By the way,
My tail got caught and almost lost.)
But your blues won't disappear
From a building's quaint veneer.
You keep saying: "I'm going to Bukhara."
Why? For what? No one knows the get-go.
So we all live in panic. Where
Will she go? Along what road
Rushes your childish caprice,
Giving us a complete surprise?
Then you'll give us all a reprimand:
Who'll come with me to ancient Samarkand?
Or, perhaps, your anguished heart
Will drive you to dusty Merv?
Or, perhaps, you'll go on
Anguish-driven to Ferganá? . . .
    Oh, Elsa, oh, Elsa!
Loving you like something else-a,
Here's my heartfelt advice:
Live without a care in life
And give up your blues —
Don't go all the way to Kathmandu.
Toss away your fantasia —
Forget about Central Asia.
Better sit quietly at home
And love . . . your student Roma.
Take a look: your dear philologist
For love of you has turned to dust.
He's forgotten folklore and Sanskrit,
Day and night at your feet does sit.

In despair at the absence of rum
He's about to drink a cup of Broma.
　　Oh Elsa, oh Elsa!
I'll tell you all about him:
Not even vodka, but something else-a
He's ready to drink your health to.
I even think he'd be pleased
If to forget your charms
They brought him methyl fumes!
　　Oh Elsa, oh Elsa!
His love for you is something else-a.

15.

I can't help but heed it,
My love for you's so deep;
If you go to Tahiti,
I shall forever weep.

PROSE

Excursions Around My Room

Chapter III

Christmas had long past, as had Shrovetide, and a trip... well, forget it. The table had only just begun little by little to take on a decent appearance, when quite by chance I came across a stamp album that thrust me into meditation. A stamp album is such an insignificant thing, but what reflections it can evoke. So I started meditating on exactly which kind of envelope would bear each stamp. Here's a pretty little Italian stamp. One can't help but think that it would be on a letter full of poetry, as poetic as its homeland, which they call "the Boot of Europe." A most prosaic comparison... And here's a blue French stamp with a depiction of the Republic; Liberté, Egalité, Fraternité—there's the Republican motto. It's only now that the color blue suits you, not before, when you needed a crimson-red color, the color of blood.

And here's a German stamp I got from my uncle's office. I know the contents of the letter it was on almost for sure: an inquiry about the number of sacks or boxes of one or another sort of goods: the same old song!

Now I'm opening the album at random—Australia. Bah! By what strange fate did Queen Victoria's portrait end up here? And here, in New Southern Belize; wherever you turn there's a portrait of Queen Victoria! Well, enough of the English! I'll take a look at America, at Africa; here and there, more Victorias... Also in Natal, even in Canada. Insatiable English! Let's take a look at Asia: Messrs Englishmen, give me a break!!! They've picked up a bit of China, they're lying in wait for Tibet, they've tightened their belts in Arabia, in . . . Messrs Englishmen, in India, that magnificent country to which we are obliged for our counting and even our very language, even there you're oppressors. Well, insatiable Messrs Englishmen, sometimes I even have doubts whether Russia belongs to you, too. Some time (in the distant future, of course) the French, in airplanes obedient to their helm, will land on the moon, and I'll make a bet there'll be an English flag there and that they poked their noses even in there, with their Victoria. Now good-bye, Messrs Englishmen, wring the last crumbs out of the poor Indians; all I have to say is that if I were in their place, I'd give you the finger. You deprive me of any desire for reflection; farewell! . . . Perhaps you are mad at me, gracious reader (if only I ever had one), for having sat too long over a stamp album. Excuse me! . . . but don't expect any further apologies from me, I'm not a fan of such empty words. Well, now it's time to continue my travels; I won't sit too long over anything more. So, I'm taking off further two months later. Sorry, two and a half, for among my readers there might be mathematicians (people whose tongues turn only on pluses and minuses), and I'm afraid of their opinion, afraid they may start saying: — What a great traveller! He waits two, two months, and because of what? — Because of a stupid stamp album, he can't even precisely determine the length and width of his own room. It's quite befitting of a mathematician, enough said! He can't define a number, and on top of that he doesn't even know the interval of time he spent doing nothing.—And those are the opinions of them that I'm scared by, it's shameful, isn't it, oh readers? But so marvelously is arranged the world: we laugh at fools, while at the same time we are afraid of their judgments. . . . Reader, you're plugging up your ears? Well, this time you're right: instead of hitting the road, I'm occupying myself with empty words. Yes, so what is this lying on the table?—Oh, my magnifying glass, an interesting thing. If only it were a microscope! It's interesting to look through it at a drop of water, on these infusorians; and if the microscope were even more perfected, one that would show an infusorian at a man's height, that would be fun. A drop of water turns into a city, and in it the infusorians scurry about. . . . Who's that there? What's this before my eyes?—Carpenters (but, understandably, from the world of infusoria) around a wall, but actually it's dust-coats, unnoticeable even for the unarmed eye, and magnified by the microscope. How they bustle about, exactly as if they were in terror. . . . Ha, ha, ha, ha, how santimoniously this fat one comes forward, just as if he were a merchant from the other side of the Moscow river; and over here, this young infusorian, just think how he hurries — a Don Juan of infusorians, honest to God a Don Juan, and how he bows to that noble feminine personage who has just turned to the "wall." And there, obviously, is the plebian part of the water—how they're fighting there, how they're quarreling there! The struggle for existence . . . whose property does it indeed consist of: not only people, but beasts, and the birds, and insects, and . . . even infusorians. And the infusoria fought, bit, hissed; one can't even list everything they did. And a noble infusorian, who accidentally happened to fall into this sphere, looked at them, having puffed up its little black lips. And if one were to show this scene to a society lady, I can just imagine how she would puff up her little lips, even if they were not black, for indeed this is nothing other than a picture of every-day life and would be a good lesson for you, society lady, despite the fact that it will not teach you the lastest fashionable dance, though, on the other hand, it will show you graphically a photo of our life. But why have these respected and not-so-respected infusorians suddenly grown alarmed?—Aha, I get it, they're being thrown into confusion by the drop, which is little by little drying up. And what if I could grab just one infusorian? . . . Oh, how stupid I am! I totally forget that I'm fantasizing. Instead of the proposed trip, I'm dreaming over a magnifying glass. Oh, this distraction, this garrulousness! I'll tie a knot in my handkerchief to remind me and start my exploration tomorrow at the crack of dawn.

Chapter IV

I'm setting out. The table is empty and looks like a desert only occasionally covered with oases (ink drops). But if one looks more closely, one can notice that these are not simply blotches, as they seemed at first, but entire arithematical operations; people who look like beasts and beasts who look like people; words that I myself am unable to read, just as in the German saying: "The poor ass, he can't even read what he himself wrote."

COMMENTARIES

PART ONE: MEMOIRS — A FUTURIAN OF SCIENCE

R.O. Jakobson's autobiograpical notes are based on tape-recorded conversations with Bengt Jangfeldt, which took place in February-March (in Cambridge, Massachusetts) and in June (on the island of Gotland) of 1977. In editing the text the editor has removed the questions and comments, thus transforming the dialogue into Jakobson's own monologue. The tape-recording consists of twelve conversations in the course of which, naturally, neither chronological nor thematic consistency were observed. Therefore, certain parts have been transposed in the interest of producing a unified text. Likewise, some insignificant corrections of a purely stylistic nature were introduced, and certain obvious mistakes and inaccuracies were corrected. The editor's own interpolations are given in square brackets. The title belongs to the editor. [The editor's title to the Russian edition was *Jakobson-Budetljanin*. The latter term was a neologism coined by the Russian Futurists to differentiate themselves from the Italian Futurists. It is derived from the form *budet* 'will be', and is more native sounding than the foreign derived term *futurist*. — Translator's note.]

The text up to p. 20 was corrected by Jakobson himself.

The text is devided into three parts: I. The Russian period of Jakobson's life; II. His emigration; III. His recollections about Majakovskij.

Fragments of the dialogue not included in the basic text are introduced in the commentaries with the abbreviation TR (= tape recording).

1.   Nikolaj Alekseevich Umov (1846-1915) was a physicist and professor of Moscow University. He was famous for his scientific-propagandistic activities. Orest Danilovich Xvol´son (1852-1934) was a physicist, a professor of Petersburg University, and a corresponding member of the Russian Academy of Sciences. He was the author of a five-volume *Course of Physics*, which went through numerous editions. The interest of young philologists in contemporary physics is attested to by a letter by

B.V. Tomashevskij to his wife, asking her to send him from Petersburg to Liège "excepts from Xvol´son about the conductivity of gases." Nevertheless, Tomashevskij's attitude to Xvol´son was somewhat sceptical, as his letter to S. P. Bobrov of May 27, 1916 indicates: "You know, there are two types of scholars: one knows a lot — that's Xvol´son—but their name is not connected to anything in science. Except for encyclopedias they can make nothing of their learning. Others . . . know little, but at the same time are capable of applying their learning." (Tomashevskij 1990, 145-46.)

2. Isaak L´vovich Kan (1895–1945) was the editor of the school journal of the Lazarev Institute, *Student's Thought*, in which Jakobson published his first literary experiments. "Later, Kan," Jakobson further recalls, "occupied himself with questions of art, both as an artist and theoretician of painting. Then, partly under my influence, he became interested in linguistics, then turned to archaeology, in connection with the ever-growing fascination of the time with Old Russian painting. Later, after the Revolution, he became an architect, a very talented one, emigrated first to Berlin and then to Prague. In Czechoslovakia there are some very interesting buildings he designed. He remained in Czechoslovakia and perished during the German occupation." (TR.) Together with Jakobson, Buslaev and Bogatyrev, Kan took part in dialectological expeditions in the districts of the Moscow Province (Jakobson/Bogatyrev 1922, 175). In his article "The Influence of the Revolution on the Russian Language" Jakobson thanks Kan for his observations used in the study (Jakobson 1921a, 31). See also the jocular poem by Jakobson addressed to Kan in Jangfeldt, ed., 1992, no. 4, 111.

3. Sergey Maksimovich Bajdin (1894–1919) was an artist. See also letter 1 to M. Matjushin and letter 6 to Elza Triolet.

4. The exhibition "Target," with works by M. Larionov, N. Goncharova, K. Malevich, M. Le-Dantju and others, was open from March 24 to April 7, 1913. The exhibition "No. 4" (Futurists, Rayonists, Primitivists) was organized by Larionov in March 1914 with the participation of V. Chekrygin and other young artists.

5. Serov's funeral took place in Moscow on November 24, 1911.

6. Both pictures are now in the collection of the Russian Museum in St Petersburg.

7. Vladimir Zhebrovskij was a schoolmate of Jakobson, who spent his summer vacations at the Zhebrovskijs' estate in the Tula province (see *SW* IV, 641).

8. Cf. a newspaper account of the event: "A student of the School of Painting, after referring to the heavy losses which Russian art had suffered in the last five years in the persons of Musatov, Vrubel', and, finally, V. A. Serov, said that the best celebration of the radiant memory of the deceased was to follow his behests" (*Russkoe slovo*, February 25, 1911).

9. The Knave of Diamonds exhibition opened on January 23, 1912.

10. Adol´f Izrailevich Mil´man (1888–1930) was a member of the Knave of Diamonds group. He participated in the exhibitions of the Knave of Diamonds in 1912 (four pictures), 1913 (at the Moscow exhibition, four pictures; at the Petersburg one, thirteen pictures), and 1914 (eighteen pictures). (The catalogue of the exhibitions is published in Pospelov 1990, 242-67.) After the February Revolution he took part in the work of the "World of Art" society and the Soviet of Organizations of Artists of Moscow (which corresponded to the Petrograd Union of Artistic Activists). His picture "A Crimean Landscape" (1916) was shown at the exhibition "A Time of Change 1905–1930" in Helsinki in 1988. "I was on good terms with Adol´f Mil´man. He even gave me one of his landscapes, which I hung in my room for a long time. He had painted it someplace near Zhiguli, where Levitan painted." (TR.)

11. Raxmaninov's "Island of the Dead" was performed on February 4, 1912 at the Assembly of Nobility. In his autobiography Majakovskij writes that at this evening, when both he and Burljuk "ran from the intolerable melodicized boredom," Russian Futurism was born.

12. In the debates arranged by the Knave of Diamonds group on February 12 and 25, 1912, David Burljuk gave two lectures on Cubism. According to A. Kruchenyx, during the second debate, which Jakobson attended, Kruchenyx and Majakovskij acted as official opponents (see Xardzhiev 1976, 11). Cf. A. Kruchenyx's memoirs: "Majakovskij delivered a whole

lecture on the fact that art corresponded to the spirit of the time, that, when comparing the art of various epochs one could notice that there was no such thing as eternal art, that it is diverse and dialectical. He spoke seriously, almost academically" (Katanjan 1985, 59).

13. V. Xlebnikov's and A. Kruchenyx's *A Game in Hell*, illustrated with lithographed drawings by M. Larionov and N. Goncharova, was ready in August, 1912, although according to *Knizhnaja letopis´*, it appeared in the second half of October.

14. Genrix Èdmundovich Tastevin (1881-1915) was a critic who at one time worked as the secretary of the Symbolist journal *The Golden Fleece* [*Zolotoe runo*]. In 1914 he published a book entitled *Futurism: On the Path toward a New Symbolism*. As the Russian delegate at the Parisian "Société des grands conférences," he invited the Italian Futurist F.T. Marinetti to visit Russia in 1914. See below.

15. A. Thibaudet, *La Poésie de S. Mallarmé* (Paris, 1913).

16. See Jangfeldt, ed., 1992, no 6 (p. 112) and pp. 262-265 above.

17. For Jakobson's translation of Mallarmé, see Jangfeldt, ed. 1992, 125.

18. Massachusetts Institute of Technology Archives and Special Collections, R. Jakobson, Manuscript Collection 72, Series 6A, 17: 63-68.1. (Further references to this manucription collection are abbreviated "The Jakobson Archive, M.I.T.")

19. Cf. Jakobson's "Retrospect": "[Tredjakovskij's] tetrameters—both iambic and trochaic—proved to display an exceptional width of tentative rhythmical variations, a license prompted by the inherited bookish pattern of syllabic versification and probably also by the flexible forms of Russian oral poetry which continuously attracted the attention of the laborious innovator. . . . The superb variability of Tredjakovskij's iambic tetrameter has been confirmed by the recent computation of Russian metricians (in particular, M. L. Gasparov)" (*SW* V, 569-570). Jakobson refers here to M.L. Gasparov's article on "Light and Heavy Verse" (1977), which the compiler of these commentaries showed him during his stay on Gotland in the summer of 1977, when Jakobson was working on the

"Retrospect" to the fifth volume of his *Selected Writings*. He was struck by the similarity between Gasparov's results and his own conclusions of sixty years before. Jakobson's work on Trediakovskij at the beginning of 1915 were summarized in a lecture on "The Influence of Folklore on Trediakovskij" at the Commission on Folklore attached to the Ethnographic Division of the Society of Lovers of Natural Science, Anthropology and Ethnography (*SW* IV, 614-633).

20. The collection appeared in the middle of December, 1912.

21. Eight of Xlebnikov's poems were united under the general title *Przheval'skij's Horse* [after the explorer's discovery of the wild Asiatic horse *Equus przewalsii*], including "On the Island of Ösel," "The Lips Sang Bobeobi," and "Veining His Winged Way in Signature of Gold." Besides the poems Jakobson mentions, the poem "Monument" and "Przheval'skij's Horse" were published in the collection.

22. One assumes the reference is to a debate on contemporary art organized by the Knave of Diamonds group on February 12, 1912, at which D. Burljuk delivered a lecture "On Cubism and Other Trends in Painting."

23. The debate took place February 12, 1913.

24. Majakovskij's appearance at the February 24th debate is not mentioned in the newspapers. His attack on Vološin is mentioned in connection with the second debate of the Knave of Diamonds (see the next footnote). Cf. Šklovskij's account of Majakovskij's speech: "He quoted the poem, changing it to read: 'If the worm of doubt has crawled up your neck,/ Squash it yourself, and don't have your servant do it for you.' If you do not doubt the new art, why do you call in the Symbolists?" (Šklovskij 1974, 26.)

25. Jakobson is referring to the "Second Debate on Contemporary Art" organized by the Knave of Diamonds group. Cf. one newspaper's review: "A Futurist appealed to the audience in a stentorian voice: 'Gentlemen, I ask for your defense against this group smearing spittle on the aspic of art.' The audience, of course, took the Futurist's side. . . . For an entire quarter of an hour the hall groaned under the weight of applause, shouts

of 'down with them,' whistles and boos. All the same, Majakovskij's decisiveness won the day." (*Moskovskaja gazeta*, February 25, 1913.)

26. In a letter to the editors of the newspaper *Russkoe slovo* (May 4, 1913), Kandinskij declared that the inclusion of four poems in prose in his book *Klänge* in Russian translation took him completely by surprise.

27. K.D. Bal´mont returned to Russia on May 5, 1913.

28. On Majakovskij's speech see Katanjan 1985, 67.

29. Jakobson is referring here to L.Ju. and O.M. Brik. See Lili Brik's memoirs about this gathering: "Majakovskij spoke boldly and with conviction, saying things of the sort that earlier it was nice 'to stomp the steps under one's feet,' but now he preferred to take an elevator. Later I saw Brjusov telling Volodja off in one of the sitting rooms of the Circle: 'On the day of a Jubilee.... Really, how can one?!' But he was clearly pleased that Bal´mont had gotten his. . . . That same evening I saw Volodja standing in front of Repin's portrait of Tolstoj and saying to a group of gentlemen surrounding him: 'One really has to be a jerk to paint like that.' Brik and I liked all of this a lot, but we continued to be indignant—I, in particular—at the scandalists, who wouldn't permit a single speech to go by without the police having to be called in and without broken chairs. I still managed not to be dragged off once [by the police, who] were checking what was going on." (Brik 1934, 59-60.)

30. The first collection *A Trap for Judges* appeared in 1910; the second—at the beginning of 1913.

31. Gorodeckij's essay mentioned by Jakobson is a review of the second collection *A Trap for Judges* and of Xlebnikov's and Kruchenyx's book *A Game in Hell*. The review incorporates the entire text of Xlebnikov's "Incantation by Laughter." Gorodeckij writes: "We encountered the name of Aleksej Kruchenyx first, but we recall Viktor Xlebnikov from the *Studio* organized by N. Kul´bin and from *A Trap for Judges*, famous for having been printed on genuine wallpaper" (*Rech´*, October 1, 1912, 269). Apart from "Incantation by Laughter," Xlebnikov's poem "Thicket" was also published in *Studio of the Impressionists* in 1910.

32. See I. P. Saxarov's collection *Tales of the Russian People* (1841), vol. 1, part 2, 46-47. "A Night in Galicia" was first published in February, 1914 in Xlebnikov's *Selection of Poems*. See also Xardzhiev 1975a. 33. According to *Knizhnaja letopis´*, *Roar!* was published by Kruchenyx's publishing house EUY at the end of December, 1913.

34. This manifesto was published only in 1930 in *Unpublished Xlebnikov*, no. 18.

35. In Kruchenyx's diaries of 1916-1918, there are a number of entries testifying to the intensity of his contacts with Jakobson: "At Jakobson's for a critique of the materials"; "tell about everything you want: the letters of Xlebnikov, Shemshurin, Jakobson, O. Rozanova"; "1) Jakobson—two essays, his new transrational verses for Kul´bin . . . 9) await 10 books (?!), ask Jakobson; 10) from Jakobson, various things, send to Kuchumov." (From a private archive; the editor would like to thank A. E. Parnis for this information.)

36. Despite Jakobson's statement that Kruchenyx preferred Xlebnikov to Majakovskij, in 1914 he published the first book about the latter, *The Verses of V. Majakovskij*.

37. In the book the date of publication is given as 1916. According to *Knizhnaja letopis´*, the book actually appeared in August, 1915. *Transrational Boog* contained two transrational poems signed "Aljagrov" (Jakobson's literary pseudonym, on which see footnote 44 below).

38. See the description of this meeting with Kruchenyx in Jakobson/Pomorska 1982, 174-176.

39. Cf. Xlebnikov's lines: "And the arrogant vaults soared – / The laws of a subterranean crowd." Majakovskij has: "Maliciously having forgotten themselves under the vaults of the law, / live downcast persons."

40. See footnote 14 above.

41. Larionov proposed throwing "rotten eggs" at the "renegade" Marinetti and pouring "sour milk" over him (see the newspaper *Rannee utro*, January 25, 1914).

42. After his lecture of January 30, 1914 in the small auditorium of the Conservatory, Marinetti visited the Literary-Artistic Circle, where Larionov was present. Cf. a slightly different version of this episode in *SW* II, 360.

43. The Alpine Rose was located at 4 Sofijka. Cf. Jakobson's memoir of 1956: "They served a carafe with vodka, marked with centimeter lines. One paid by the centimeter, according to how many centimeters had been consumed. Majakovskij said: 'How many centimeters have I drunk?'" (Jakobson 1956a). [In Russia vodka was usually served by weight, 100 grams being a regular serving size — Translator's note.]

44. Apart from his joint publication with A. Kruchenyx, *Transrational Boog*, Jakobson signed letters, poems and articles with this pseudonym right up to 1919. According to Jakobson himself, the pseudonym Aljagrov (variant *Ja*ljagrov) should be deciphered as follows: Alja + g + ro + v. "Alja" (or "Ljalja") was the name of his girlfriend, and "ro" is R(oman) O(sipovich). In the variant *Ja*ljagrov there is also a play on his family name, Ja(kobson).

45. Jakobson is here speaking about the summer of 1914.

46. Majakovskij lived in Lubjanskij Thruway from 1919 until his death. See p. 66 above.

47. See footnote 54 below.

48. In his "Letter about Malevich" Jakobson assigns his visit to Malevich to the year *1914* (Jakobson 1976, 293), but one must assume that it ocurred in 1915, when he was "already a student" at Moscow University.

49. Jakobson also assigns this meeting to Christmas *1914* in his "Letter about Malevich" (see the previous note). Cf. a similar attitude toward Majakovskij on the part of one of the "very 'leftist' founders of Futurism" after a reading of the poem *War and the World*: according to O. M. Brik, the unnamed opponent "shouted that 'this is an outrage, it's anti-artistic, it's in the vein of Leonid Andreev, it's not worthy of a leftist poet'" (cited from Percov 1969, 307).

50. Cf. a letter from Malevich to Matjushin (June, 1916): "The word 'as such' should be transformed 'into something,' but this 'something' remains *dark*. Thanks to this, many of the poets who have declared a war against thought, against logic, have been forced to get stuck in the meat of the old poetry (Majakovskij, Burljuk, Severjanin, Kamenskij). Kruchenyx is still leading a battle against this old meat, not letting himself stop for long in one place, but this 'into something' hangs over him. Without finding this 'into something,' he will be forced to suck up the same old meat." (Malevich 1976, 190-91.)

51. Jakobson is probably referring to his poem "How Many Fragments Have Scattered," where the urban theme in the poetry of early Futurism is parodied. (See poem 7 on p. 253 above.)

52. On *Transrational Boog* see footnote 37 above. In the book *Transrationalists* (1922), Kruchenyx cites one of "Aljagrov's unpublished poems": "kt.vest' mgl zl l' jas." (See poem 5 on p. 249 above.)

53. From the poem "Words' Farewell" (see p. 254 above).

54. In a letter of June, 1916 Malevich writes Matjushin that "the new poets waged a war against thought, which had enslaved free sound, and tried to bring the letter closer to the idea of the sound (and not to music)" (Malevich 1976, 190). He later expounded these ideas in his essay "On Poetry" (1919).

55. In 1908 Albert Sechehaye formulated the tasks confronting a new scientific disciple which he termed "phonology." See Sechehaye 1908 and Jakobson's discussion of it in *SW* I, 312. 56.

56. Cf. E. Kovtun's commentary to his letters in Malevich 1976, 194.

57. Josef ˇima (1891-1971). Cf. Jakobson/Pomorska 1982, 111 and Toman 1987, 320.

58. Karel Teige (1900-1951) was the main theoretician of the Czech avant-garde in the 1920's and the founder, together with Nezval, of the poetic group Devětsil. Jakobson's ties with the Czech avant-garde are analyzed in detail in Linhartová 1977, Toman 1987, and Effenberger 1983. See also footnote 152.

59. The letter was written in January-February (?), 1914 and published in part in Xardzhiev 1976, 56-57.

60. In fact, the photographs used in Rodchenko's collages for the first edition of Majakovskij's *About That* were shot by A. Shterenberg.

61. A.A. Markov (1856-1922), a professor at Petersburg University, was a mathematician who specialized in the theory of numbers and of probability. Jakobson is referring to his use of probability chains in analyzing Pushkin's *Eugene Onegin* (see Markov 1913).

62. P. D. Pervov was a professor at V. Lepeshinskaja's Municipal Woman's Professional School and the author of textbooks and anthologies of the classical languages.

63. The inhabitants of the village of Novinskoe, where Jakobson and Bogatyrev were conducting fieldwork, took the young folklorists for German spies and tried to murder them, but at the last minute they managed to escape. See *SW* IV, 634-644.

64. A.A. Buslaev (1897–1964?) was one of the seven founders of the Moscow Linguistic Circle and served as its president from September, 1920 until March, 1922. His grandfather was the famous philologist F.I. Buslaev (1818–1897).

65. On Husserl's influence on Jakobson, see Holenstein 1975.

66. Cafe Tramblé was located at 5 Petrovka St.

67. In Elsa Triolet's novel *Wild Strawberry* (1926, 168) she describes a man named Radlov as "a tombstone to himself."

68. Tamara Begljarova, a friend of Elsa Triolet.

69. A.N. Vertinskij (1889–1957) often appeared on stage in his younger years in the costume of Pierrot. Despite Vertinskij's reaction to Majakovskij's presence in the audience, relations between the two poets were entirely friendly. According to L.Ju. Brik (1963, 347), Majakovskij liked to quote Vertinskij's songs. Cf. Vertinskij's autobiographical notes

about his meetings and mutual appearances with Majakovskij (1990, 87-88, 91, 93-94).

70. Sologub's play was performed on January 2, 7, 11, 17 and 22, 1917 in Komissarzhevskaja's Theater.

71. The first volume of *Collections on the Theory of Poetic Language* [*Sborniki po teorii poèticheskogo jazyka*] appeared in 1916 (the military censor's approval is dated August 24, 1916); the second is dated 1917 and appeared at the very beginning of the year (censor's approval dated December 24, 1916). The first issue contains Shklovskij's article "Transrational Language and Poetry"; the second—Brik's "Sound Repetitions." Both books carried the publishing imprint OMB, i.e. O.M. Brik.

72. V. Shklovskij, *The Resurrection of the Word* (1914).

73. This excerpt is published in Winner 1977, 508. The beginning of Jakobson's translation of *A Cloud in Trousers* into French was first published in Jangfeldt, ed. 1992, 125-126 from the editor's tape-recording of Jakobson's own recitation from memory. It reads as follows:

Vous direz, le délire de la maladie?

Non, c'était,
c'était à Odessa.

"Je viens à quatre," Marie m'a dit.

Huit.
Neuf.
La onzième commença.

Voici le soir
dans le froid nocturne
s'en fuit des fenêtres,
décembreux,
sinistres.

Vers le dos décrepit ricannent et hurlent
les lustres.
[...]
Âpre, comme un mot de dédain,
tu entras, Marie,
et tu m'as dit,
en tourmentant tes gants de daim:
"Savez-vous,
je me marie."

74. Cf. L. Ju. Brik's memoirs: "Father died. I returned from the funeral in Moscow. Elsa came to Petersburg [...], Volodja came from Finland. We whispered to Elsa pleadingly: 'Don't ask him to read.' But Elsa didn't listen to us, and for the first time we heard *A Cloud in Trousers*." (Brik 1934, 62.)

75. Maurice Grammont (1866-1946) was a phonetician and expert on French verse.

76. In her last book, *La mise en mots*, Elsa Triolet reminisces about her French tutor, Mademoiselle Dache: "La jeune personne qui m'appris le français était née à Moscou de parents français, avait fait ses études dans une école française moscovite et en gardait un accent russe que j'ai fidèlement attrapé! Elle pouvait avoir seize ans quand elle apparut à la maison. [. . .] J'avais dans les six ans et je savais déjà lire et écrire en russe." (Triolet 1969, 82.)

77. Cf. Shklovskij's letter to Jakobson in his book *The Third Factory*: "When we met on Osja's couch, Kuzmin's poems hung above the couch. You were younger than me, and I tried to convince you of the new faith. With the inertia of your weight, you accepted it." (Shklovskij 1926, 68.) Jakobson and Bogatyrev wrote about the differences between OPOJAZ and the Moscow Linguistic Circle at that time: "whereas the Moscow Linguistic Circle proceeds from the proposition that poetry is language in its aesthetic function, the Petrograders insist that the poetic motif is far from being an unfolding of the linguistic material" (Jakobson/ Bogatyrev 1922, 31).

78. Majakovskij returned to Petrograd on March 30 or 31 (April 13, New Style), 1917, after a week-long stay in Moscow, where he appeared at a meeting of the Soviet of Organizations of Moscow Artists with information from the Petrograd Soviet of Artistic Activists (Katanjan 1985, 128). The reason for Jakobson's trip to Petrograd was his participation at the Seventh Congress of the Consitutional Democratic Party in April, 1917. The Congress took place on March 25-28 (April 7-10, New Style), which puts in doubt either Katanjan's chronicle or Jakobson's own dating. Jakobson states the details in a letter he wrote to his attorney, Professor Arthur Sutherland, on April 23, 1953 in connection with his having been served a subpoena to appear before the U. S. House of

Representatives' Un-American Activities Committee (the subpoena was later squelched, in all probability after the intervention of President Dwight David Eisenhower, who had known Jakobson during his tenure as President of Columbia University, when he had defended him against attacks for holding the Masaryk Professorship, funded in part by the Czech government): "As a student of Moscow University, I was for the Russian Constitutional Democratic Party which advocated a constitutional monarchy on the British model. In 1917-1918, I was an active member of this party and preserved personal ties with its leader Miliukov until the last war during which he died. In 1917-1918, I was a member of the Presidium of the University faction of this party and as such I actively participated in the national convention of the Constitutional Democratic Party, April 1917 in St. Petersburg. When in the spring of 1918 arrests among the members of this faction took place I managed to escape and hid in the country for several months. When in 1919 the party went underground, I continued to cooperate." (The Jakobson Archive, M.I.T.; the editor is grateful to Stephen Rudy for bringing this information to his attention.)

79. The exhibition of Finnish artists in Petrograd opened on April 3 (16), 1917 at 2:00 p.m. in the art gallery of N.E. Dobychina on the Field of Mars, after which, at seven in the evening, there was a banquet at the restaurant Donon on 24 Mojka St. At the opening of the exhibition there were present, apart from the Finnish artists, M. Gor´kij—"who wanted to speak the four Finnish words he knew: Eläköön Suomi, Rakastan Suomi"— A. Benois, V. Figner, E. Breshko-Breshkovskaja, representatives of the Provisional Government (Miljukov, Rodichev), N. Rerix, N. Al´tman and "the president of the Moscow futurists, David Davidovich Burljuk," who expressed the desire of arranging a Russo-Finnish exhibition "with the participation of our artists and, above all, of the group he represented" (A.G-s., *Hufvudstadsbladet*, April 22, 1917). According to the newspaper *Rech´* (April 5, 1917), Majakovskij also spoke at the opening.

80. One assumes that the reference is to the sculptor Ville Vallgren (1855-1940), who gave an "enthusiastic" speech in French at the banquet which "was interrupted by applause and cries of bravo" (A.G-s., *Hufvudstadsbladet*, April 25, 1917). The banquet is described both in the newspapers and in the memoir literature. A week after the banquet O. Leshkova

wrote to M. Le-Dantju: "At the banquet for the opening of the exhibition . . . Dobychina (its organizer) seated . . . Majakovskij with Gor´kij. A. Benois began telling Zdanevich how much he loved and respected him, and Gor´kij began telling Majakovskij the same. . . ." (Katanjan 1985, 526). D. Burljuk recollects: "Donon had a grand reception, to which all artistic Petrograd was invited. Miljukov, the Minister of Foreign Affairs, Rodichev, the Minister for Relations with Finland, sat next to one another in the middle of the most lengthy table. In the places of hosts sat Gor´kij, the Chairman of the Commission for the Preservation of Monuments, and the tall, dark-complexioned, brilliant Finish artist Gallen Rissojanen [Burljuk here contaminates the names of A. Gallen-Kallela and O. Rissanen—B.J.], the writer Bunin, Konstantin Somov, Aleksandr Benois and others. Speechs were devided over supper. Gor´kij didn't deliver one. . . . Gor´kij was jolly, made jokes, but in his witticisms were carping and peevishness (decent wine and the ever weakening health of the artist.)" (Burljuk 1973.) I. Bunin recollects in horror Majakovskij's central role, noting that everything he saw in Petrograd at the time "harmoniously and significantly was linked with the Homeric disgracefulness poured out at this banquet." Bunin described how "Majakovskij dominated everyone," shouting cat-calls at all the speakers, including the Minister of Foreign Affairs Miljukov. "But then the French Ambassador rose. Obviously, he was quite convinced that the Russian hooligan would give up before him. He couldn't have been more wrong! Majakovskij instantly drowned him out with an even greater stentorian roar. As if that wasn't enough, the hall immediately broke into a wild and senseless fury: Majakovskij's comrades-in-arms also began to shout, stomp their boots on the floor, beat their fists on the table, to laugh, howl, scream, and grunt." (Bunin 1950, 53–54.) Bunin's memoirs are supported by the newspaper account: "The atmosphere, which became more and more heated, created ever newer orators, and frequently a bold Futurist leapt on the table and tried to drown out the noise with all the strength of his lungs" (*Hufvudstadsbladet*, April 25, 1917). After midnight the "celebration" was moved to the nightclub "Stopping-place of Actors" [*Prival Komediantov*], recalls Burljuk (1973).

81. Lenin arrived in Petrograd the evening of April 3 (16), 1917, so that Brik, obviously, went directly from the reception to the Finland Station.

82. Cf. the newspaper accounts of the days: "Kshesinskaja's Palace unexpectedly became Lenin's headquarters. . . . A crowd gathered below. From time to time one of Lenin's 'disciples' would appear on the balcony, at times his 'follower,' citizenness Kollontaj, would speak, who proved to be the only one in the Congress of Deputies who was sympathetic to the teachings of Communism. They made speeches that are bearable only in the fresh air." (*Novoe vremja*, April 6 [19], 1917.)

83. "To Himself the Beloved Author Dedicates These Lines."

84. I.e., the question of "sound repetitions," to which Brik devoted his first article in the field of poetics, which was published in the second issue of *Collections on the Theory of Poetic Language* (1917).

85. The collection *To Two* (1918). On Kuzmin and Majakovskij see Seleznev 1989.

86. Jurij Jurkun (1893-1938), a prose writer, the author of *Swedish Gloves* (1914) and other books, was Kuzmin's life-long companion. See Sudejkin's 1916 portrait of him in *Pamjatniki kul'tury 1989*, 136. He was repressed under Stalin.

87. The artist Vladimir Ivanovich Kozlinskij (1891-1967) studied in 1911-1917 in the Higher Artistic School of the Academy of Arts. He was the author of several drawings in the album *Heroes and Victims of the Revolution*, 1918, with captions by Majakovskij.

88. On May 2, 1919 Stanislav Gurvic-Gurskij delivered a lecture in the Moscow Linguistic Circle "On Abbreviations in Factory Terminology (On the Material from One Enterprise)," which was attended by Jakobson, Bogatyrev, and Majakovskij, among others.

89. Cf. L. Ju. Brik's autobiographical note: "Majakovskij wouldn't let his partners at cards recollect themselves. He would break millioneers with limits, he would bluff, make jokes, declame. And he would get up from the table only with the winnings." (Archive of L.Ju. Brik.)

90. Chemin de fer in the Briks' salon entered Russian poetry; cf. K. Bol'shakov's poem "Le chemin de fer," dated March 1915 and dedicat-

ed to L.Ju. Brik (the collection *Solnce na izlete* [Sunset], Moscow, 1916). Cf. also Jakobson's jocular verses: "Chemin de fer/ pljus banque ouvert/ milej Volode vsex affairs./ Shestnadcat´ ras/ pokryl on nas/ i vse my vozopili 'pass'./ Brosaet v zhar/ nash Vol´demar,/ napilsja krov´ju kak komar./ Shestnadcat´ raz..." (TR). In Jakobson's article "The Influence of the Revolution on the Russian Language," he lists the word "vikzhel´" as an example of a new abbreviation: "*vikzhel´* (All-Russian Executive Committee of Railwaymen) is also used with the meaning of the card game 'chemin de fer,' a particularly complex metonymy, connected not with the metaphoric name of the game, but with the same word in its primary meaning," and *vikzhel´nut´* as a verbal neologism ending in *-nut´* with a humorous tinge (1921a, 11, 5).

91. The reference is to the summer of 1919.

92. The reference is to a game of bouts-rimés at the Briks' in May 1919. Jakobson's poem begins with the words: "When we to Voronezh do go,/ We'll get as drunk as a cobbler." See poem 10, p. 256, and Katanjan 1975.

93. Brik graduated from the Juridical Faculty of Moscow University in 1911. His thesis, on the theme of "Solitary Confinement," and other documents relating to his studies are preserved in the Central State Historical Archive in Moscow (f. 418, op. 320, d. 174; I am grateful to A.V. Valjuzhenich for this information).

94. Cf. Jakobson's afterword to the reprinted edition of Brik's essays on poetics: "During the summer of 1919, spent in Puskino, Brik became greatly interested in the sociological aspect of pictorial art. His main concern was the development of two simultaneous trends, French impressionism and the Russian *Itinerant artists*. Brik's interpretation of Zola's *L'Œuvre*, of Perov's and Kramskoj's writings and biographies, and of Russian art reviews published in the late nineteenth century was indeed illuminating, and such problems as art production and consumption, demand and supply, the art market and painters' competition were clearly sketched. These views, immediately picked up and absorbed by V. Shklovskij, later underlay some of the latter's reasonings on literature, art, and their social prerequisites after Shklovskij loudly repudiated his so-called 'formalist' creed." (1964, 79-80.)

95. Osip Borisovich Rumer (1883–1954) was a philologist and translator of both Mickiewicz and Omar Khayyam.

96. In this book Shklovskij turns to the All-Russian Central Executive Committee (VCIK) with a request for permission to return to Russia.

97. The date is verified by a certificate of the Political Division of the Moscow GPU, according to which Brik entered the organization on June 8, 1920 (Archive of L. Ju. Brik).

98. On the similarities between Blok's poem "The Terrible World" ("Night, a street, a lamppost, a drugstore") and Majakovskij's long poem *Man*, see Stahlberger 1964, 62-63.

99. The reading at the poet's V. Amari (M. Cetlin) took place at the end of January, 1918, in the company of K. Bal´mont, Vjacheslav Ivanov, Andrej Belyj, Ju. Baltrushajtis, D. Burljuk, V. Kamenskij, I. Èrenburg, V. Xodasevich, M. Cvetaeva, B. Pasternak, A. Tolstoj, P. Antokol´skij, V. Inber and others. The newspaper *Mysl´* (January 28, 1918) has an account of the enthusiastic reaction of the representatives of the older generation to Majakovskij's poem. Various participants in the evening have written memoirs about the reading (see Katanjan 1985, 138-139).

100. Cf. the reminiscences of A. Chicherin: "Belyj delivered an empassioned speech about Majakovskij's poetic talent and literary style. In passing, he said that after the Symbolists, Majakovskij was the greatest Russian poet since he was speaking his own, unexpectedly new word." (Katanjan 1985, 140.)

101. Elsa and her mother lived on Golikovskij Lane.

102. The Cafe of Poets, which opened in fall of 1917, continued the old futurist tradition from the Stray Dog Cafe and the Stopping-Place of Actors. Immediately after moving to Moscow in the beginning of December Majakovskij became a regular at the Cafe, which was located at Nastas´inskij Lane and the corner of Tverskaj St.

103. Among the numerous, short-lived anarchistic organizations was a group called "instant socialists."

104. Among the constant guests of the Cafe were anarchists, for whom the place served as a "convenient secret rendezvous" (Spasskij 1940, 109). Majakovskij's close friend L. A. Grinkrug, who was at the cafe almost every evening, recalls: "Anarchists, who had occupied the neighboring building of the former merchants' club on M. Dmitrovka, came quite often. From time to time they created scandals by shooting their guns" (from the Archive of B. Jangfeldt). The anarchists, from their side, regarded the futurists as their allies, and the *Gazeta Futuristov* [Futurists' Newspaper], published in March 1918, figures in a list of anarchist organs printed in their journal *Revoljucionnoe tvorchestvo* [Revolutionary Creation], I-II (1918). In the night of April 11-12, 1918 the Cheka carried out raids on the strongholds of the Moscow anarchists; within two days, no doubt in connection with this, the Cafe of Poets was closed.

105. "We'll wash the cities of the worlds / with the flood of a second deluge" ("Our March").

106. See footnote 109. The full text of the translation is given in the first edition of this book (B. Jangfeldt, ed. 1992, 126).

107. Vladimir Robertovich Gol´cshmidt, a "futurist of life," was one of the organizers of the Cafe of Poets and a propounder of a philosophy of "health and sun." His main contribution to the history of futurist épatage was that he would break boards from the stage of the Cafe over his head. Gol´cshmidt was closely tied to the anarchists. After the Cafe's closing he ended up in the Far East, according to D. Burljuk; the latter saw him for the last time in Japan.

108. On the poster for the evening it was announced that "brilliant translators will read brilliant translations of my [i.e., Majakovskij's] brilliant poems: French, German, Bulgarian" (Katanjan 1985, 145). Jakobson had translated into French fragments of *A Cloud in Trousers* (see B. Jangfeldt, ed. 1992, 125-26) and "Our March." In a conversation with Stephen Rudy, Jakobson stated that in his absence P. Bogatyrev read his translations (letter of S. Rudy to B. Jangfeldt, Dec., 11, 1989). Jakobson's absence was explained by the fact that in the spring of 1918 he hid in the countryside for several months in order to avoid arrest for his membership in the Kadet party (see footnote 78). V. Nejshtadt also read his German translation of Majakovskij at the Cafe of Poets (see the memoirs of Nejshtadt cited in Shapir 1989, 66).

109. Cf. the inexact text in Nejshtadt's memoirs (1940, 104). See the analysis of Jakobson's translation in Shapir 1989, as well as Vallier 1987. Nejshtadt and Jakobson were friends from childhood and schoolmates at the university. He met in the summer of 1906, when they were neighbors at the dacha: "I saw him in the garden," recalls Nejshtadt, "with a book in his hands. 'Boy, what are you reading?' 'Jules Verne's *Black India.*'—'Is it interesting?'—'Oh, yes!' Thus we met. He gave me *Black India* to read and I was charmed by it." (Shapir 1989, 66.)

110. The reference is to the poetess Natalija Poplavskaja, the sister of the poet Boris Poplavskij (1903-1935).

111. Jakobson's memoirs shed new light on the instant departure of Burljuk from Moscow after the Cheka's raid on the anarchists in April 1918. The fate of his older brother Nikolaj (b. 1890) is unclear; according to Markov, it is most likely that he served in the White Army and was killed in 1920 (Markov 1968, 318, 413). Vladimir Burljuk (b. 1886) is believed to have died in 1917.

112. Jacques is Jakov L'vovich Izrailevich, who together with his brother Aleksandr associated with the Briks and Majakovskij in the 1910's. He is mentioned in a letter of Majakovskij to L. Ju. Brik of April 1918. He was also a regular at the Stray Dog Cafe. See *Pamjatniki kul'tury* 1984, 249, as well as his portrait by Sudejkin (Kogan 1974, 138).

113. Cf. L.Ju. Brik's unpublished memoirs: "After the filming in Moscow [the reference is to work on "Shackled by Film" in June 1918—B.J.] we returned to Petrograd and moved to the dacha (a family pension) in Levashovo. There I received yet another letter from I[zrailevich]. In Moscow I had received a multitude of them, so lengthy that I didn't read them to the end, and it didn't enter my head to answer even one of them, let alone to tell Volodja about I[zrailevich]. Now a letter had been sent to the dacha, full of reproaches and demanding an immediate meeting. Volodja read it and in a delirium of jealousy totally incomprehensible to me rushed off to Petrograd. Osja and I also went. We were at home when Volodja came and told us that he had met I. on the street (it had to be [in public]), that the latter flung himself at him and they started fighting. The police managed to break them up, took them both to the station, and I. told them to call Gor'kij, whose frequent guest I was, and

they released them both. Volodja was quite gloomy as he related all this
and showed us his fists, which were all black and blue, so hard had he
been hitting I." ("That's the Way it Was.") The enmity of Majakovskij
toward Gor´kij actually goes back to the spring of 1918, when Gor´kij
played a dubious role in spreaking rumors that Majakovskij had venere-
al disease. In this drama both Ja.L. Izrailevich and K.I. Chukovskij took
part (see L.Ju. Brik's letter to Gor´kij in this regard in Majakovskij/Brik,
1986, 244). On the relations between Majakovskij and Gor´kij see also
Aseev 1983, 502-505, and Babkin 1984, 306-309. Both memorists
underscore Gor´kij's unwillingness to meet Majakovskij or even hear
about him at the end of the 1920's.

114. Cf. Jakobson's recollections of 1956: "I was on very good terms with
Gor´kij, and in Petersburg at the end of 1919 (I was reading a lecture
there [see p. 80 above]) I was at his place often. I was usually with Viktor
Borisovich Shklovskij at Gor´kij's, and in general the name of
Majakovskij was not in favor there. Later, I recall, Gor´kij, when he
came to Prague and Berlin (I met with him both in Prague and in
Berlin—in Saarow), asked me to write something for the journal *Beseda*.
And at this point he and I quarreled. He didn't want me to give him any-
thing about Majakovskij." (1956a.)

115. Jakov Grigor´evich Bljumkin (1892?–1929) was a Chekist, a Left
Socialist Revolutionary, and the assassin of the German ambassador
Mirbach (summer 1918). Sentenced to death, but pardoned. He
returned to the Cheka, became one of Trockij's retinue; executed in 1929
for his links to Trockij. Cf. Jakobson's recollections of 1956: "at the next
table sat a man who soon joined us at our table, the murderer of
Mirbach—Bljumkin—and if I'm not mistaken, Vadim Shershenevich.
. . . Majakovskij began speaking about the fact that it was necessary to
put an end to the cult of Gor´kij: 'Let's go, you Bljumkin and I, and
speak out against Gor´kij.' This didn't mean that they should go immediately and speak; it was a form of bravado. Then he started making
wicked jokes on Gor´kij's account." (1956a; the episode is also related in
Brown 1973, 71.) Bljumkin's behavior in the presence of Majakovskij
and Jakobson was typical of him. In a similar way he waved a revolver at
Osip Mandel'shtam several times, threatening to kill him. Cf. the memoirs of N. Mandel´shtam about a "skirmish" between Mandel´shtam and
Bljumkin, when the poet spoke out against Bljumkin's Chekist activities:

"Bljumkin said he would not tolerate any interference in his business and that he would shoot M. too if he dared to 'meddle.' It appeares that Bljumkin threatened M. with his revolver during this first argument between them. This was something Bljumkin did at the slightest provocation — even, I was told, at home with his family. . . . In M.'s opinion, Bljumkin, terrible as he was, was by no means an utter savage. M. always said that Bljumkin never had any intention of killing him. . . . Brandishing a revolver, shouting and raving like one possessed, Bljumkin was simply indulging his temperament and his love of external effects— he was by nature a terrorist of the flamboyant type which had existed in Russia before the Revolution." (Mandelstam 1970, 105-6.)

116. V.A. Antonov-Ovseenko (1884-1938) was the Soviet ambassador to Czechoslovakia in 1924-1929. Repressed under Stalin (see below). On the bliny dinner at Jakobson's see the memoirs of Jaroslav Seifert. Seifert also mentions receptions at the Soviet Embassy: "There were mainly unusual people there, and among them the brilliant personality of the ambassador, Antonov-Ovseenko, whom we immediately took a liking to. Roman Jakobson was also there. He came up to us and was instantly our friend. And we—also right away—adopted him as one of our own." (Seifert 1983, 198.)

117. The evening of the "Selection of the King of Poetry" took place on February 27, 1918 in the Polytechnical Museum. According to V. Kamenskij, Severjanin was chosen after an "underhanded" counting of the votes (1974).

118. "A Soviet Alphabet" was written in the second half of September, 1919, and appeared in October of that year. Cf. Majakovskij's recollections: "It was written as a parody on an old pornographic alphabet. . . . It was written for use by the army. There were witticisms there that weren't fit for salons, but which went quite well in the trenches. . . . After writing the book I took it to the Central Printing House to have it typed. There was a typist there who hadn't yet been purged, who told me with great malice: 'Better I should lose my job than type this filth.' So it started. Further on, no one wanted to print the book. . . . I had to publish it myself. . . . I made three to five thousand copies by hand and carried the whole weight on my back to distribute it. This was genuine work by hand at the time of the most ominous encirclement of the Soviet

Union." (A speech at the House of the Komsomol on March 25, 1930; *PSS* 12, 428-29.)

119. The reference is to the poster "Raëk" dated December 10, 1919 (*PSS* 4, 32). It is interesting that the text has the rhyme word "Voronezh," which figures in the game of bouts-rimés that Jakobson and Majakovskij took part in in May of the same year. (See poem 10 on p. 256 above.)

120. L.Ju. Brik hints at the fact that Majakovskij's work at ROSTA was to a significant degree precisely a "source of earnings" for him. Cf. her letter to the poet of November 17, 1921, where she proposes that he become the Moscow representative of "a certain *very important* capitalist" in Riga, who was ready to publish the books of the Futurists in Latvia: "He would like someone in Moscow to take exclusive responsibility for that. He proposes to *supply* that person with provisions and money. I would like you to agree to be that person, Volosik—in the first place, it's very interesting, and in the second place it would give you the possibility of giving up the posters completely." (Jangfeldt, ed. 1982/1986, 74.)

121. "In what is strength?—In this cocoa" is a quotation from an advertising jingle from the Tea Board (Chaeupravlenie) in 1924. Jakobson examines the question of the interrelation of lyrics and advertisement texts in Majakovskij's work in his essay "New Lines by Majakovskij" (Jakobson 1956, 198 ff.).

122. The pro-German government of Hetman Pavel Skoropadsky (1873–1945) existed from the end of April until November 1918. In December Skoropadsky fled to Germany. During the entire summer there were negotiations underway in Kiev between the government of the R.S.F.S.R. and the Hetman's Ukrainian government.

123. Xristian Georgievich Rakovskij (1873–1941) played a key role in the Bolsheviks' fight against the efforts of the Ukraine to create a government independent from the R.S.F.S.R. and in 1919 headed the Soviet governments established briefly there. In the trials of 1938 Rakovskij was sentenced to twenty years in prison; in 1941 he was sentenced in absentia to be shot.

124. In the beginning of July the Russian delegation, with Rakovskij at its head, gave the Ukrainian part of the commission a map with the borders of the Ukraine indicated. This map represented "the maximum of the concessions that the Russian delegation can make" (*Izvestija*, 1918: 141 [405], July 8th). Within a month's time Rakovskij reported that "the work of the peace conference is going more slowly than we would wish. The main question—that of borders—is still not decided, though we have devoted more than seventeen sessions to it" (*ibid.*, 1918: 165 [429], August 4th).

125. Vladimir Maksimovich Friche (1870-1929) was a writer, a Marxist, and for a certain time after the October revolution the commissar of foreign affairs under the Moscow Soviet. He played a leading role in the attacks on the artistic and literary avant-garde that began in 1919.

126. Ol´ga Davydovna Kameneva (1883-1941), Trockij's sister and the wife of Kamenev, was the head of the Theatrical Division of the People's Commissariat of Enlightenment. She was repressed under Stalin. On Jakobson's episode with typhus, cf. the chapter devoted to him in Shklovskij's *Third Factory*: "Remember the nightmare you had during your bout of typhus? In the nightmare you had lost your head. (Typhus patients always make this claim.) In the nightmare, you were being tried for having betrayed science. And I condemned you to death." (Shklovskij 1926, 66.)

127. Cf. the announcement in the paper *Art* (1919: 3,12) about the establishment in IZO of a Collegium for the preparation of an Encyclopedia of Visual Arts, including "both essays of a general nature on questions of the Visual Arts, as well as terminology and biomonographs of artists, sculptors and architects."

128. The artist Aleksandr Vasil´evich Shevchenko (1882-1948).

129. The artist V.F. Franketti, a member of the directors of the society "Moscow Salon," was chosen in spring 1919 to be a member of the Moscow Collegium of IZO, together with A.M. Rodchenko and V.M. Strzheminskij. An article "V.F. Franketti" was planned in the series of monographs about artists issued by the publishing section of IZO (*Art*, 1919: 4,22,2).

130. In February 1919 a monograph entitled *Kandinskij* appeared, written by the artist himself.

131. The Petrograd newspaper *Art of the Commune* appeared from December 1918 until April 1919.

132. Konstantin Andreevich Umanskij (1901–1945). The first issue of the newspaper *Art* appeared in April 1919. Jakobson published two essays there: "Futurism" (1919: 7, 2.8) and "The Tasks of Artistic Propaganda" (1919: 8, 5.9), both of which are included in the present volume in English translation. The book Jakobson refers to is: Konstantin Umansky, *Neue Kunst in Russland 1914–1919* (1920).

133. A one-volume *Everything Composed by Viktor Xlebnikov* was included in a list of editions by the publisher IMO on July 18, 1919, and on August 28th of the same year Jakobson signed a contract with IMO for the preface to this edition (see footnote 169).

134. "Xlebnikov's Testament" was published in no. 6 of *The Unpublished Xlebnikov* (Moscow, 1928); it is republished as an appendix to the reprint edition of Xlebnikov's works (*SP*, 3, 529-30).

135. The reference is to the collection *Creations, 1906–1908* (1914, edited by David Burljuk) and the collection *Stopgap* (1913). Cf. Xlebnikov's "open letter," presumably dated 1914: "In the collections *First Volume of the Poems of V. Xlebnikov, Stopgap*, and *The Journal of the Russian Futurists*, David and Nikolaj Burljuk continue to publish poems under my name that are worthless, and in addition make changes in them. . . . I demand . . . that the pages from the collection *Stopgap* containing my poem 'Infinity' be destroyed." (*SP* 5, 257.)

136. Antonina (Tonja) Gumilina (1895-1918) was an artist and a member of the Knave of Diamonds group. At her only solo exhibition, organized by IZO, seventy-three watercolors were shown. Xardzhiev (1981, 281-82) dates the exhibition 1920. However, a joint visit to the exhibition by Jakobson and Xlebnikov could have taken place only in 1919, in view of the fact that Xlebnikov left Moscow in April of that year. On Gumilina see below and the article "In Memory of Gumilina" in *Sredi kollekcionerov*, 1922: 3, 34-37.

137. Xlebnikov left Moscow at the end of April 1919.

138. *The Newest Russian Poetry. A First Sketch* (Prague, 1921). (The book is dated May, 1919.) See the reviews by G. Vinokur (1921), V. Zhirmunskij (1921), B. Tomashevskij (1921) and V. Vinogradov (1922).

139. The meeting took place on May 11, 1919. The lecture was entitled "On the Poetic Language of Xlebnikov's Works." Present were members of the Moscow Linguistic Circle (P.G. Bogatyrev, O.M. Brik, A.A. Buslaev, F.M. Vermel', G.O. Vinokur, V.I. Nejshtadt, O.B. Rumer, P.P. Sveshnikov), as well as specially invited guests—L.Ju. Brik and V.A. Buslaev. In the rough draft of his memoirs about Majakovskij, Nejshtadt recalls: "Majakovskij attended Jakobson's lecture on Xlebnikov (11.V.1919). He was supposed to leave for Petrograd on the 9th, but put off the trip, since he was very interested in this lecture, about which he inquired." (Cited according to Shapir 1990, where the minutes of the meeting are published.) At the end of November or beginning of December of the same year Jakobson presented the same lecture at the Petrograd House of Writers, and in a year's time—at a meeting of OPOJAZ in Petrograd (Jakobson 1987, 411).

140. The verses are from the poem "Sisters-Lightening" (2nd wing, "Execution Square"):

> From the beehive of the street
> Bullets like bees.
> The chairs shake.
> The happy one turns pale.
> Along the long streets, like a flight of bullets,
> Against the machine gun
> Hits and harvests
> With bullets the leafy wreath,
> Rottens
> The shepherd's day.

Jakobson cites these verses in *The Newest Russian Poetry* as "an example of a complex composition of analogies": "Here, in the first two lines there is established a parallelism in sound imagery *(ulica* 'street' - *ulej* 'beehive', *puli* 'bullets' - *pchëly* 'bees'), in which, moreover, the subject of the first line is juxtaposed to the subject of the second, while the object of the first is linked to the object of the second by contiguity. In the fifth line there is a parallelism in sound imagery between the subject of the first and second lines (*po ulice* 'along the street' - *puli polet* 'a flight of bullets').'' (Jakobson 1921, 41; note the variant reading in the fifth line, which Jakobson gives as *po ulice* 'along the street', whereas Xlebnikov's *SP* has *po ulicam* 'along the streets.') These verses from "Sisters-Lightening" so fascinated Jakobson that he translated them into Czech; see Jangfeldt, ed. 1992, 126. In Xlebnikov 1968-1972 (3, 380), the editors note that the first two parts of the poem "were conveyed to R. Jakobson at the beginning of 1919."

141. The publisher IMO, where *Everything Composed by Viktor Xlebnikov* was supposed to appear, was financed by IZO.

142. Majakovskij's necrology of Xlebnikov was published in the journal *Krasnaja nov'* (1922: 4). The necrology concludes with the words: "After Xlebnikov's death, there appeared in various journals and newspapers articles about him full of sympathy and understanding. I have read these articles with disgust. When will this comedy of posthumous kindness finally end? Where were those writers when Xlebnikov, abused by his critics, wandered about Russia alive? I know some still living who may not be his equals, but are neglected as much as he was. Let us finally drop this reverence for hundred-year anniversaries, this honoring of posthumous publications! Let us have articles about the living! Let us have bread for the living! Let us have paper for the living!" (*PSS* 12, 28; cited from the translation by J. Rosengrant in E. J. Brown, ed., 1973, 88.)

143. In the last months of his life Xlebnikov lived at the artist's Petr Miturich (1887-1956), who led the ill poet to quarrel with his old friends. Xlebnikov died on June 28, 1922 in the village of Santalovo. In August Miturich wrote Majakovskij a letter in which he accused him of appropriating Xlebnikov's manuscripts. (The letter became known after the Nichevoki printed it as an appendix to the collection *Dog's Box*, 1922; it was reprinted as an introduction to Al'vek's brochure *Xlebnikov's Hangers-On*, 1927.) In October 1922 G.O. Vinokur and Jakobson attested to Majakovskij's innocence on a page of the poet's notebook. Jakobson testified as follows: "With the following I hereby attest that V.V. Majakovskij commissioned me to edit the *Collected Works* of Xlebnikov in spring of 1919 and gave me in that connection a series of Xlebnikov's manuscripts. In view of the fact that the edition was not realized, the materials prepared for publication, together with other materials of the

publisher IMO were kept by me and before my departure abroad in spring
of 1920 were conveyed in toto by me for preservation in the archive of
the Moscow Linguistic Circle to the secretary of the Circle, G.O.
Vinokur, about which fact I informed O.M. Brik at the time. The manuscripts were locked up in the archive of the Circle and remain there
untouched to the present day. The manuscripts in the Circle were not
given out to anyone. R. Jakobson. October 28, 1922" (Katanjan 1985,
550, where other details of this "affair" are adduced.) Majakovskij himself thought that Jakobson had taken the manuscripts with him to
Prague, as he writes in his necrology of Xlebnikov (*PSS* 12, 27).

144. In 1913 D. Burljuk gave a lecture on "Pushkin and Xlebnikov" several
times, i.e., November 3rd in the Tenishev School in Petersburg and
November 11th in the Polytechnical Museum in Moscow. Cf. the newspaper account of the first: "Pushkin has grown old for us, and it is
enough for us to get to know him as adolescents. There is genuine depth
in Pushkin only in 'Egyptian Nights'; all the rest is shallow. We—the
lecturer sums up to the loud laughter of the audience—find ourselves in
relation to Pushkin at a right angle. Xlebnikov is completely different.
He is a strong, unusual, colossal, genius of a poet, and this is felt not only
by those who are capable of appreciating a vase, apart from the idea of
what has been poured into it." (*Rech'*, November 4, 1913.)

145. The reading took place no earlier than March, when the collection had
not yet been titled *My Sister Life*, and no later than May, 1919, when
Majakovskij included Pasternak's book in a list of proposed editions to
be published by IMO. (Pasternak's receipt of August 29, 1919 for 9,000
roubles for "my book of poems *My Sister Life*, which has been sold to the
publisher IMO" is preserved in the archive of L.Ju. Brik.) After the reading at the Briks', Pasternak presented L. Ju. Brik with a manuscript of
the collection specially prepared for her, with the inscription: "This copy,
which behaved so shamefully, is written for Lili Brik, with best feelings
for her, devotedly B. Pasternak" (archive of L.Ju. Brik). On this manuscript see footnote 1 to letter 6 of Jakobson to Elsa Triolet from October
11, 1920 (p. 320 in the present edition). Cf. also Pasternak's own recollections of this reading: ". . . reading first to Majakovskij the poems from
My Sister, I heard from him ten times more than I counted on hearing
from anyone" (Pasternak 1985, 215). L.Ju. Brik recalls Majakovskij's
enthusiastic attitude to Pasternak's poetry: "Majakovskij was in love with

the enticing, practically mysterious Pasternak. He knew him by heart, for many years always read *Above the Barriers, Themes and Variations, My Sister Life.* . . . One should add here the whole of Pasternak. For me all his poems are meetings with Majakovskij." (Brik 1963, 342, 344.)

146. Jakobson has in mind the following lines from his essay "On a Generation that Squandered Its Poets": "Modern Russian poetry after 1910 is largely defined by these names [Xlebnikov and Majakovskij]. The verse of Aseev and Sel´vinskij is bright indeed, but it is a reflected light. They do not determine but reflect the spirit of the times. Their magnitude is a derivative quantity. Pasternak's books and perhaps those of Mandel´shtam are remarkable, but.theirs is chamber verse: new creation will not be kindled by it. The heart of a generation cannot take fire with such verses because they do not shatter the boundaries of the present." (Jakobson 1931, 9; cf. p. 211 above.)

147. Boris Fedorovich Malkin (1891–1938), a Left Socialist Revolutionary, from August to November 1917 a member of the All-Russian Central Executive Committee (VCIK), in May 1918 joined the Bolshevik party, in 1918–21 was head of the Central Publishing House, in 1921–22—of the Ural State Publishing House. One can assume that Jakobson is referring here to the book for IMO of August 29, 1919, when the receipts mentioned in footnote 169 below were signed.

148. From the poem *Man.*

149. "Randbemerkungen zur Prosa des Dichters Pasternak," *Slavische Rundschau* 7, 1935 (cf. the translation in Jakobson 1987, 301-17: "Marginal Notes on the Prose of the Poet Pasternak").

150. *Safe Conduct* in the Czech translation of Svatavá Pírková-Jakobson with a postscript by R. Jakobson was published by Manes in December 1935. In the same year the Czech poet Josef Hora (1891-1945) published his Czech translations of Pasternak's poetry (Melantrich Publishers). Cf. Pasternak's poem "All accumulations and debts . . ." (1936), with the line: "I just came out as a book in Prague. . . ." In a letter to Josef Hora (Nov. 15, 1935) Pasternak wrote about the strong impression this translation made on him: "I am unable to judge the objective merits of your translations. I do not know how they sound to the Czech ear and whether

they have much to offer the Czech reader. But in an inexplicable way *they gave me an immense amount. . . .* Why does your collection hold such power over me? Let me say, without exaggerating: there wafts from it such a poetic freshness that its very presence in the room has become for me a central experience. It's as if what served you as the original had never been published, and had only been silently carried in me as an assumption. And your translations are the first manifestation of that, not even in Czech, but in any human language." Further Pasternak writes: "having already dispatched my last letter [of October 14, 1935] I remembered suddenly that I had not conveyed my greetings to Roman Jakobson, with whom you are acquainted. I have never forgotten my own bright, even if short-lived, acquaintance with him. From all my soul I wish him health and happiness. We frequently remember him here with the same and unchangeable warmth. If there is anything in my letter that you can't make out (I write in an impermissible way for a writer, disconnected and verbose)—show it to R.O. [Jakobson], and he will correct my inadequacies, i.e. will give you supplementary explanations, if they are needed." (*Voprosy literatury,* 1979:7, 184.)

151. Cf. Jakobson/Pomorska 1983, 143.

152. Vítězslav Nezval (1900–1951), Jaroslav Seifert (1901–1987), Vladislav Vančura (1891–1942), Konstantin Biebl (1898–1951). Jakobson's close and warm ties with the Czech avant-garde and scholarly world are attested to in the small Festschrift devoted to him in 1939: *Romanů Jakobsonovi. Pozdrav a díkůvzdání.* It included, i.a., Nezval's poems "Roman Jakobson" and "Dopis Romanů Jakobsonovi," Arne Novák's "Tvůrči znalec staročeského básnictví," and the anonymous poem "Slóvce M." See also the memoirs of J. Seifert (1985, 297-305, and footnote 116 here) and V. Nezval (1978, 154-56), as well as K. Pomorska's "Postscript" to Jakobson/Pomorska 1983, 176-79.

153. Julian Tuwim (1894–1953), Kazimierz Wierzyński (1894–1969), Louis Aragon (1896–1982). Jakobson met Tuwim and Wierzyński, who had fled Poland, in New York during World War II (Jakobson/Pomorska 1983, 179). His friendship with Elsa Triolet linked him to Aragon. See his articles "O slovesnom iskusstve Kazimira Vezhin´skogo" and "Le Métalangage d'Aragon" *(SW* III).

154. Gerasim Davidovich and Evgenija Grigor´evna Gur´jan.

155. F.N. Afremov, one of the founding members of the Moscow Linguistic Circle.

156. Cf. *A Sentimental Journey*: "He took me into the archive, locked me in, and said: If there's a search at night, rustle, and say that you're a piece of paper" (Shklovskij 1923, 216). This occurred at the beginning of fall, 1918. One must assume, along with the commentator to Shklovskij's book *The Hamburg Reckoning* that Jakobson is also the "comrade philologist" with whom Shklovskij stayed later (Shklovskij 1990, 503).

157. In *A Sentimental Journey*, the person hiding in the bushes by the Church of Christ the Saviour is identified as "a certain officer, who had escaped from Jaroslavl´ . . . after the uprising [of the Left Socialist Revolutionaries in the summer of 1918]." (Shklovskij 1923, 213.)

158. Cf. Shklovskij's account: "I ended up at a comrade's (who didn't have anything to do with politics), dyed my hair, which came out violet. We had a good laugh. I had to shave my head. I couldn't spend the night at his place." (Shklovskij 1923, 216.)

159. In Shklovskij's account the document was signed not by Trockij, but by Sverdlov, and not at the request of L. Rejsner, but of M. Gor´kij: "I went to Aleksej Maksimovich [Gor´kij], who wrote a letter to Jakov Sverdlov. . . . Sverdlov received me without suspicion. I told him I wasn't a White and he didn't interrogate me. He gave me a letter on an official form of the Central Executive Committee and in the letter he asked that the Shklovskij case be closed." (Shklovskij 1923, 243.) A different story relates to Larisa Rejsner: she had asked him to "liberate" her husband, Fedor Raskol´nikov, who had been imprisoned in Reval. This proved to be unnecessary—"the English traded him for something or other"—but Shklovskij went to Petrograd "with some sort of fantastic document signed by her" (*ibid.*, 244).

160. In February 1922 it was announced that 47 representatives of the party of Socialist Revolutionaries had been arrested. Their trials began on June 8, 1922. In the middle of March 1922 Shklovskij fled to Finland, where he lived for a while in the village of Raivola (now Roshchino) near the

Russian-Finnish border (where the Finnish poetess Edith Södergran also lived at the time). The second part of *A Sentimental Journey,* "A Writing Table," was begun in May 1922 in Raivola (see Shklovskij 1923, 187) and completed in Berlin later in the same year.

161. Jurij Jakovlevich Bal´shin (1871–1938).

162. Majakovskij moved into Lubjanskij Thruway in the fall of 1919. Cf. Jakobson's letter of Dec. 19, 1920 to Elsa Triolet, concerning the real reason for the move: "By fall 1919 they had ceased living together, Volodja moved in next door to me, and in the winter they broke up" (see letter 11, p. 127, in the present edition).

163. This first Pushkino summer is not mentioned in Katanjan's chronicle of Majakovskij's life, but it was precisely during this summer that the dog Shchen was found, about which L.Ju. Brik writes in her book *Shchen* (Molotov, 1942).

164. Lev Aleksandrovich Grinkrug (1889–1987), one of the closest friends of Majakovskij and the Briks. On his biography see B. Jangfeldt, ed. 1986, 195.

165. Cf. Jakobson's recollections: " In 1917 I undertook to analyze along these lines a single text which was included in Kirsha Danilov's collection and which stands on the boundary between lyrical and epic poetry. It was a short specimen (twenty-one lines) of the remarkable cycle of poems on grief. I promised to contribute an article on the subject to the forthcoming issue of the *Collection on the Theory of Poetic Language,* which OPOJAZ was preparing at the time. The issue appeared in 1919, but without my article, which I rightly considered as an immature sketch that needed extension and revision in light of more precise principles of linguistic analysis. I allowed this analysis of these twenty-one lines of the "Grief" poem to ripen for half a century before using it in my monograph on grammatical parallelism and its Russian facet, published in 1966 in the American journal *Language.* Even this monograph is in my eyes only a preliminary sketch." (Jakobson/Pomorska 1983, 102.)

166. P. G. Bogatyrev, *Czech Puppet Theater and Russian Folk Theater* (1923). Jakobson's and Bogatyrev's joint work on the folk theater began earlier

than the summer of 1919: "we assiduously worked [on the manual of Russian folk theater] during the winter months of 1919 at a temperature of 24° F in our room on Lubjanskij Thruway, with ice in our inkwell instead of ink, to the accompaniment of the sound of gun-fire from the neighbouring street" *(SW* VII, 301).

167. The reference is to the artist Èduard Gustavovich Shiman (1885–1942), who frequently visited the Briks, and the artist Antonina (Tonja) Gumilina, whom Shiman married not long before her suicide in 1918.

168. In the screenplay *How Are You?* (*PSS* 11, 129-148), Majakovskij learns from the newspaper about a girl who has shot herself with a revolver. It was written at the end of 1926. L. Kuleshov was named its producer, but the film was never shot. The scenario has a clearly autobiographical character and seems, as it were, a continuation of the poem *About That.* See Jakobson's analysis of the scenario (1956).

169. On the estimate attached to the letter to Lunacharskij, there are the follownig signatures: "Members of the editorial board of IMO: V.V. Majakovskij, O. Brik; for the secretary: R. Jakobson." The estimate is dated July 18, 1919 (*PSS* 13, 403). Four receipts of Jakobson's dated August 29, 1919 are preserved stating that he received money from IMO for 1) an article (two printer's sheets) "On the Revolutionary Verses of V. Majakovskij" for a collection of essays on Majakovskij, *Ivan. An Epic of the Revolution,* 2) translations of poems into French for the book *Russians, Germans, French* (a collection of the latest Russian poets in German, French and English translation), 3) the article "Futurism" (half a printer's sheet) for the collection *Art of the Commune,* and 4) an introductory essay (in four printer's pages) "Approaches to Xlebnikov" for the *Collected Works* of Xlebnikov. (Archive of B. Jangfeldt.) Jakobson's article on "Futurism" had already been published in the seventh issue of the newspaper *Iskusstvo* for 1919 (August 2) and "Approaches to Xlebnikov" was published as a separate book in Prague in 1921—*The Newest Russian Poetry.* The other planned works were not realized. (See also footnote 145 about Pasternak's receipt.)

170. Cf. Jakobson's recollections of 1956: "Before he had finished the poem, in the end of 1919, Vladimir Vladimirovich read *150,000,000* to Shklovskij and me at my room on Lubjanskij Thruway. He asked us

what we thought the weak passages were. We indicated some such passages to him, and he replied: 'What do you think, I don't see this? Of course, there are many weak passages, but I see still other things you don't see.'" (Jakobson 1956a.)

171. Cf. in the same concluding part of the poem: "Everyone sing and everyone hear/ the solemn hymn of the world." See also Jakobson's analysis of the "drum lines" in *150,000,000* (1971).

172. The reading took place at the Briks' apartment in the first half of January, 1920 (Jakobson 1956a).

173. Vladimir Dmitrievich Bonch-Bruevich (1873–1955) was the organizer and first director (1933–1939) of the Literary Museum in Moscow.

174. This textual variant was first published in the collection *Smert' Vladimira Majakovskogo* (Jakobson 1931).

175. Cf. Lenin's note of May 6, 1921, written after he had received the book *150,000,000* as a present from Majakovskij: "Nonsense, stupidity, double-dyed stupidity and pretentiousness. In my opinion, only one out of ten such things should be published and *in no more than 1500 copies* for libraries and eccentrics. And Lunacharskij should be whipped for his futurism." *(Kommunist,* 1957: 18.) Cf. Jakobson's discussion of the matter in Jakobson/Pomorska 1983, 107-9, as well as Jangfeldt 1987.

176. Cf. Jakobson's reminiscences of 1956: "Vladimir Vladimirovich spoke very passionately. He said that it was precisely thus that one should understand the topic of the revolution, that it's naturalistic depiction would be laughable and that it should be an epic. And this was quite characteristic of him: that a genuine epic, a genuine long poem should already be, first of all, about the future. . . . Lunacharskij compared *150,000,000* to Blok's 'The Twelve.' . . . In essence, the title *150,000,000* was a polemical reply to 'The Twelve.' It was not twelve who made the revolution, but *150,000,000* ! . . . . In general, his titles often had a polemical character. In particular, his 'Letter to Tat'jana' was a unique polemic with Tat'jana's answer to Onegin's letter. Once, when I asked him: what are you up to? (this was quite a long time ago, before the revolution), he answered: 'I'm rewriting world literature. I rewrote *Onegin,*

then I rewrote *War and Peace,* and now I'm rewriting *Don Juan.* But this *Don Juan,* as you know, has not been preserved. . . . The theme of the work was as follows: Don Juan was a man with one love, and all of his attractions were coincidental, not genuine. Finally, the last—his true love—turns out to be a personal tragedy." (1956a.)

177. Lunacharskij reacted critically several times to this thesis of the thoreticians of the so-called Formal School, "who affirmed that honesty and art are antipodes" (*Krasnaja nov´,* 1921: 1; Lunacharskij 1967, 253). Judging from the evidence, O.M. Brik also spoke at this evening with the same argumentation; in an essay of 1929, Lunacharskij ascribes to him the words about "painted" and "marble columns" (Lunacharskij 1967a, 43). In 1923, the People's Commissar recalled: "When Majakovskij read . . . *150,000,000,* I asked him: did he write it sincerely or insincerely. He didn't reply, since if he said 'sincerely,' he would have been attacked by the Briks, who said that Pushkin himself wrote insincerely, and so on. Brik irreligiously conflated two questions that night. He thought that it was all the same to ask whether a column which was depicted in the stage design was made of genuine stone or whether it was decorated with paint, or to ask whether a poet is sincere when he writes or whether he is lying, pretending." (Lunacharskij 1967, 662.)

178. At the Theatrical School attached to the First State Theater of the R.S.F.S.R Jakobson taught a course on "Russian Language." One of his students was the famous linguist A.A. Reformackij (see Reformackij 1970, 14-15).

179. The first classes at The State Institute of Declamation began on October 20, 1919. The Chairman of the Presidium of the Institute was V.K. Serezhnikov, and its teachers included, among others, Vjacheslav Ivanov, P. Kogan, D. Ushakov, and Ju. Ajxenval´d. Jakobson was named a professor at the Institute in November 1919. (*Vestnik teatra,* 1919: 44, Dec. 2-7.)

180. The opening ceremony of the Institute took place on November 27, 1919 (see the report in *op. cit.*).

181. This reading took place later in January of 1920.

182. Adol´f Grigor´evich Men´shoj (Gaj) was a journalist and a worker in the Commissariat of Foreign Affairs. In 1919-1920 he worked in ROSTA. He was later repressed. See p. 82 above.

183. Cf. Jakobson's reminiscences of 1956: "Someone said that it was to a significant extent a return to the tradition of Derzhavin's odes; someone spoke about the connection of the poem to the byliny, someone spoke about its link to Nekrasov, and so on. Vladimir Vladimirovich made notes about whom said what, then said: 'I hear that here are Derzhavin, Pushkin, Nekrasov, and so on. It is not the one, nor the other, nor the third, but all of Russian literature and beside that something different.'" (1956a.)

184. Similar images are often encountered in Majakovskij's poetry. Cf., for example, the poem "Bureaucratish" (1922): ". . . above me rise/ inaccessible forts,/ the grey bastions of Soviet chancelleries"; or the poem "Comrades, Let Me Share with You My Impressions of Paris and of Monet" (1923): "Let us stand . . ./ and further at a turtle's pace!/ Next stop:/ Station 'Member of the Collegium'/ Next stop:/ Exit of 'Two Secretaries.' . . ." Cf. also the first draft of the poem *The Fifth International*, which refers to Lenin and his secretary Fotieva: "You think a secretary and a door bother me?/ I'll fly through their mass/ Like radium./ Put around a hundred ranks of guards/ . . . No barrier will silence me,/ Even if they multiply the Kremlin's walls by four./ From the asphalt I'll call out and deafen their ears/ with the roar of a song that's begun to boil." (*PSS* 4, 306.)

185. In the film scenario "Forget About the Fireplace" (1927) and in the play *The Bedbug* (1928), into which Majakovskij transferred the theme and basic characters from the scenario (which has never been produced), the author paraphrases the first stanza of a song based on Ja. Polonskij's poem "The Recluse" in *The Bedbug*: "On Lunacharskij Street / I recall an old house—/ with a marvelous wide staircase, / and an elegant window."

186. On the theme of the "revolution of the spirit" in Majakovskij see Jangfeldt 1976, 51-71.

187. From Majakovskij's poem "To Proletarian Poets" (1926).

188. The theme of the resurrection of the dead is particularly clear in the poem *About That*: "Revive me,/ if for nothing else,/ because/ Russians, I,/ a poet,/ cast off daily trash/ to wait for you./ Revive me/ if only for that!/ Revive me,/ let me live my due!" Jakobson: "The poet's vision of the coming resurrection of the dead is vitally linked with the materialistic mysticism of Fëdorov" (1931, 24; cf. p. 225 above).

189. Cf. Jakobson's reminiscence of how, in spring 1920, after his return from Reval to Moscow, Majakovskij "made me repeat several times my somewhat confused remarks on the general theory of relativity": "the idea of the liberation of energy, the problem of the time dimension, and the idea that movement at the speed of light may actually be a reverse movement in time—all these things fascinated Majakovskij. I'd seldom seen him so interested and attentive." (1931, 24; cf. p. 225 in the present edition.)

190. From the poem "Iranian Song" (1921).

191. Cf. the reminiscences of the artist V.O. Roskin: "They lived together—the poet and the theoretician. These were terrible years. The Jakobsons' former cook baked rolls and fed them something. In the evening they wrote, in the day went to the IZO Department of the People's Commissariat for Enlightenment, which was located by Red Square in the building of a former lyceum." (Jakobson 1987, 410.)

192. The play "So Who Spends Their Time Celebrating Holidays" was written in March-April 1920 for the State Experimental Stage Studio of the Theater of Satire. It was meant for the spectacles for May Day, but was presented only in 1922 in the Club of the Military Artillery School "The Shot."

193. The mentioned play, as well as two others written for the same occasion, were first published in the almanac *With Majakovskij* (Moscow, 1934).

194. M. M. Pokrovskij (1896-1942) was the rector of Moscow University.

195. Cf. the article "The Influence of the Revolution on the Russian Language": "Spirtoshvili—a Moscovite word from 1919, indicated a secret seller of liquor and wine . . . since the majority of them were from the Caucasus" (Jakobson 1921a, 22).

196. See pp. 59-60 above.

197. Shklovskij's father was a mathematician. On Shklovskij's relatives see *A Sentimental Journey* (Shklovskij 1923, 318 ff.).

198. V. Shklovskij's "Letter to Roman Jakobson" begins with a reference to this Nadja: "Nadja has gotten married." The letter was published in *Knizhnyj ugol,* 1922: 8 and is reprinted in Shklovskij 1990, 145-46. The person in question is Nadezhda Filippovna Fridljand, over whom Shklovskij "had a duel with someone" in spring of 1920 (see Shklovskij 1990, 164, 503). Jakobson had known her since childhood. "Both of our fathers were originally from Dvinsk and studied in the same class," recalls N. Fridljand (in a letter to B. Jangfeldt of June 28, 1990). "Their friendship continued in their mature years. My first memory is of the dacha our parents rented together. I was seven, Roma—eleven. . . . The neighboring children would drop by, and we would have loud games. Everyone, that is, except for Roma. He would sit at a table in the garden, surrounded by books and notebooks, and to all our invitations to 'come play' would answer: 'later.' Or he wouldn't answer at all." N. Fridljand saw Jakobson in Riga in the spring of 1919, and before his departure for Prague he tried to convince her to come with him: "You have to be crazy to stay in this country. You'll later regret this bitterly." Nevertheless, N. Fridljand stayed in Russia and saw Jakobson again only in 1976, when she immigrated to America. In 1989 she published a book of stories and reminiscences about her artistic life (under the name N. Kramova).

199. It has not been possible to ascertain when the lectures mentioned took place in the House of Writers. Jakobson read his lecture on Brjusov, "A Model of Scholarly Charlatanism (on Brjusov's *Science of Verse*)," in the Moscow Linguistic Circle on September 23, 1919, with Majakovskij present (Shapir 1991, 52). Jakobson later set forth his objections to Brjusov in an article "Brjusov's Versology and the Science of Verse" (1922). On February 1, 1920 Jakobson delivered another lecture at Chukovskij's on "the emancipation of poetry from semantics, on the weakening of the referential element," this time at the House of Arts (Chukovskij 1979, 274), and on February 7th he gave a report to the Moscow Linguistic Circle on "the philological life of Petrograd" (Shapir 1991, 52).

200. On Janov's father see p. 33. If G. Janov was "five years younger" than Jakobson, he was at the time not even twenty years old!

201. Jakobson stayed in Reval from the beginning of February until the fourth of April 1920 in the capacity of a "member of the trade delegation of Centrosojuz and a colllaborator of ROSTA" (Jakobson 1987, 427).

202. Mixail Jul´evich Levidov (1891–1942) was a writer and journalist; after Reval he worked in the publications bureau of the Soviet trade delegation in London. After returning to Russia, he joined LEF. Repressed under Stalin.

203. Arturo Cappa was a lawyer and brother of Benedetta Cappa, the future wife of Marinetti. A communist, he was the author of the book *L'arte e la rivoluzione* (Milan, 1920). Cappa was far from being the sole Italian futurist with communist sympathies: see footnote 9 (pp. 332f below) to the essay "New Art in the West."

204. Nikolaj K. Klyshko (1880–1937) was an Old Bolshevik. During World War I he was a member of the Bolshevik section of the R.S.D.R.P. in London (together with Litvinov, Kerzhencev and others). After the October revolution he worked for a while as V.V. Vorovskij's assistant in the State Publishing House (GOSIZDAT), then served in Soviet trade and diplomatic missions abroad, including Sweden and Norway. Repressed under Stalin.

205. Jakobson was in Reval from the beginning of June until July 3, 1920.

206. Jakobson agreed with me that his account here about Teodor Nette was contaminated with his letter of March 2, 1963 about his acquaintanceship with the Latvian diplomatic courier, a copy of which he gave me during our work on the current memoirs. The letter later appeared in *SW* VII, 363-65.

207. Janis Rainis (Jānis Pliekšāns, 1865–1929) was a Latvian poet and playwright. In 1897–1902 he was exiled to Russia for participating in the fight for democracy and later emigrated to Switzerland. In 1920 he returned to his homeland, where he became director of the National Theater and later Minister of Enlightenment.

208. *On Czech Verse, Primarily in Comparison with Russian* (Prague, 1923). On the Cafe Derby, cf. Ju. Tynjanov's letter to V. Shklovskij from the end of 1928: "I'm sitting in the Cafe Derby with Roman, we're talking a lot about you and making various plans. We've elaborated the principal theses (for OPOJAZ) and are sending them to you for amplification and confirmation." (Tynjanov 1977, 533.)

209. A citation from Majakovskij's poem "To Comrade Nette, the Steamboat and the Man" (1926).

210. The poem was published without an indication of the author.

211. As far as can be determined, this note was never published.

212. Nette's scholarly proclivities are attested to by the fact that in his article "The Influence of the Revolution on the Russian Language" Jakobson thanks him for philological observations that are used in the work (Jakobson 1921a, 31).

213. The literary scholar and folklorist A.A. Skaftymov (1890–1968) was a professor at Saratov University from 1921 on.

214. Pavel Nikolaevich Mostovenko (1881–1939) was in 1921–1922 the representative of the R.S.F.S.R in Lithuania and Czechoslovakia. According to Shklovskij, Mostovenko helped him to return to Russia: "One of my acquaintances (through Roman), Pavel Nikolaevich Mostovenko, was in Moscow and submitted a statement on the necessity of concluding my case. He spoke about it with Kamenev, Lunacharskij and, it seems, Zinov´ev. The statement was given to Enukidze and was supposed to go to the All-Russian Central Executive Committee [VCIK]." (A letter of November 1922 to his wife; Shklovskij 1990, 507.)

215. G.V. Chicherin (1872–1936) was the Commissar for Foreign Affairs from 1918 to 1930. As Jakobson recalls further: "I never met Chicherin. He was a unique person, from a very aristocratic family of Italian origin. (His ancestor was, in Moscovite Russia, under one of the Ioanns, an Italian translator, a *cicerone;* hence the name Chicherin.) He graduated from the Philological Faculty of Petersburg University. One of my acquaintances, who also graduated from the same faculty, Jastrebov, who

later became a professor, told him: 'I envy you, you graduated with distinction.' 'Yes,' Chicherin answered, 'but there isn't a single subject to
which I am attached.' And so he entered the diplomatic service, in
Tsarist Russia. Then one fine day he went to the Embassy and declared
that he had become a Social Democrat and left the service. Chicherin
wrote letters to Levin; I read them myself: 'Send me books, I love Czech
literature and Czech poetry very much. (In emigration he was for the
most part in Prague.) Send me, if you can, the latest volume of poems by
Vrchlický; I value him greatly.' Levin sent him the books he wanted, and
also sent him *Švejk*, which we also found quite interesting. In one letter
he wrote to Levin: 'You say you're bored in Prague. But you're not right.
It is a country with a philistine gloss, but under this are hidden passions,
the same passions that are reflected in the Slavonic dances of Dvořák
and in Czech poetry, in the poetry of Neruda. This will be one of the
brightest of revolutions.'" (TR.)

216. V. A. Antonov-Ovseenko was the Soviet ambassador to Czechoslovakia
in 1924–1929. See footnote 116.

217. Cf. the letter of the All-Russian Society for Cultural Relations with
Foreign Countries (VOKS) in the name of its representative in
Czechoslovakia, the embassy's advisor Naum Kaljuzhnyj, of February 8,
1927: "Majakovskij is travelling at his own expense and is counting on
an organized collaboration in arranging a reading and lodgings, which
comrade Jakobson has kindly agreed to offer him, since he does not wish
to stay at a hotel" (Archive of L.Ju. Brik). As a matter of fact,
Majakovskij stayed at the Hotel Julius, Vaclavská 22. Cf. Majakovskij's
description of his trip to Prague in his essay "How I Traveled" (1927):
"At the Prague railway station was Roma Jakobson. He is the same. He's
gained some weight. Work in the press agency of the Prague Embassy
has added to him a certain solidity and diplomatic circumspection in
speech." (*PSS* 8, 331.)

218. The evening at the Soviet Embassy took place on April 25th.

219. Mathesius' translation appeared as a separate edition in Prague in 1925.

220. The evening took place on April 26 in the "Vinohrad People's House."
Cf. the essay "How I Travelled": "I read a lecture on 'Ten Years of Ten

Poets.' Then *150,000,000* was read in Prof. Mathesius' translation. The third part was 'Me and My Verses'" (*PSS* 8, 332). On the various newspaper reviews of the evening see Jakobson's letter, sent to Majakovskij several days after his apppearance and cited by the poet in his essay.

221. Majakovskij's quarrel with the State Publishing House over his honoraria is reflected in the poet's correspondence with its manager (*PSS* 13, 112, 114-15, 127, 129-30). Majakovskij was usually paid by the line, but in a letter of March 16, 1929, the director of the State Publishing House, A. B. Xalatov wrote that in connection with the "disadvantageousness" of this system, "it is essential urgently to make a motivated proposition to comrade Majakovskij about changing the agreement in relation to the system of payment (making it per page)" (IMLI, 18-2-35). Majakovskij, however, demanded payment of 75 kopecks per line and received a certificate from the Federation of Writers (FOSP) about the justifiability of such a demand: "Payment of 75 kopecks per line in relation to poetic works being issued in their first book edition, keeping in mind the usual payment of our publishers and the qualifications of Comrade Majakovskij as a writer, is considered normal" (*ibid.*). Judging by Xalatov's letter of June 15, 1929 to the Associate Director of the Literary-Artistic Division of the State Publishing House, G. Sandomirskij, the publisher agreed to Majakovskij's conditions (*ibid.*).

222. Jakobson had indicated already in 1931 the similarity of Majakovskij's and Karamzin's perception of Russia and France, in his essay on the Russian myth of France: "Der treue Sohn des russischen Kaiserreiches, Karamzin, sagt in 1790 vom revolutionären Paris: Ich möchte in meinem lieben Vaterland leben und sterben; aber nach Rußland gibt es für mich kein angenehmeres Land als Frankreich. Und 1925 schreibt Majakovskij, der Dichter Sovjetrußlands, der nie Karamzin gelesen hatte, vom Nachkriegs-Frankreich: Ich möchte in Paris leben und sterben, wenn es kein Land Moskau gäbe. Das gleiche Motiv variiert 1847 Belinskij." (Jakobson 1931a, 637.)

223. Adolf Hofmeister (1902–1973) was a Czech artist and caricaturist. On November 3, 1929 Majakovskij was present at the opening of an exhibition of his caricatures in Paris. See Hofmeister's reminiscences about Majakovskij (Majakovskij 1988, 347-50, which also has a reproduction of a caricature of Majakovskij in 1927 by Hofmeister).

224. On the way to Paris in mid-February 1929, Majakovskij "spent a day at my place in Prague," Jakobson recalls (1956, 187). According to a letter cited by V.A. Katanjan, negotiations about producing *The Bedbug* were preceded by a letter from the representative of VOKS in Prague, N. Kaljuzhnyj, to VOKS in Moscow dated January 21, 1929, with a request for a copy of the play (1985, 584).

225. Cf. also the following lines in *About That*: "Perhaps in my childhood,/ actually,/ I'll find ten tolerable days." The theme of time and aging is a leitmotif of the entire oeuvre of Majakovskij. See Pomorska 1981, 341-353.

226. Cf. Jakobson's essay "For and Against Viktor Shklovskij": "Majakovskij often spoke about the dramatic alternation of genres and about their dramatic collision, about the battle of lyric and antilyric elements both in his poetry and in his written or oral testimony about his poetry. . . . The quarrel of pro and contra, the pressure of the lyric, again calling him to write about the one and the other and answering attacks on the lyric, such is the inner law of Majakovskij's life and literary path" (1959, 309). The notion of the cyclical nature of Majakovskij's work is developed by Jakobson in his essay "New Verses by Majakovskij": "In Majakovskij's work love poems and lyrical cycles regularly alternate with lyro-epic poems about world events" (1956, 180-181). After the first lyrical cycle (*A Cloud in Trousers, A Backbone Flute*) there followed the "civic poem" *War and the World*, replaced in turn by the lyric poem *Man*, after which *150,000,000* was written, etc.

227. Majakovskij met Tat´jana Aleksandrovna Jakovleva (1906-1991) in Paris in 1928. Jakobson made her acquaintance in America, and some of Majakovskij's letters to her were published by Jakobson in 1956. Cf. Elsa Triolet's reminiscences: "I made Tat´jana's acquaintance in Paris in 1928, just before Majakovskij's arrival, and told her: 'You're of Majakovskij's stature.' So it was because of this 'stature,' as a joke, that I introduced Volodja to her. Majakovskij fell deeply in love with her at first glance. . . . At the time Majakovskij needed love, he counted on it, desired it. . . " (Triolet 1975, 64, 65).

228. Thus, for example, in December 1916, Elsa received a letter from Majakovskij with a line from *A Cloud in Trousers*—"my nerves are already giving way under their feet"—and immediately set off for

Petrograd to see him. "All my life I was afraid that Volodja would kill himself" (Triolet, 1975, 33; see also the correspondence of Majakovskij and Elsa Triolet: Majakovskij/Triolet 1990).

229. The group of Left-wing activists in art who sided with the revolution called themselves "Komfuty" (Communist-Futurists). It included Majakovskij, Brik, Punin, Kushner and others. On the history of the "Komfuty" see Jangfeldt 1976, 92-118.

230. A quote from the poem "A Letter of the Writer Vladimir Majakovskij to the Writer Aleksej Maksimovich Gor'kij" (1926).

231. See Majakovskij's autobiography, "I Myself": "Burljuk would say: Majakovskij has a memory like a road in Poltava,—everyone leaves one of their galoshes on it."

232. This took place, in all likelihood, in 1916 (see Blok 1982, 100). Cf. K.I. Chukovskij's diary entry for December 8, 1920: "Majakovskij told me, in a most amusing way, the story of how he went to see Blok a long time ago. It was Lili's nameday, and she was making bliny; she insisted that he not be late. He went to Blok's, having decided that he would return at a certain time. Lili had asked him to get some of Blok's latest books— with an autograph.—I went. I sit down. Blok keeps talking and talking. I look at my watch and figure: ten minutes for conversation, ten minutes to ask for the books and autographs, and three minutes for the preparation of the autographs. Everything went well—Blok proposed the books himself and said that he wanted to make a dedication. He sat down at the table, took his pen—and sits for five minutes, ten, fifteen. I'm in a state of horror—I want to scream: hurry up!—and he keeps sitting and thinking. I politely say: don't strain yourself, write the first thing that comes to mind—he keeps sitting with the pen in his hand and keeps thinking. The bliny had fallen through! I rush about the room like a madman. I'm afraid to look at my watch. Finally Blok finishes. I slammed the book shut, smearing it slightly, thanked him, ran off, and then I read: 'To Vl. Majakovskij, about whom I have been thinking so much lately'" (Chukovskij 1980, 304-5). On Majakovskij's attitude toward Blok's poetry, cf. Lili Brik's memoirs: "In 1915, when we met, Majakovskij was still bewitched by Blok" (Brik 1963, 332).

233. Cf. Jakobson's reminiscences about K.P. Bogatyrev: "It isn't easy to read the noisy semantics of a still unconscious human being, and even our Moscow guest Vladimir Majakovskij would shudder when the little boy Bogatyrev would run into the room" (Bogatyrev 1982, 230).

234. Cf. L.Ju. Brik's diary for January 23, 1930: "Volodja's relatives would irritate him to such an extent that he would positively shudder. Even though [his older sister] Ljuda would drop by our place once in three months. I even went to his room and said: 'You have to at least talk to Ljuda for half an hour or at least open the door; otherwise, she won't leave.' And he answered: 'I can't, she gets on my nerves!!!' And he became all contorted while saying it. It was terribly unpleasant for me." (Archive of L.Ju. Brik.)

235. Shchen was Majakovskij's dog in 1919-1920. See Lili Brik's memoir of 1942. Majakovskij often signed his letters to Lili Brik as "Shchen," with a drawing of a dog.

236. Anna Axmatova recalled a similar utterance of Majakovskij's in a conversation with L.Ja. Ginzburg: "Remember what Majakovskij said: say whatever you want about my poems; only don't say that the earlier ones were better than the latest." (Ginzburg 1989, 361.)

237. L.Ju. Brik recalls that in the first years of her marriage to O.M. Brik they read Kierkegaard's book *In vino veritas* together. (Brik 1934, 63.)

238. E. A. Lavinskaja tells how on April 16, 1930 she saw the Chekist Ja. S. Agranov, surrounded by a group of writers from LEF: "I approached, and he handed me some sort of photograph, warning me to look at it quickly and not to show it to anyone else. It was a photograph of Majakovskij, outstretched on the floor like someone crucified, with his arms and legs spread out and with his mouth wide-open in a cry of despair. They explained to me: 'It was taken immediately, when Agranov, Tret´jakov and Kol´cov entered the room.'" (Lavinskaja 1968, 330.) The memoirs of V. Polonskaja, who was in the apartment when Majakovskij shot himself, do not contain this information.

PART TWO — LETTERS

Letters 1-3 are addressed to A. E. Kruchenyx and M. V. Matjushin. Apart from these three letters addressed to older futurist colleagues, there exists a letter of Jakobson to V. Xlebnikov from February 1914. Fragments of this letter have been published by N. Xardzhiev: "Remember, Viktor Vladimirovich, how you told me that our alphabet is too poor for poetry and that one ends up in a blind alley with verses composed of letters? I become more and more convinced that you are mistaken. Recently I came to a curious discovery, which is why I am writing you. This novelty is interlacings of letters, a sort of analogy to musical chords. It achieves a simultanism of two or more letters and, moreover, a diversity of graphic combinations which establish various interrelations of letters. All of this enriches verse and opens new paths. . . . When I asked you what you had come to, the answer was—numbers. You know, Viktor Vladimirovich, it seems to me that verses made out of numbers are realizable. The number is a two-edged sword, extremely concrete and extremely abstract, arbitrary and fatally exact, logical and nonsensical, limited and infinite. Pardon the rhetoric. You know numbers, and therefore, even if you recognize that the poetry of numbers is an unacceptable paradox, but a sharp one, please try and give me at least a small model of such verse." (Xardzhiev 1976, 57.) Xardzhiev also states that his archive contains a letter of Jakobson to Kruchenyx with a reference to the above letter to Xlebnikov.

F. T. Marinetti, by the way, also arrived at the poetry of numbers. In March 1914 he published a manifesto entitled "Lo splendore geometrico e meccanico e la sensibilità numerica," in which he writes: "My love for precision and essential brevity has naturally given me a taste for numbers, which live and breathe on the page like living beings in our new numerical sensibility. . . . I always intuitively introduce numbers that have no direct significance or value between the words-in-freedom, but that . . . express the various transcendental intensities of matter and the indestructible correspondences of sensibility." (Marinetti 1973, 158-59.) The catalogue *The Futurist Imagination* (Yale

University Art Gallery, New Haven, 1983) reproduces an example of Marinetti's poetry of numbers from c. 1914–1915 (?) (Cat. no. 59, p. 28). On the principal difference in the Italian and Russian Futurists' approach to the word, see Jakobson 1921, 6-9; cf. pp. 176f above.

Letter 4 is addressed to the mother of L. Ju. Brik and Elsa Triolet in London. Letters 5-17 are addressed to Elsa Triolet in Paris (5-13, 17) and in Berlin (14-16).

LETTER 1.

The letter is not dated. In his essay "From Aljagrov's Letters," written in 1979, where it was first published (minus the postscript), Jakobson dates it February 1914. (On the dating, see note 15.) It is published from a photocopy of the original, which is in the archive of A. E. Parnis. Jakobson's own annotations to the letter from his article "From Aljagrov's Letters" (see *SW* VII, 357-61) are given in the footnotes in quotes, followed by his initials. The remaining annotations are the editor's.

1. "Using habitual words"—R.J.

2. Jakobson speaks of a letter "to Kruchenyx with a poem which is an indirect parody of Majakovskij" (see p. 25 above), i.e. apparently the poem "How Many Fragments Have Scattered," but in the present letter there is a reference to a poem in which "all the words" are in the masculine gender, but no such poem has been found.

3. "*Samovityj*, 'self-centered', according to Xlebnikov's terminology"—R.J.

4. "*Prugva* is from Old Russian *prug* 'locust' by analogy with *bukva* 'letter'"—R.J.

5. Lukashevich, "who in 1846 published his numerous bold fantasies on language"—R.J. In his book *Futurism and Madness. Parallels to the Creative Work and Analogies to the New Language of the Cubo-Futurists* (Saint Petersburg, 1914), Dr. E.P. Radin cites one of the theses of P.A.

Lukashevich (from his book *Spell-Casting, or the Holy Language of Gods, Magicians, and Heathen Priests,* Petrgorod [sic: for Petersburg], 1846, p. 24): "Every letter [*bukva*] or locust [*prugva*] should be spoken exactly as it is."

6. The reference is, perhaps, to the collection mentioned in the postscript, *Onanism,* which never appeared. Cf. Jakobson's note to this passage: "This planned publication was never realized. Of all the joint literary projects only one booklet written by Kruchenyx and Aljagrov, daringly and opulently decorated by Ol´ga Rozanova (1886-1918) . . . was published in 1915 (though dated 1916). The title of this booklet, *Zaumnaja gniga,* jokingly blends *kniga,* 'book,' with *gnida,* 'nit.' The collage of the cover alluding to a buttoned heart consists of a red colored heart with a genuine white button affixed to it. The catalogue of the Exhibition, *Paris-Moscou 1900–1930,* at the Centre Pompidou, 1979 (pp. 425, 428) appraises the book as 'l'un des plus beaux du futurisme russe.'"—R.J.

7. "A one-volume series of futurist texts published in Petersburg, January, 1914, and prohibited by the censorship as 'amoral.'"—R.J. The Futurists' collection *Roaring Parnassus* appeared in January-February, 1914. (The official date of issue, according to *Knizhnaja letopis´,* was February 5-12.)

8. "Symbolists grouped around the publishing center Musaget"—R.J.

9. Stepun: "Russian philosopher and critic (1884-1965)"—R.J.

10. "The Lithuanian symbolist painter Mikalojus Čiurlionis (1875-1911)"—R.J. According to the newspaper *Russkie vedomosti* (January 17, 1914), Vjacheslav Ivanov's lecture "Čiurlionis and the Problem of the Synthesis of the Arts," delivered on January 16th, "only partially touched on the named artist" and expressed Ivanov's own concept of the artist as creator of myth and of future synthetic art as mystery" (see *Russkaja literatura* 1972, 571).

11. "Cf. Gisela Erbslöh, *Pobeda nad solncem, ein futuristiches Drama von Kručenych,* (played in Petersburg, Dec. 1913), Munich, 1976"—R.J.

12. "The Snow Queen"—R.J.

13. D. P. Martynov: "Russian provincial school principal, author of the book *Revelation of the Mystery of Human Language,* 1898, with innumerable delirious etymologies referred to in Radin's book cited above"—R.J.

14. *"Budetljanin,* Xlebnikov's term corresponding to 'futurist'"—R. J.

15. "Written during Marinetti's Russian sojourn in February 1914"—R. J. Judging by this phrase, the letter was written during Marinetti's visit to Russia and was addressed to Kruchenyx in Petersburg, where Marinetti stayed from February 1st until the 8th, 1914. When the Italian Futurist arrived in Moscow on January 26th, the main representatives of Russian Futurism were absent: Majakovskij, Burljuk and Kamenskij were conducting their tour of Russia, whereas Xlebnikov and Kruchenyx were in Petersburg. Therefore, a debate with the Cubo-Futurists did not take place, and, on his departure from Moscow, Marinetti proposed arranging a meeting with various Russian Futurists after his return from Petersburg "with the aim of clarifying the points on which they diverge from Italian Futurism and on elaborating a general program" (Xardzhiev 1975, 128). On Marinetti's visit to Moscow, see above pp. 20-22.

16. "Particularly in questions of poetic language"—R.J.

17. "Large Moscow bookstore on Kuzneckij Most"—R.J.

18. Severjanin: "The ego-futurist poet (1887-1942)"—R.J.

19. There is no such collection with this title. It is not to be excluded that this was the preliminary title for the collection *Transrational Boog.*

LETTER 2.

The beginning of the letter is lost. It can be dated, tentatively, by its contents (it was clearly written after the beginning of the war on August 1, 1914). Jakobson's translation of Mallarmé's sonnet "Une dentelle s'abolit" is appended to the letter. It is published from a photocopy of the original, which is in the archive of A. E. Parnis.

1. It is possible that the reference is to the last parts of the novel *Petersburg*, which appeared in April 1914.

2. Kruchenyx's book *Actual Stories and Drawings of Children* appeared in 1914.

3. The reference is to a phrase from Kruchenyx's book *Explodity* (St. Petersburg, 1913): "On the 27th of April at 3 o'clock in the afternoon I instantaneously mastered completely all languages."

LETTER 3.

The letter is addressed to the artist M. V. Matjushin (1861-1934). It is dated by the contents. When I sent Jakobson a copy of the letter, at the end of 1977, he informed me that he had returned from Petrograd to Moscow during the first days of the New Year, and the premiere of Goldoni's play mentioned in the letter took place on January 27, 1915. Excerpts from the letter are cited in Jakobson/Pomorska 1982, 163-64. It is printed here in full for the first time from a photocopy of the original in The Institute of Russian Literature (IRLI), f. 656, the archive of M.V. Matjushin.

1. As Jakobson informed me, the reference is to "reestablishing" contact with Malevich, with whom he had already become acquainted in 1913. On Malevich and Morgunov see p. 24 above.

2. Jakobson had taken E. Guro's book *Baby Camels of the Sky* (Petersburg, 1914), to the editorial offices of the newspaper *Russkie vedomosti* to be reviewed (cf. Jakobson/Pomorska 1983, 163).

3. On Jakobson's friend, the artist S. Bajdin, see above, p. 6.

4. On January 1, 1915 a German submarine sank the English dreadnought Formidable. Jakobson is referring to certain of Xlebnikov's mathematical calculations as proof for the "predication" having come true.

5. N.S. Goncharova did the scenery for Goldoni's play "The Fan." The play premiered in the Kamenyj Theater on January 27, 1915.

6. The reference is to two poems from the collection *The Goblet Seething with Thunders*. In the edition of 1916 the third line of the poem "A Polonaise of Champagne" of 1912 still reads "*Golubku i jastreba! Rejxstag i Bastiliju*" ["Dove and Hawk! The Reichstag and the Bastille"], while in the edition of 1918 "Reichstag" is replaced by its Swedish counterpart "Riksdag." In the poem "Nelly" (1911), the last line—"*Introdukcija— Gauptman, a final—Pol′ de Kok*" ["The introduction is Hauptman, and the finale—Paul de Kock"]—permits the replacement of Hauptman by Huysmans both in meter and in sense, but there are no printed versions that reflect this change. On January 25, 1915 Severjanin read, together with Blok, Sologub, Axmatova and others, at the Town Council for an evening of poetry called "Writers to Soldiers"; the reference may be to this reading. (I'm grateful to R. Kruus for bringing this to my attention.)

7. Ekaterina Genrixovna Guro (Nizen), 1874-1972, was the sister of Elena Guro. She contributed to the first of the collections *A Trap for Judges* and was the translator of the Russian edition of Gleizes' and Metzinger's book *On Cubism* (St. Petersburg, 1913).

8. Ol′ga Konstantinovna Matjushina (1885-1975), a writer, was the second wife of Matjushin.

LETTER 4.

The letter is addressed to Elena Jul′evna Kagan (1872–1942), the mother of Elsa Triolet, in London. It is dated by its contents. The letter and Jakobson's letters to Elsa Triolet are preserved in the archive of Elsa Triolet in the Centre National de la Recherche Scientifique (CNRS) in Paris, and are published here from photocopies of the originals.

1. Lilja = L.Ju. Brik. In 1918 Elsa married the French officer André Triolet and went abroad with him.

2. The linguist G.O. Vinokur (1896–1947) worked at the time in the Embassy of the R.S.F.S.R. in Reval. After a while he became the head of the Press Bureau of the Embassy of the R.S.F.S.R. in Riga. During these years Jakobson corresponded with Vinokur; excerpts of his letters can be found in Shapir 1990.

3. Izrail´ L´vovich Kan, Jakobson's schoolmate at the Lazarev Institute. See above, p. 5.

LETTER 5.

Jakobson dates the letter without indicating the year. It is addressed to Elsa Triolet in Paris and is dated on the basis of its contents.

1. See the letter to E. Ju. Kagan from mid-September 1920.

2. On Jakobson's activities in 1917-1920 see above, pp. 17-89.

3. For her first time abroad Elsa Triolet lived with her husband on Tahiti. See her book *On Tahiti* (Leningrad, 1925) and Jakobson's poem in this edition (p. 259).

4. An error of memory: Jakobson spent the summer of *1919* with the Briks in Pushkino. Cf. letter 11 of December 19, 1920: "last summer."

5. One assumes that the diary was kept in the safe of Moscow Linguistic Circle along with Xlebnikov's manuscripts. See above, pp. 59-60.

6. Jakobson is referring to spotted typhus, which he contracted in Riga in the winter of 1919. See above, pp. 54-55.

7. The reference is to the collection *Everything Composed by Vladimir Majakovskij* (Moscow, 1919). See the next letter.

LETTER 6.

The letter is mistakenly dated November 11 by Jakobson, without an indication of the year. The last phrase ("Today is my birthday") dates it *October* 11.

1. Jakobson's statement that L.Ju. Brik planned to enter into a "fictitious marriage" with him and go abroad is quite interesting. Her intention to emigrate is testified to by B. L. Pasternak's parting words on the manuscript of *My Sister Life*, which he gave to L.Ju. Brik in spring 1919. His pencilled dedication, hinting at an up-coming trip to America by L.Ju. Brik, was written later, in October 1919 (Pasternak 1989, 533):

    > Let the rhythm of the October trifle
    > Serve as the rhythm
    > For a flight from bungling
    > To a country where there's Whitman,
    > And at a time when the colors are flowering
    > Of variously colored Guards,
    > I wish you Chicago dawns
    > To dawn upon you.

    The dating of this impromptu is confirmed by another of Jakobson's letters to Elsa Triolet of December 19, 1920 (no. 11), where he speaks of a serious crisis in the relations between L. Ju. Brik and Majakovskij: "Lili long ago got tired of Volodja. . . . It ended in endless quarrels. . . . By the fall of 1919 they had ceased living together, Volodja moved in next door to me, and in the winter they broke up." One can assume that the idea of emigration was partly connected to these changes in Lili Brik's personal life, but judging by Pastenak's sharp parting words there may have been political motives as well.

2. Jakobson preserved Elsa Triolet's diary after her departure from Russia in the summer of 1918. See above, p. 36.

3. On the artist Sergej Bajdin see letter no. 3 to M. V. Matjushin and p. 6 above.

4. The reference is to Majakovskij's poem *150,000,000*, which he was unable to publish in Russian and therefore gave to Jakobson when the latter was going abroad. See above, p. 85.

LETTER 7.

Jakobson dates the letter "the 14th," without indicating the month and year. It is dated by its contents: Jakobson left the Red Cross Mission in September 1920. Judging by the following letter, it was not sent immediately, but together with that letter: "Today is the *19th*, and I had already written you on the 14th, but didn't send it off until now."

1. I. e., the Red Cross Mission.

2. Judging by this phrase, Jakobson planned to visit O. M. Brik in Moscow.

LETTER 8.

This letter is dated by its contents.

1. I. e., Majakovskij's poem *War and the World* (1917).

2. The reference is to the manuscript of the poem *150,000,000*. Cf. letter 6 of October 11, 1920.

3. Cf. letter 5 of September 17, 1920.

4. The book on Xlebnikov came out in Prague at the beginning of 1921 under the title *The Newest Russian Poetry. A First Sketch* (see letter 13 of January 25, 1921). Jakobson read it "in the form of a lecture" in the Moscow Linguistic Circle in May 1919, in the Petrograd House of Writers at the end of 1919, and in OPOJAZ in the spring of 1920.

5. Pavel Nikitich Sakulin (1863–1930) was a literary scholar who after the Revolution headed the Society of Lovers of the Russian Word.

6. In the collection *Poetics* (Moscow, 1919), three articles by Viktor Shklovskij appeared: "On Poetry and Transrational Language," "The Connection Between Devices of Plot Construction and General Stylistic Devices," and "Art as Device." See Shklovskij 1916, 1919a, and 1919b.

7. Elsa lived with her mother on Golikovskij Lane on Pjatnickaja Street.

8. A quote from *A Cloud in Trousers*: "I swear with all my pagan strength!/ Give me/ any/ beautiful/ young girl—I won't waste her soul. . . ."

9. Henri Barbusse's book *Le Feu* (1916) appeared in Russian in Moscow in 1919 in S.V. Gal'perin's translation: *Ogon': dnevnik odnogo goroda.*

10. The French writer Pierre Benoit's novel *L'Atlantide*; the Russian translation appeared in 1922.

11. O.M. Brik, V.B. Shklovskij, A.E. Kruchenyx.

LETTER 9

The letter is dated by Jakobson without indicating the year.

1. The reference is to the book on Xlebnikov's work.

2. At the time Jakobson's parents and his younger brother Sergej lived in Berlin.

LETTER 10.

The letter is dated by Jakobson without indicating the year.

1. Lev Aleksandrovich Grinkrug, a friend of Majakovskij and the Briks. See notes 164 (p. 299) and 104 (p. 286) above.

2. Cf. p. 32 above about this period, the end of 1916: "This was a time of a great, passionate friendship between Elsa and me." Jakobson proposed to Elsa at the time. Cf. the chapter "Wild Strawberry, Get Married" in Elsa Triolet's autobiographical book *Wild Strawberry* (Moscow, 1926), 88-90.

3. As before, the reference is to the poem *150,000,000*.

4. See Letter 11 of December 19, 1920 about a planned trip to Moscow.

LETTER 11.

The letter is dated by Jakobson without indicating the year.

1. A paraphrase of the poem "Brother Writers" (1917): "If ones like you are creators—/ I spit on all art."

2. The reference is to the summer of 1919, which they spent together in Pushkino.

3. In the fall of 1919 Majakovskij moved into a room in the Staxeev House on Lubjanskij Thruway, where Jakobson lived. See above, p. 66.

4. Stanislav Gurvic-Gurskij, an acquaintance of Elsa's. See Triolet 1975, 32-33, and p. 42 above.

5. Boris Anisimovich Kushner (1888–1937) was a writer and poet, one of the founders of OPOJAZ; in 1918–1919 he collaborated with Brik and Majakovskij in IZO, the Fine Arts Division of the People's Commissariat of Enlightenment (Narkompros). He was repressed under Stalin.

6. The reference is to a heliographic edition of a manuscript text of the four Gospels of the New Testament made by the abbot Procopius (died c. 1030; in 1204 canonized by the Catholic Church) in the Czech monastery of Sázava: *Notice sur l'évangéliare slavon de Reims dit Texte du Sacre*, Reims, 1899. The first part is written in Cyrillic; the second—in Glagolitic.

7. See above, p. 62.

8. Mademoiselle Dache was the French tutor of Jakobson and Elsa. See above, p. 36.

LETTER 12.

The letter is dated by its contents—December 25, 1920 in the Old Style, January 7, 1921 in the New Style.

1.   Elsa Triolet's father, U.A. Kagan, was a member of the Literary-Artistic Circle, which organized a Christmas ball every year.

2.   The letter of Prince N. S. Trubetzkoy to Jakobson from Sofia is dated December 12, 1920. After receiving it, Jakobson apparently inquired of Trubetzkoy about the perspectives for work in Bulgaria. Cf. Trubetzkoy's letter of February 1, 1921: "You ask whether it is possible to get you a job in Bulgaria." Considering the difficulties of obtaining work in Sofia, Trubetzkoy advises Jakobson to use his "stay in Prague to get a doctorate there." Further, Trubetzkoy dissuades Jakobson from the thought of returning to his homeland: "You had better not go to Moscow for the time being, as the possibility of [ending up in] the Great Lubjanka [prison and headquarters of the secret police] is not to be excluded. Of course, perhaps, sooner or later we'll all end up there, but in the given case better later than sooner." (Jakobson 1975, 9, 10.)

3. From Majakovskij's poem *War and the World*: "You take pain and grow and grow it."

LETTER 13.

The letter, sent by registered airmail, is dated by Jakobson and addressed to Madame André Triolet, 1 Avenue Emile Déschanel, Paris.

1.   I. e., Jakobson's first book, *The Newest Russian Poetry*.

2.   The Russian publisher Ja. Povolockij and Co. in Paris (13, rue Bonaparte).

LETTER 14.

The letter is dated by Jakobson without an indication of the year. Letters 14-16 are addressed to Elsa Triolet in Berlin, where she moved in October 1922 and resided until the end of 1923. See Triolet 1975, 39-40.

1. Sof´ja Nikolaevna Jakobson, née Fel´dman (1899–1982), Jakobson's first wife.

2. Jakobson met Elsa in Berlin in October 1922, when Shklovskij, the Briks and Majakovskij were there. See the following note.

3. The relations between Elsa and Shklovskij formed the basis for the latter's novel in letters *Zoo, or Letters Not About Love* (Berlin, 1923). In her first letter the heroine Alja (= Elsa) writes about a "second" suitor (Jakobson is implied) who "continues to insist on the fact that he loves me. In exchange, he demands that I turn with all my unpleasantnesses to him." At the end of September 1922 Shklovskij visited Jakobson in Prague, and in October of the same year they saw each other in Berlin. Cf. Shklovskij's letter to M. Gor´kij of September 18, 1922: "[Roman Jakobson] sends me one telegram in the morning and one at night. I'm going to visit him on Monday. I love him like a lover." (Shklovskij 1993, 35.) Cf. also Shklovskij's letter to his wife in Moscow: "I lived in Prague, but they received me very poorly, since they decided that I was a Bolshevik. . . . Now I'm in Berlin with Roma. Roma doesn't want to let me leave Prague. But I'm staying here." (Shklovskij 1990, 503.) Contacts between Jakobson and Shklovskij were reestablished in the second half of the 1920's in connection with the attempts to resurrect the tradition of OPOJAZ; see the correspondence of Jakobson, Shklovskij and Tynjanov (Tynjanov 1977, 531-33) and Jakobson's letter to Shklovskij (Shklovskij 1990, 519).

4. Elsa lived with her mother on Golikovskij Lane in Moscow in 1915–1918.

5. On Elsa Triolet's diary, see letter 6, note 2.

6. An allusion to Shklovskij's book *A Sentimental Journey*, published in Berlin in January 1923.

LETTER 15.

The letter is dated in a hand other than Jakobson's without an indication of the year.

1.   In his "Letter to Roman Jakobson," published in the journal *Knizhnyj ugol* (1922: 8) and reprinted in the Berlin journal *Veshch´* (1922: 1-2), Shklovskij informs him that "Nadja has gotten married" (see p. 305 above, note 198) and goes on to explain: "I am writing you about this in a journal, even though it is a small one, because life has been compressed. If I wanted to write a love letter, I should just sell it to a publisher and get an advance." (Shklovskij 1990, 145.) As a matter of fact, the letters of the heroine Alja in the novel *Zoo* are actual letters of Elsa Triolet. Jakobson answered Shklovskij's letter, in which he asks him to return to Russia, with the dedication to his book *On Czech Verse* (Prague, 1923): "To V.B. Shklovskij (instead of an answer to a letter in *Knizhnyj ugol*)."

LETTER 16.

The letter is dated by Jakobson and addressed to "Frau André Triolet, Hagelbergerstr. 37[1], Berlin SW 47."

1. It was not possible to establish the source of this quote.

LETTER 17.

The letter is dated by Jakobson without an indication of the year. Judging by the context, it was sent to Paris, where Elsa Triolet returned at the end of 1923.

1. Shklovskij returned to Russia at the end of September - begining of October 1923. See p. 307 above, note 214.

2. Sharik is perhaps Majakovskij's acquaintance Dubinskij (actual name Mojsha Livshic), a left poet who worked in the Comintern.

3. V. Xodasevich and N. Berberova left Berlin on November 4, 1923 for a visit to Prague. They saw Jakobson often: November 9, 13, 20, 23, 24, 25, 27, 29 and December 1 and 5 (according to Xodasevich's notes; cf. Berberova 1969, 203-4). Berberova recalls: "Roman Jakobson comes after dinner. Along the black streets, Xodasevich, he, and I champ through the liquid snow and mud, sink into it, slip on the sidewalk—we are going to an ancient tavern. In the tavern Xodasevich and Roman will carry on long conversations about metaphors and metonymies. Jakobson suggests to Xodasevich that he translate into Russian a long poem of the Czech romantic Mácha. 'Perhaps from Mácha to Mácha you could set yourself up in Praha?' he says pensively. But Xodasevich is not enchanted by Mácha and returns to the poem." (*Ibid.*, 208.)

4. In the summer of 1923 Jakobson was in Germany, where he met with Majakovskij and the Briks. It is possible, of course, that he is speaking of a later trip.

5. It is possible that the reference is to manuscript of Elsa Triolet's first book, *On Tahiti*, published in Leningrad in 1925.

PART THREE — ESSAYS

The first four essays by R.O Jakobson published here originally appeared in Soviet newspapers and journals just prior to and after his departure from Russia at the beginning of summer, 1920. Two of them—"Futurism" and "The Tasks of Artistic Propaganda"—are programmatic articles dedicated to questions of modern art which were published in the organs of the Division of Visual Arts of the People's Commissariat of Enlightenment (IZO). The other two, "New Art in the West" and "Dada," are accounts of new trends in Western art and literature. A. Parnis advances the thesis that the article "Cubism," published in the newspaper *Iskusstvo* (1916: 6, July 8) and signed with the initials R.Z., could also have been written by Jakobson for the proposed *Encyclopedia of Visual Arts*, though he states that "for a definitive resolution of this question further investigations are needed" (Jakobson 1987, 418). In his conversations with the editor of the present volume, Jakobson speaks about an essay on "Pictorial Semantics" written for the above-mentioned encyclopedia, but does not mention the article on Cubism (see above, p. 56). At the beginning of September 1975, I inquired of Jakobson about an article "On Painting" published in *Gazeta Futuristov* (March 15, 1918) signed by N. Jakobson; he replied that the essay was not by him, adding that D. Burljuk had asked him to contribute to the newspaper but that he had not written anything for it. In this regard Jakobson spoke of another essay he had written for the Soviet press, a review of reminiscences of Dostoevskij by either his daughter or wife. The book in question is either *Dostoevskij v izobrazhenii ego docheri L. Dostoevskoj* (Moscow-Leningrad, 1922) or *Vospominanija A. G. Dostoevskoj* (Moscow-Leningrad, 1925). In his conversation Jakobson says that he "composed a notice" about Majakovskij's poem *150,000,000* for the Berlin newspaper *Nakanune*, but it has not been possible to locate it.

FUTURISM

The essay "Futurism," signed under the initials R.Ja. and printed in the news-
paper *Iskusstvo* (Moscow 1919: 7, August 2), the organ of the Moscow
Division of IZO, is a variant of two articles published in the Petrograd newspaper *Zhizn' iskusstva*, namely "Devices of Old Painting" (1919: 199-200,
July 27) and "Futurism as an Aesthetic and Scientific System" (1919: 226,
August 27). Minor variant readings between these versions are mentioned by
A. Parnis in Jakobson 1987. It is published here according to the original
newspaper publication, with the correction of obvious misprints and taking
into account the text as printed in *SW* III, 717-722. In preparing the article
for publication in his *Selected Writings* Jakobson changed the text slightly.
   [Translator's note: I used the text in *SW*—S.R.]

1.   A. Gleizes and J. Metzinger, *Du cubisme* (Paris, 1912). The book
     appeared in a Russian translation by E. Nizen, edited by M. Matjushin,
     O kubizme (Saint Petersburg, 1913).

2.   See C. Stumpf, *Über den psychologischen Ursprung der Raumvorstellung*
     (Leipzig, 1873), 112-13.

3.   The Russian term *ustanovka* (orientation, set) is a calque for German
     Einstellung, a philosophical term designating apperception, the view-
     point or mental set crucial in the perceiver's constituting an object.
     [Translator's note—S.R.]

4.   From Goncharov's novel *Oblomov* (Oblomov's dream).

5.   From the "technical manifesto" of Futurist painting (1910), signed by
     the artists Umberto Boccioni, Carlo Carrà, Luigi Russolo, Giacomo
     Balla and Guino Severini. See *Manifesty ital'janskogo futurizma*
     (Moscow, 1914), translated by V. Shershenevich.

6.   Cf., for example, Majakovskij's poem "To the Other Side" (1918): "We
     covered the world with a complete 'Down With!'"

7.   These and the following six quotations are free paraphrases from the
     books O.D. Xvol'son, *The Principle of Relativity* (Saint Petersburg, 1914)

and N.A. Umov, *The Characteristic Features and Tasks of Contemporary Natural Scientific Thought* (Saint Petersburg, 1914). (On the influence of physics on the young science of the time, see above, p. 3.)

8. A. Bogdanov's (A.A. Malinovskij, 1873–1928) theses on collectivistic ideology. See his book *The Science of Social Consciousness (A Short Course of Ideological Science in Questions and Answers)*, Moscow, 1918.

9. Cf. Carrà's manifesto "The Painting of Sounds, Noises and Smells" (1913).

10. An inexact quote from Gleizes' and Metzinger's *Du cubisme*.

11. On "false recognition" see also *The Newest Russian Poetry*, where Jakobson refers to Aristotle's *Poetics* (Jakobson, 1921, 29).

12. Aristotle's *Poetics* (IV, 1448B, 15-19), in Kenneth A. Telford's translation (Chicago, 1961), 6-7.

13. A quote from Xemnicer's fable "A Student of Metaphysics."

THE TASKS OF ARTISTIC PROPAGANDA

The article was published in the last issue of the newspaper *Iskusstvo* (1919; 8, Sept. 5), on the occasion of the "Day of Soviet Propaganda" (Nov. 7), signed Aljagrov and with an editorial note: "Published as a matter for discussion." On the "Day of Propaganda," Majakovskij, Malevich, Rodchenko and others, whose aesthetic views Jakobson was close to, spoke at a meeting on "The New Art and Soviet Power." The article was first reprinted by A. Parnis (Jakobson 1987), unfortunately in an incomplete form, with the last paragraph omitted. It is published here from the original newspaper edition.

1. The Moscow Universal Store "Muir and Merilise" (now the Central Universal Store, CUM).

2. From the foreword to Karl Marx's *Zur Kritik der politischen Oeconomie* (1859): "Aus Entwicklungsformen der Produktivkräfte schlagen diese Verhältniße in Fesseln derselben über."

3. Jakobson has in view the "conciliatory" essay of D. Burljuk, written "under the thunder of the misfortunes of war," "From Now On I Refuse to Speak Poorly Even About the Works of Fools. United Aesthetic Russia!" (in the collection *A Spring Contractorship of the Muses*, Moscow, 1915).

4. Cf. V.I. Lenin, *The Proletarian Revolution and the Renegade Kautsky* (Moscow,1918): "Having fallen in love with the 'purity' of democracy, Kautsky unexpectedly . . . takes formal equality (thoroughly false and hypocritical under capitalism) for a factual one."

5. The reference is to the Division of Fine Arts (IZO) of the People's Commissariat of Enlightenment (Nakompros). The tendency of the representatives of this organization "to sharpen the struggle of artistic currents" led, actually, to the closing of the journal *Iskusstvo* by the authorities: the issue with Jakobson's article was the last to appear.

NEW ART IN THE WEST

The article was published in the journal *Xudozhestvennaja zhizn'* (Moscow 1920 : 3, March-April) and signed with the initials R. Ja. In his commentaries to the article's republication (Jakobson 1987, 426-427), A. Parnis cites a multitude of data testifying to Jakobson's authorship. To these convincing arguments one can add still another: when the editor of the present edition gave Jakobson a xerox of the essay in 1975, he immediately stated that he was its author; his authorship is thus unquestionable. The article was written during Jakobson's first stay in Reval, from February 1 to April 4, 1920. (See above, p. 81.) It is published from the original journal edition.

1. Th. Däubler, *Im Kampf um die moderne Kunst* (Berlin, 1919); all further quotes from Däubler are to this edition. According to the version spread

by G. Apollinaire (*Mercure de France,* Oct. 16, 1911; *Les Peintres cubistes,* Paris, 1913), the word "cube" was first used by Henri Matisse upon seeing a canvas by Braque at the Salon d'Automne in 1908. But the originator of the term was more likely Louis Vauxcelles, the critic of the notable Parisian journal *Gil Blas,* who in his review about Braques' exhibition at Kahnweiler's Gallery wrote: "He despises form, reduces everything, places and figures and houses, to geometrical schemes, to cubes" (*Gil Blas,* Nov. 11, 1908; cf. E. Fry 1966, 50). By the way, Vauxcelles had earlier christened yet another movement in art—Fauvism (1905). Paul Cassirer was an editor, publisher, and devotee of modern art. Max Pechstein (1881-1938) was one of the leading expressionist artists. The French artist Julien-August Hervé exibited nine canvases at the 1901 Salon des Indépendants under the common title "Expressionism."

2.   F. Landsberger, *Impressionismus und Expressionismus* (Leipzig, 1919). The following citations are taken from this book.

3.   From a letter of Vincent van Gogh to his brother Theo dated ca. August 1888; cited from H. Chipp, ed. 1968, 34-35.

4.   H. Bahr, *Expressionismus* (Munich, 1914).

5.   A possible misprint; one assumes that the author has in mind Joachim Kirchner's book *Junge Berliner Kunst* (Wasmuth's Kunsthefte, 6. Heft, 1919).

6.   The German playwright Friedrich Hebbel (1813–1863).

7.   The article "Proletarian Art (from a letter of I.E. Repin)" is a reprint from the newspaper *Novaja russkaja zhizn'* (Helsinki, Feb. 5, 1920). Repin's negative attitude toward the political changes in Russia found a curious expression in his refusal to help V. Shklovskij stay in Finland. (He motivated his refusal by the fact that Shklovskij used the new, "Bolshevik," orthography; cf. p. 65 above.)

8.   N.B. Simakov, "Artistic Politics," *Segodnja* (Riga, 1920 : 50, March 2).

9.   There is no book by Marinetti with this title. A. Parnis' suggestion that Jakobson might have gotten information about a new work by Marinetti

from the Italian Communist Arturo Cappa, whom he met in Reval in the spring of 1920, is reasonable (Jakobson 1987, 429; cf. p. 82 above). It is possible that Jakobson is referring to a book with a similar title which appeared in 1919, *Democrazia futurista*, and was reprinted in its entirety in the journal *L'Internazionale*, the organ of the "revolutionary syndicalists." The following year Marinetti published another book on politics, *Al di là del Comunismo* (Milan, 1920).

10. Such Italian Futurists as Duilio Remondino, Vinicio Paladini, Carlo Frassinelli, Ivo Pannaggi, Piero Illari, and Umberto Barbaro belonged to this leftist, pro-Bolshevik group. Like the members of the Russian avant-garde, they were convinced that "Futurist art will become the art of communist society, the art of the proletariat," as Arturo Cappa formulated it (*L'arte e la rivoluzione*, Milan, 1921). The leaders of the Italian Communist Party, like the ideologists of the Soviet Communist Party, took an extremely negative attitude toward the verbal experiments of the Futurists; thus, for example, in 1922 the Central Committee of the Italian Communist Party attacked the advocates of "Workers' Futurism" (*Futurismo operaio*) as a decadent trend that should be eradicated, and, in particular, V. Paladini for his brochure *1 + 1 + 1 + 1. Dinamite. Poesie Proletarie. Rosso più nero*, published by the Turin section of the Proletcult in spring of 1922.

DADA

The article was published in the journal *Vestnik teatr* [Theatrical Herald], 1921: 82 (February) under the general subtitle: "Letters from the West"; it is signed with the initials R. Ja. All the quotations in the article are taken from the Dadaist collection *Dada Almanach*, edited by Richard Huelsenbeck (Berlin, 1920), which was issued to coincide with the end of the First International Dada Fair (*Große Internationale Dada-Messe*), which opened in Berlin on June 5, 1920. At the beginning of July Jakobson travelled through Berlin on his way to Prague; it is possible that he visited the Dadaists' exhibition. The article is published according to its first edition with the correction of certain inaccuracies. On Jakobson's and the Russian avant-garde's ties with Dadaism, see Jakobson 1987, 435, and Jangfeldt's article "Roman Jakobson, *Zaum'* and Dada" (1991). Authorial notes, as opposed to editorial ones, are so indicated.

1. The Treaty of Versailles went into effect in January, 1920.

2. "Things have gone particularly badly for believers in the 'order of things' [*bytoviki*] in Russia. One of them complained to me bitterly: 'What can one write, when there is no "established order of things" [*byt*] left'. And they've gone over to the Whites (Kuprin, Chirikov, Andreev, Bunin, Averchenko, Merezhkovskij, A. Tolstoj). But they haven't found *byt* even there. And so they've been busy, some with tearful petitions (Andreev), some with pogrom-like proclamations (Kuprin), some with outright sponging (Merezhkovskij)." [Author's note.] The heavily loaded term *byt* suggests "the order of things," "mores," "convention," "daily grind." See Jakobson's discussion of this term in relation to Majakovskij in his essay "On a Generation that Squandered Its Poets" in the present volume, pp. 214-17.

3. This expression became popular after the Chief of Police A.A. Makarov spoke at the State Duma in connection with the shooting at the Lena gold-fields in 1912 (Jakobson 1987, 436).

4. The reference is to anti-semitic attacks on Einstein in the German press.

5. O. Spengler, *Der Untergang des Abendlandes,* vol. 1. The second volume appeared in 1922.

6. An inexact quote from V. Xlebnikov's "A Conversation of Two Persons," originally published in *Union of Youth* (1913: 3); cf. Xlebnikov 1968-1972 V, 183 and the English translation in Xlebnikov 1987, 288-91.

7. N.I. Buxarin, *The Economics of the Transitional Period,* part 1 (Moscow, 1920).

8. [Translator's Note: References to *Dada Almanach* are abbreviated as *DA,* followed by two page references separated by a semicolon, the first to the original edition, the second to the English translation edited by Malcolm Green (London: Atlas, 1993).] R. Huelsenbeck, "Introduction," *DA* 3; 9.

9. T. Tzara, "Dada Manifesto 1918," *DA* 117; 122.

10. All three quotes are from Huelsenbeck's "Introduction," *DA* 4, 5, 7; 10, 11, 12.

11. C. Ribemont-Dessaignes, "Dadaland," *DA* 97-98; 103-104. The text is cited with abbreviations.

12. T. Tzara, "Dada Manifesto 1918," *DA* 123; 126.

13. R. Huelsenbeck, "First Dada Lecture in Germany," *DA* 108; 113.

14. F. Picabia, "Cannibal Dada Manifesto," *DA* 48; 56.

15. T. Tzara, "Dada Manifesto 1918," *DA, passim.*

16. W. Mehring, "Revelations," *DA* 73; 80.

17. Abbreviated quotes from R. Huelsenbeck, "First Dada Lecture in Germany," *DA* 107; 112. R. Huelsenbeck, "Introduction," *DA* 3-4; 9.

18. "What Did Expressionism Want?," *DA* 35; 44.

19. T. Tzara, "Dada Manifesto 1918," *DA* 117; 122.

20. R. Huelsenbeck, "Introduction," *DA* 8; 13.

21. After he goes mad, the hero of V.F. Odoevskij's story "The Improv-visatore" (1833) "ceaselessly speaks poetry in some sort of language that is a mixture of all languages."

22. A reference to an essay by A. Kruchenyx which compares a bill from the "Triumphal Gates Laundry" with "eight lines from Onegin—in an anguish of mad regrets, and so on," claiming that its "style is higher than Pushkin!" (*Secret Vices of the Academicians,* Moscow, 1916, 14).

23. Cf. the poster "Art is Dead. Long Live Tatlin's New Machine Art!" which was hung at the Dada exhibition in Berlin and is reproduced in *DA* 41; 48.

24. A quote from T. Tzara's "Negro Songs," *DA* 143; 147.

25. This and the following two quotations are taken—somewhat inexactly—from Huelsenbeck's "Introduction," *DA* 5, 4, 8; 10- 13.

26. During the first anniversary of the October Revolution artists painted the grass in the Alexander Park in Moscow.

27. T. Tzara, "Zurich Chronicle," *DA* 13; 18.

28. W. Mehring, "Revelations," *DA* 62; 69.

29. This quote (from an essay by Jean Cocteau) is given in a list of "Newspaper Reviews from Around the World" about Dada in *DA* 43; 51.

30. An inexact quote from T. Tzara, "Dada Manifesto 1918," *DA* 122, 125.

31. The reference is to rumors about the possible emigration of Einstein to England; he was being badgered in Germany for being a pacifist and a Jew. Einstein received the Medal of the Royal Society in 1925.

32. H. Baumann, "A Personal Dadaist Matter," *DA* 33; 42.

33. T. Tzara, "Zurich Chronicle," *DA* 22; 28.

34. R. Huelsenbeck, "Introduction," *DA* 4; 10.

35. T. Tzara, "Dada Manifesto 1918," *DA* 117-18; 122.

36. T. Tzara, *ibid.*, 123; 126.

37. R. Huelsenbeck, "First Dada Lecture in Germnay," *DA* 106; 112.

38. F. Picabia, "Letter to Madame Rachilde," *DA* 109; 114.

39. R. Huelsenbeck, "Introduction," *DA* 4; 10.

40. "In order to characterize somewhat this milieu, so distant from present-day Russia, I will note a few features. In post-war Berlin the favorite

places for spending one's time in a jolly, comfortable way are the clubs
and cafes of homosexuals. In Berlin there also appears a daily newspaper
of wide circulation, *Homosexuelle Nachrichten.* In Germany a two-volume
study by the scholar Blüher, *Die Rolle der Erotik in der männlichen
Gesellschaft,* enjoyed a stormy success. Its main proposition: 'It is not economic nor ideological factors that condition the rise and development of
social and political life, but the erotic attraction of male toward male.'"
[Author's note.] The reference to Tzara is to his "Zurich Chronicle," *DA*
11; 15. H. Blüher's book was published in Jena in 1917–1918.

41. An inexact rendering of the last line of Huelsenbeck's "Introduction,"
    DA 9; 14.

TRANSLATOR'S NOTE

The last two critical works by Jakobson included here did not appear in the
first, Russian edition of this book. They have been added for the convenience
of the English reader, since they represent the most important works by
Jakobson on Xlebnikov and Majakovskij, two of the main "heroes" of this
book. The first is a translation by Edward J. Brown of extensive excerpts from
Jakobson's first book, *The Newest Russian Poetry,* which was written in 1919
and published in 1921. It is one of the first attempts to analyze the poetry of
Xlebnikov and remains one of the best. The second essay, also in Edward J.
Brown's translation, "On a Generation That Squandered Its Poets," was written after Majakovsky's suicide and published in 1931. Though it is outside the
time frame of this edition proper, it is both a valuable introduction to
Majakovskij's work and one of Jakobson's most empassioned and brilliant literary-critical essays.

THE NEWEST RUSSIAN POETRY: VELIMIR XLEBNIKOV [EXCERPTS]

Jakobson's first major scholarly monograph, *Novejshaja russkaja poèzija.
Nabrosok pervyj: Podstupy k Xlebnikovu* [The Newest Russian Poetry. A First

Sketch: Approaches to Xlebnikov] was first published in Prague at the beginning of 1921. It was written as a preface for an unrealized edition of Xlebnikov's collected works in 1919 and presented in lecture form several times that year; on the history of the text see pages 293 and 321 n. 4 of the present edition. The translation of major excerpts reprinted here is by the late Professor Edward J. Brown of Stanford University. It originally appeared in his important anthology *Major Soviet Writers: Essays in Criticism* (London-Oxford-New York: Oxford University Press, 1973), pp. 58-82. The editor and publisher would like to thank Oxford University Press for their kind permission to republish it in the present volume. The notes to the text are by E.J. Brown, with the exception of a few notes by Jakobson to the original edition, which are so indicated.

1. *Stoglav* (literally *The Hundred Chapters*), a collection containing the decisions of a sixteenth-century Russian Church Chronicle.

2. Russian literary scholars of the early part of the century.

3. Premier of the Provisional Government in 1917, under whose rule counterfeiting was not uncommon.

4. A.S. Griboedov (1795–1829), a dramatist, author of *Woe from Wit.* Ermolov was the commander of Russian armies in the Caucasus, on whose staff Griboedov worked.

5. Syllabo-tonic is the technical name for the traditional metrical system of Russian nineteenth-century poetry.

6. This article was written in 1919.

7. Filippo Tommaso Marinetti (1876–1944) was an Italian poet who founded the futurist movement in literature.

8. A.E. Kruchenyx (1888–1968), one of the most active members of the futurist group, and a close collaborator of Xlebnikov.

9. L.V. Shcherba (1880–1944), a Russian linguist, professor at the University of Petersburg [later Leningrad University].

10. Having accepted such a definition of poetry, we can term the method of research resulting from it expressionistic. [Author's note.]

11. Franz Saran, a German philologist who specialized in problems of rhythm and meter.

12. Hans Sperber, a German linguist who emphasized the importance of emotional factors in the development of language.

13. Compare the hyperbole used in everyday parlance: "That's quick: one foot here, the other there." [Author's note.]

14. The pun is not translatable: "*ostavat'sja s nosom*" actually means "to be cheated."

15. Simeon Polocskij (1629–1680), a Russian cleric and literary man, one of the earliest Russian poets.

16. M.V. Lomonosov (1711–1765), a Russian scientist and poet, a pioneer in the development of modern metrics.

17. G.R. Derzhavin (1743–1816), and N.A. Nekrasov (1821–1877), were poets and, in their time, innovators in verse form.

18. Eduard Hanslick (1825–1904), author of *Vom Musikalische-Schönen* (Leipzig, 1854).

19. Vjacheslav Ivanov (1866-1949), another leading symbolist poet.

20. A.M. Peshkovskij (1873-1933), a Russian linguist and a specialist in the problems of syntax.

21. A.A. Fet (1820-1892), one of the leading lyric poets of the nineteenth century.

22. O.M. Brik (1888-1945), a leading theoretician of the Russian formalists.

23. Literally "obese clouds," where an etymological relationship of "obese" and "cloud" is suggested by phonetic similarity.

24. *Molnienosna,* literally, "bearing lightning."

25. Josef Zubat˝ (1885–1931), a Czech linguist, interested in problems of comparative grammar.

26. I.F. Annenskij (1856–1909), a Russian poet who belonged to the "decadent" movement.

27. See his article *"Zvukovye povtory"* ["Sound Repetitions"] in *Poètika* (Petrograd, 1919). [Author's note.]

28. Elena G. Guro (1877–1913), a poet and member of the Cubo-futurist group.

29. Franz von Stuck (1863–1928), a German painter who specialized in allegorical subjects.

30. F.F. Fortunatov (1848–1914), a Russian linguist, interested in comparative linguistics.

31. V K. Trediakovskij (1703–1769), a poet and theoretician of verse, one of the creators of the metrical system in use during the late eighteenth and the nineteenth century.

ON A GENERATION THAT SQUANDERED ITS POETS

This essay, Jakobson's response to Vladimir Majakovskij's suicide on April 14, 1930, first appeared in a shorter German version in *Slavische Rundschau.* The full Russian text, entitled *O pokolenii rastrativshem svoix poètov,* appeared in a booklet, together with an essay by D. Svjatopolk-Mirskij, *Smert' Vladimira Majakovskogo* [The Death of Vladimir Majakovskij], Berlin: Petropolos, 1931. The translation reprinted here by E.J. Brown, which first appeared in his *Major Soviet Writers: Essays in Criticism* (London-Oxford-New York: Oxford University Press, 1973), pp. 7-32, has been slightly revised by Stephen Rudy. It is reprinted here with the kind permission of Oxford University Press. The notes are by E.J. Brown, except as indicated.

1. Il´ja L´vovich Sel´vinskij (1899–1968), the leader of a modernist group of poets known as "constructivists." Nikolaj Aseev (1889–1963) was a poet close to the futurist movement.

2. When we say "chamber" (*kamernaja*), we certainly do not intend to detract from the value of their work as poetic craftsmanship. The poetry of Evgenij Baratynskij or of Innokentij Annenskij, for instance, might be called "chamber verse." [Author's note.]

3. Xlebnikov himself describes his own [alter ego's] poetic death using suicide imagery: "What? Zangezi's dead!/ Not only that, he slit his own throat./ What a sad piece of news!/ What sorrowful news!/ He left a short note:/ 'Razor, have my throat!'/ The wide iron sedge/ Slit the waters of his life,/ He's no more." [Author's note.]

4. Leonid Nikolaevich Andreev (1871-1919), a writer of short stories and plays pessimistic in content and symbolic in manner.

5. "New name,/ tear off!/ fly/ into the space of the world dwelling/ thousand-year-old/ low sky,/ vanish, you blue-ass!/ It is I./ I, I/ I/ I/ I/ the inspired sewage-disposal man of the earth."

6. A nearly untranslatable Russian word which suggests "mores," "convention," the "established way of life," the "daily grind," "middle-class values," and so forth.

7. *Komi*, an aboriginal non-Russian minority who live north and east of the Ural mountains and speak a language belonging to the Finno-Ugrian group.

8. Petr Jakovlevich Chaadaev (1794-1856), author of a famous "philosophical letter" which was highly critical of Russian culture and Russian life.

9. Nikolaj F. Fëdorov (1828-1903) was a Russian philosopher who maintained that the physical resurrection of the dead should become a major project of Christendom.

10. The title of an early collection of poems.

11. Bela Kun (1886?–1940?), Hungarian Communist, head of the short-lived Hungarian Soviet government in 1919.

12. These are all prominent poets of the first three decades of the nineteenth century.

PART FOUR — VERSE AND PROSE

JUVENILIA

Poems 1 and 2 are published from copies in the Jakobson Archive at M.I.T. which appear to be transcribed in Jakobson's mother's handwriting.

FUTURIST POEMS

Poem 3 is a fragment of a poem Jakobson worked on in June of 1914; it is quoted by the author in *SW* VII, 358. Poems 4 and 6 were published in *Transrational Boog* (1915).

Poem 5 is cited in A. Kruchenyx's book *Transrationalists* (Petrograd, 1922), 16.

Poem 7, "How Many Fragments Have Scattered" is an "oblique satire" of Majakovskij's urban poetry; see p. 25 above. The note "(sic)" belongs to the author. The manuscript of the Russian original is in the Archive of A.E. Parnis and contains comments in Kruchenyx's hand in the margins. The poem is signed Roman Jaljagrov. In his preserved letters and poetics manuscripts Jakobson used the signature R.Ja. or Roman Jaljagrov. The form Aljagrov is used in *Transrational Boog* (1915) and the essay "The Tasks of Artistic Propaganda" (1919).

Poem 8. The original is in the Archive of A. E. Panis. The margins contain comments in Kruchenyx's hand. In the fourth line the word *blednotelyj* 'pale-bodied' is replaced by the word *melotelyj* 'chalk-bodied', apparently in the same hand; cf. p. 25 above.

JOCULAR POEMS

Poems 9-10 were written in March-April 1919 at the Briks' apartment on Poluèktovyj Lane in Moscow. Besides Jakobson, Majakovskij and Pasternak took part in a game of bouts-rimés. Xlebnikov was also present. In the first round, all the rhyme pairs were given; in the second—only the words to be rhymed, which included: Voronezh, *stel'ka* 'insole', *na stenu* 'up/on the wall', *masle* 'butter', Punin, and Al´tman. The word "Voronezh" is explained by the fact that Jakobson and Majakovskij "had planned to go to Voronezh to rent a place for the summer" (Katanjan 1975, 82; cf. p. 43 above). The original manuscripts are in the Archive of L.Ju. Brik.

Poem 11 was incribed in the beginning of 1920 in the album that the writer Kornej Chukovskij kept at his summer dacha in the Finnish village Kuokkala outside Petersburg. It was jokingly called *Chukokkala*, mixing the writer's name and that of the village, and contains remarkable autographs of Russian writers and artists of the period. (See Chukovskij 1979, 20.)

Poem 12 is dated 1918 or 1919 conjecturally on the basis of its content. The mention of Roederer champagne is not fortuitous; Jakobson told the editor of the present volume that before the revolution he had composed advertising jingles for that brand. Martin Ivanovic Lacis (1888–1938) was, from mid-1918, the head of Cheka, the difficult but successful work of which he reported on in the book *The Extraordinary Commissions in the Battle with the Counter-revolution* (Moscow, 1921). He was repressed under Stalin. Nikolaj Vasil´evich Krylenko (1885–1938) was a professional revolutionary who at the beginning of 1918 "transferred to the Department of Justice in the division for extraordinary trials, where with [his] direct participation show trials were conducted" (*Dejateli SSSR i Oktjabr´skoj Revoljucii*, Moscow, 1989, 469). He was repressed under Stalin. The original manuscript of the poem is in The Jakobson Archive, M.I.T.

POEMS TO ELSA TRIOLET

Poems 13-15 relate to the period of the "great, warm friendship" between Jakobson and Elsa, which had begun at the end of the summer of 1916. The second poem is not dated, but it was written prior to June 27, 1918, when Elsa graduated from the Division of Architecture and Construction of the Moscow Women's Construction School. From the Elsa Triolet Archive, CNRS, Paris.

Poem 15: the Epigraph to Elsa Triolet's first book, *On Tahiti* (Leningrad, 1925).

PROSE

This prose fragment, signed with the initials R.Ja. was published in the same issue of the school journal *Student's Thought [Mysl' uchenika]*, as was the poem "The Nightingale" (see Jangfeldt, ed. 1992, 112-14). The first two chapters were published in the first issue of the journal, which has not been preserved, and a continuation was proposed for the third issue. The text is published from a copy of the journal preserved in Jakobson's Archive, which contains an insignificant correction by hand.

LIST OF ILLUSTRATIONS

Frontispiece. Roman Osipovich Jakobson. Moscow, 1918. The Jakobson Foundation.

Illustrations

12. L.Ju. and O.M. Brik, R.O. Jakobson, V.V. Majakovskij. Bad Flinsberg, July 1923. The Jakobson Foundation.

13. Philological meeting in Brno, late 1926. From left to right: R.O. Jakobson, N.S. Trubetzkoy, P.G. Bogatyrev, and N.N. Durnovo. The Jakobson Foundation.

14. The folklorist P.G. Bogatyrev with a leopard cub. Prague Zoo, 1928. The Jakobson Foundation.

15. From top to bottom: Karel Teige, R.O. Jakobson, Vítězslav Nezval. Brno, 1933. The Jakobson Foundation.

16. R O. Jakobson. Gotland, 1977. Archive of Bengt Jangfeldt.

LIST OF WORKS CITED

Note on transliteration of Russian: the system used in this bibliography and throughout the volume is a modified form of that followed in the *International Journal of Slavic Linguistics and Poetics*, the main exceptions being that digraphs are used instead of the diacritical sign *háček*, e.g. *ch* rather than *č*, and that the "soft sign" (*mjagkij znak*) is represented by a prime mark (´) so as to avoid confusion with the English apostrophe.

While this bibliography cannot claim to be exhaustive, an attempt has been made to include the original Russian titles of works cited in the text in English translation, with the exception of newspapers and journals. Where English translations are available, they have been noted. [Translator's note — S.R.]

Alekseev, M.P. *et al*, eds., 1976. *Ezhegodnik rukopisnogo otdela Pushkinskogo doma na 1974 god* [Yearbook of the Manuscript Division of the Pushkin House for 1974]. Leningrad.

Al´vek, 1927. *Naxlebniki Xlebnikova* [Xlebnikov's Hangers-On]. Moscow.

Apollonio, U., ed., 1973. *Futurist Manifestoes*. London.

Armstrong, D. and C. H. van Schooneveld, eds., 1977. *Roman Jakobson. Echoes of His Scholarship*. Lisse.

Aseev, N., 1983. "Iz vospominanij o Majakovskom (Majakovskij i Gor´kij)" [From Reminiscences of Majakovskij (Majakovskij and Gor´kij)], *Literaturnoe nasledstvo* 93: *Iz istorii sovetskoj literatury 1920-x i 1930-x godov*. Moscow.

Babkin, D., 1984. "Vstrechi s Majakovskim" [Meetings with Majakovskij], in *V. Majakovskij v sovremennom mire*. Leningrad.

Ball, H., 1974. *Flight Out of Time. A Dada Diary*, ed. by J. Elderfield. New York.

Bann, Stephen and John E. Bowlt, eds., 1973. *Russian Formalism: A Collection of Articles and Texts in Translation.* Edinburgh.

Berberova, N., 1983. *Kursiv moj.* New York, 2nd ed. Cf. the English translation: *The Italics are Mine.* New York, 1969.

Blok, A., 1982. "Darstvennye nadpisi Bloka na knigax i fotografijax" [Blok's Dedications on Books and Pictures], *Literaturnoe nasledstvo* 92:3: *Aleksandr Blok. Novye materialy i issledovanija.* Moscow.

Bogdanov, A., 1918. *Nauka ob obshchestvennom soznanii (kratkij kurs ideologicheskoj nauki v voprosax i otvetax)* [The Science of Social Consciousness (A Short Course in Questions and Answers)]. Moscow.

Bogatyrev, K., 1982. *Poèt-perevodchik Konstantin Bogatyrev. Drug nemeckoj literatury* [The Poet-Translator Konstantin Bogatyrev. A Friend of German Literature], ed. V. Kazak. Munich.

Bogatyrev, P., 1923. *Cheshskij kukol'nyj i russkij narodnyj teatr* [Czech Puppet and Russian Folk Theater]. Berlin-Petrograd.

Brik, L., 1934. "Iz vospominanij" [From Reminiscences], in the almanach *S Majakovskim* [With Majakovskij]. Moscow.

———, 1942. *Shchen (Iz vospominanij o Majakovskom)* [Shchen. From Reminiscences about Majakovskij.] Molotov.

———, 1963. "Majakovskij i chuzhie stixi" [Majakovskij and the Poetry of Others], in *V. Majakovskij v vospominanijax sovremennikov.* Moscow.

———, "Dnevnik" [Diary]. Archive of L. Ju. Brik.

———, "Kak bylo delo" [Thus It Went]. Archive of L. Ju. Brik.

Brik, O., 1917. "Zvukovye povtory" [Sound Repetitions], in *Sborniki po teorii poèticheskogo jazyka* [Collections on the Theory of Poetic Language] II. Petrograd.

———, 1964. *Two Essays on Poetic Language* (= Michigan Slavic Studies, 5). Ann Arbor.

Brown, C., 1973. *Mandelstam.* Cambridge.

Bunin, I., 1950. *Vospominanija* [Memoirs]. Paris.

Burljuk, D., 1973. "Moe znakomstvo s Alekseem Maksimovichem Gor'kim (1915–1917 gg.)" [My Acquaintance with Aleksej Maksimovich Gor'kij (1915–1917)], in *Knigi. Arxivy. Avtografy.* Moscow.

Buxarin, N., 1920. *Èkonomika perexodnogo perioda* [The Economics of the Transitional Period], 1. Moscow.

Chipp, H., ed., 1968. *Theories of Modern Art. A Sourcebook by Artists and Critics.* Berkeley-Los Angeles.

Chukovskij, K., 1979. *Chukokkala.* Moscow.

——, 1980. "Iz dnevnika (1919–1921)" [From a Diary (1919–1921), a publication of E. Chukovskaja], *Voprosy literatury* 10.

Effenburger, V., 1983. "Roman Jakobson and the Czech Avant-Garde Between the Wars," *American Journal of Semiotics* 2/3.

Erbslöh, G., 1976. *Pobeda nad solncem, ein futuristiches Drama von Kručenych.* Munich.

Foster, S., ed., 1988. *"Event" Arts and Art Events.* Ann Arbor.

Gasparov, M., 1977. "Legkij i tjazhelyj stix" [Light and Heavy Verse], *Studia Metrica et Poetica* (Tartu) 2.

Geroi i zhertvy revoljucija [Heroes and Victims of the Revolution]. Moscow, 1918.

Ginzburg, L., 1989. *Chelovek za pis'mennym stolom* [A Man at his Writing Desk]. Leningrad.

Gleizes, A. and J. Metzinger, 1912. *Du cubisme.* Paris. Cf. the partial English trans. in Chipp, ed., 1968, 207-216.

Guro, E., 1914. *Nebesnye verbljuzhata* [Baby Camels of the Sky]. St. Petersburg.

Hamsun, K., 1920. *Hunger.* New York.

Holenstein, E., 1975. *Roman Jakobsons phänomenologischer Strukturalismus.* Frankfurt.

——, 1987. "Jakobson's Philosophical Background," in Pomorska *et al.*, eds., 1987, 15-32.

Huelsenbeck, R., ed., 1920. *Dada Almanach.* Berlin. Cf. the English trans., ed. by M. Green, *Dada Almanac* (London, 1993).

Ivanov, Vjacheslav V., 1987. "Poètika Romana Jakobsona" [Roman Jakobson's Poetics], in Jakobson 1987, 5-22.

Jakobson, R., *Selected Writings* (abbreviated in this volumes as *SW*).I. *Phonological Studies* (1966). II. *Word and Language* (1971). III. *Poetry of Grammar and Grammar of Poetry,* ed. S. Rudy (1981). IV. *Slavic Epic Studies* (1966). V. *On Verse, Its Masters and Explorers,* ed. S. Rudy and M. Taylor (1979). VI. *Early Slavic Paths and Crossroads,* ed. S. Rudy (1985). VII. *Contributions to Comparative Mythology. Studies in Linguistics and Philology, 1972-1982,* ed. S. Rudy (1985) VIII. *Major Works, 1976-1980,* ed. S. Rudy (1987). [The series, with its supplementary volumes, has been renamed *Collected Works.*]

——, 1921. *Novejshaja russkaja poèzija. Nabrosok pervyj.* [The Newest Russian Poetry. A First Sketch.]. Prague. (Reprinted in *SW* V, 299-354; cf. the partial English translation in this volume, pp. 173-208.)

——, 1921a. "Vliv revoluce na rusk˝ jazyk" [The Influence of the Revolution on the Russian Language], *Nove Atheneum*, II.

——, 1922. "Brjusovskaja stixologija i nauka o stixe" [Brjusov's "Verseology" and the Science of Verse], *Nauchnye izvestija* [Akademicheskogo centra Narkomprosa RFSSR], 2, 222-40.

——, 1923. *O cheshskom stixe, preimushchestvenno v sopostavlenii s russkim* [On Czech Verse, Primarily in Comparison with Russian]. Prague. (Cf. *SW* V, 3-121.)

——, 1931. "O pokolenii, rastrativshem svoix poètov" [On a Generation that Squandered Its Poets," in R. Jakobson and D. Svjatopolk-Mirskij, *Smert´ Vladimira Majakovskogo*. Berlin. (Reprinted in *SW* V, 355-81; cf. the English translation in the present volume, pp. 209-24.)

——, 1931a. "Der russische Frankreich-Mythus," *Slavische Rundschau*, III.

——, 1934. "Co je poesie?" in *Volné smery* 30. (Cf. the English translation, "What Is Poetry?", in *SW* III, 740-750.)

——, 1935. "Randbemerkungen zur Prosa des Dichters Pasternak," *Slavische Rundschau*, VII. (Reprinted in *SW* V, 416-32; cf. the English trans., "Marginal Notes on the Prose of the Poet Pasternak," in *Pasternak: Modern Judgments*, ed. by D. Davie and A. Livingstone, London, 1969, 131-51 and reprinted in Jakobson 1987a, 301-17.)

——, 1956. "Novye stroki Majakovskogo" [New Verses of Majakovskij], *Russkij literaturnyj arxiv.* New York.

——, 1956a. "Besedy s R.O. Jakobsonom o Vl. Majakovskim" [Conversations with R.O. Jakobson about V. Majakovskij]. Stenogram of a meeting of the Section for the study of the life and work of V.V. Majakovskij, May 24, 1956, Gor´kij Institute of World Literature (IMLI).

——, 1959. "Za i protiv Viktora Shklovskogo" [Pro and Contra Viktor Shklovskij], *International Journal of Slavic Linguistics and Poetics*, I/II. (Cf. *SW* V, 406-412.)

——, 1964. "Postscript" in Brik, O., 1964. (Cf. *SW* V, 557-59.)

——, 1970. "La mise en mots," *Les Lèttres françaises*, 1340.

——, 1971. "The Drum Lines in Majakovskij's *150,000,000*," *California Slavic Studies*, VI. (Cf. *SW* V, 413-415.)

——, 1975. *N. S. Trubetzkoy's Letters and Notes.* The Hague-Paris.

——, 1975a. "Les Règles des dégats grammaticaux," in *Langue,*

Discours, Société, ed. by J. Kristeva, J.-C. Milner and N. Ruwet. Paris. (Cf. "On Aphasic Disorders from a Linguistic Angle" in *SW* VII, 128-40.)

———, 1976. "Message sur Malévitch," *Change,* 26/27.

———, 1987. *Raboty po poètike* [Works on Poetics]. Moscow.

———, 1987a. *Language in Literature,* ed. by K. Pomorska and S. Rudy. Cambridge, Mass.

Jakobson, R. and P. Bogatyrev, 1922. "Slavjanskaja filologija v Rossii za gg. 1914-1921," *Slavia,* 1.

Jakobson, R. and K. Pomorska, 1983. *Dialogues.* Cambridge, Mass. [Cf. the original Russian edition, *Besedy,* reprinted in *SW* VIII, 437-582.]

Jangfeldt, B., 1976. *Majakovskij and Futurism 1917-1921.* Stockholm.

———, 1986. "Vladimir Mayakovsky and Lili Brik," in Majakovskij/ Brik 1986, 3-41.

———, 1987. "Eshche raz o Majakovskim i Lenine (Novye materialy)" [Once More on Majakovskij and Lenin (New Materials)], *Scando-Slavica,* 33.

———, 1990. "Vmesto predislovija" [In Place of a Preface], in Majakovskij/Triolet 1990.

———, 1991. "Roman Jakobson, *zaum´* i dada" [Roman Jakobson, Zaum´ and Dada], in *Zaumnyj futurizm i dadaizm v russkoj kul'ture.* Bern-Berlin-Frankfurt-New York-Paris-Vienna.

———, ed., 1992. *Jakobson-Budetljanin. Sbornik materialov.* [Jakobson the Futurist. A Collection of Materials.] Stockholm. [The first, Russian, edition of the current volume.]

Jangfeldt, B. and N. Nilsson, eds., 1975. *Vladimir Majakovskij. Memoirs and Essays.* Stockholm.

Kamenskij, B., 1974. *O Majakovskom* [On Majakovskij], *Literaturnaja gazeta,* 14.

Katanjan, V., 1975. "Ne tol´ko vospominanija" [Not Just Recollections], in Janfeldt and Nilsson, eds., 1975, 73-85.

———, 1985. *Majakovskij. Xronika zhizni i dejatel'nosti* [Majakovskij. A Chronicle of His Life and Activities]. Moscow.

Kogan, D., 1974. *S. Ju. Sudejkin.* Moscow.

Kruchenyx, A. E., 1914. *Stixi V. V. Majakovskogo* [The Verses of V. V. Majakovskij]. St. Petersburg.

———, 1916. *Tajnye poroki akademikov* [Secret Vices of the Academicians]. Moscow.

———, 1922. *Zaumniki* [Transrationalists]. Petrograd.

Kuzmin, M., 1918. *Dvum* [To Two]. Petrograd.

Lacis, M., 1921. *Chrezvychajnye komissii po bor'be s kontrrevoljuciej* [The Extraordinary Commissions in the Battle with the Counter-revolution]. Moscow.

Lavinskaja, E., 1968. "Vospominanija o vstrechax s Majakovskim" [Recollections of Meetings with Majakovskij], in *Majakovskij v vospominanijax rodnyx i druzej*. Moscow.

Lemon, L. and M. J. Reis, eds., 1965. *Russian Formalist Criticism: Four Essays*. Lincoln, Nebraska.

Lenin, V., 1918. *Proletarskaja revoljucija i renegat Kautskij* [The Proletarian Revolution and the Renegade Kautsky]. Moscow.

Linhartová, V. "La Place de Roman Jakobson dans la vie littéraire et artistique tschécoslovaque," in Armstrong and van Schooneveld, eds., 1977, 219-236.

Lukashevich, P., 1846. *Charomutie, ili Svjashchennyj jazyk bogov, volxvov i zhrecov* [Spell-Casting, or the Holy Language of Gods, Magicians, and Heathen Priests]. St. Petersburg.

Lunacharskij, A., 1967. *Sobranie sochinenij v 8-i tomax* [Collected Works in Eight Volumes], 7. Moscow.

———, 1967a. *Ibid*, 8.

Majakovskij, V., 1955–1961. *Polnoe sobranie sochinenij* [Complete Collected Works], 1-13. Moscow. (Abbreviated throughout this volume as *PSS*.)

———, 1988. *Ja zemnoj shar chut' ne ves' oboshel. . . .* [I've Practically Walked Across the Entire Globe]. Moscow.

Majakovskij/Brik, 1986. *Love is the Heart of Everything. Correspondence Between Vladimir Mayakovsky and Lili Brik, 1915–1930*, ed. by B. Jangfeldt. New York.

Majakovskij/Triolet, 1990. *"Dorogoj djadja Volodja. . . ." Perepiska Majakovskogo i El'zy Triolet 1915-1917* ["Dear Uncle Volodja. . . ." The Correspondence of Majakovskij and Elsa Triolet 1915–1917], compiled and edited by B. Jangfeldt. Stockholm.

Malevich, K., 1919. "O poèzii," *Izobrazitel'noe iskusstvo* 1. (Cf. the English translation, "On Poetry," in his *Essays on Art*, ed. T. Andersen, Copenhagen, 1971, 73-82.)

Mandel'shtam, N., 1970. *Vospominanija*. N.Y. Cf. the English translation: *Hope Against Hope. A Memoir* (N.Y., 1970).

Marinetti, F.T., 1973. "Geometrical and Mechanical Splendour and the Numerical Sensibility," in Apollonio, U., ed., 1973.

Markov, A., 1913. "Primer statisticheskogo issledovanija nad tekstom

Evgenija Onegina, illjustrirujushchij svjaz´ ispytanij v cep´" [An Example of Statistical Investigation on the Text of *Eugene Onegin*, Illustrating the Connection of Trials in a Chain], *Izvestija Imperatorskoj Akademii Nauk*, 6th series, vol. VII, No. 3 (Feb. 15, 1913), 153-162.

Markov, V., 1968. *Russian Futurism. A History*. Berkeley-Los Angeles.

Martynov, D., 1898. *Raskrytie tajny jazyka chelovecheskogo i oblichenie nesostojatel'nosti uchenogo jazykoznanija* [Revelation of the Mystery of Human Language and an Exposure of the Flimsiness of Scientific Linguistics]. Place of publication unknown.

Motherwell, R., ed., 1981. *Dada Poets and Painters* (3rd edn.). Boston.

Nejshtadt, V., 1940. "Iz vospominanij o Majakovskom" [From Recollections about Majakovskij], *30 dnej*, 9/10.

Nezval, V., 1978 (1959). *Z mého života*, ch. 38. Prague.

Onchukov, N., 1909. *Severnye skazki* [Northern Fairy Tales]. St. Petersburg.

Pamjatniki kul'tury, 1984. A. Parnis, R. Timenchik, "Programmy 'Brodjachej sobaki'" [The Programs of "The Stray Dog"], *Pamjatniki kul'tury. Ezhegodnik 1983*. Leningrad.

——, 1989. A. Konechnyj, V. Morderer, A. Parnis, R. Timenchik, "Artisticheskoe kabarè 'Prival Komediantov'" [The Artistic Cabaret "The Stopping-Place of Actors"], *Pamjatniki kul'tury. Ezhegodnik 1988*. Leningrad.

Pasternak, B., 1985. *Izbrannoe v 2-x tomax* [Selected Works in Two Volumes]. Moscow.

——, 1989. *Sobranie sochinenij v 5-i tomax* [Collected Works in Five Volumes], 2. Moscow.

Percov, V., 1969. *Majakovskij. Zhizn´ i tvorchestvo (1893-1917)*. Moscow.

Pomorska, K., 1978. "The Autobiography of a Scholar," in Pomorska *et al.*, eds., 1987, 3-13

——, 1981. "Majakovskij i vremja" [Majakovskij and Time], *Slavica Hierosolymitana*, 5/6.

Pomorska, K. *et al.*, 1987. *Language, Poetry and Poetics: The Generation of the 1890s: Jakobson, Trubetzkoy, Majakovskij* [*Proceedings of the First Roman Jakobson Colloquium, at the Massachusetts Institute of Technology, October 5-6, 1984*]. Berlin-New York-Amsterdam.

Pospelov, G., 1990. *Bubnovyj valet. Primitiv i gorodskoj fol'klor v moskovskoj zhivopisi 1910-x godov* [The Knave of Diamonds. The

Primitive and City Folklore in Moscovite Painting of the 1910's]. Moscow.

Radin, E., 1914. *Futurizm i bezumie. Paralleli tvorchestvy i analogii novogo jazyka kubo-futuristov* [Futurism and Madness. Parallels to the Creative Work and Analogies to the New Language of the Cubo-Futurists]. St. Petersburg.

Reformatskij, A., 1970. *Iz istorii otechestvennoj fonologii* [From the History of Phonology in the Fatherland]. Moscow.

Rudy, S., comp. and ed., 1990. *Roman Jakobson 1896-1982. A Complete Bibliography of his Writings. Berlin-N.Y.*

Russkaja literatura, 1972. *Russkaja literatura konca XIX-nachala XX v. 1908-1917* [Russian Literature of the End of the 19th- Beginning of the 20th Century, 1908-1917]. Moscow.

Saxarov, I. P., 1841. *Skazanija russkogo naroda* [Tales of the Russian People], 1. St. Petersburg.

Sechehaye, A., 1908. *Programme et méthodes de la linguistique théorique.* Paris.

Seifert, J., 1985. *Všecky krásy sveta.* Prague.

Seleznev, L., 1989. "Mixail Kuzmin i Vladimir Majakovskij," [Mixail Kuzmin and Vladimir Majakovskij], *Voprosy literatury*, 11.

Severjanin, I., 1916. *Gromokipjashchij kubok* [Goblet Seething with Thunders]. St. Petersburg.

Shapir, M., 1989. "Russkaja tonika i staroslavjanskaja sillabika. Vl. Majakovskij v perevode R. Jakobsona" [Russian Tonic Verse and Old Church Slavonic Syllabic Verse], *Daugava*, 8.

——, 1990. "Prilozhenija" [Supplement], in Vinokur 1990.

——, 1991. "Materialy po istorii lingvisticheskoj poètiki v Rossii (konex 1910-x - nachalo 1920-x godov)" [Materials on the History of Linguistic Poetics in Russia (end of the 1910's-beginning of the 1920's], *Izvestija Akademii Nauk SSSR. Serija literatury i jazyka,* 50:1.

Shklovskij, V., 1914. *Voskreshenie slova.* St. Petersburg. Cf. the English trans., "Resurrection of the Word," in Bann and Bolt, eds., 1973.

——, 1916. "Zaumnyj jazyk i poèzija," in *Sborniki po teorii poètich- eskogo jazyka* [Collections on the Theory of Poetic Language] I, 1- 15. Petrograd. Cf. the English trans., "On Poetry and Trans-Sense Language," *October* 34 (Fall 1985), 3- 24.

——, 1919a. "Svjaz´ priemov sjuzhetoslozhenija s obshchimi priema- mi stilja," in *Poètika: Sborniki po teorii poèticheskogo jazyka*, 115-50.

Petrograd. Cf. the English translation, "The Connection Between Devices of Plot Formation and General Devices of Style," in Bann and Bowlt, eds., 1973.

——, 1919b, "Iskusstvo kak priem," *ibidem*, 101-114. Cf. the English translation, "Art as Device," in Lemon and Reis, eds., 1965.

——, 1923. *Sentimental'noe puteshestvie.* Moscow-Berlin. Cf. the English translation by Richard Sheldon: *A Sentimental Journey. Memoirs, 1917-1922.* Ithaca-London: Cornell University Press, 1970.

——, 1926. *Tret'ja fabrika.* Moscow. Cf. the English translation by Richard Sheldon: *Third Factory.* Ann Arbor: Ardis, 1977.

——, 1974. "O Majakovskom" [On Majakovskij], in his *Sobranie sochinenij v 3-x tomax* [Collected Works in Three Volumes], 3. Moscow.

——, 1990. *Gamburgskij schet. Stat'i, vospominanija, èsse (1914–1933)* [The Hamburg Reckoning. Essays, Reminiscences, Essays (1914–1933)]. Moscow.

Sobachij jashchik [Dog's Box]. Moscow, 1922.

Spasskij, S., 1940. *Majakovskij i ego sputniki* [Majakovskij and His Fellow-Travellers]. Leningrad.

Stahlberger, L., 1964. *The Symbolic System of Majakovskij.* The Hague-Paris.

Stumpf, C., 1873. *Über dem psychologischen Ursprung der Raumvorstellung.* Leipzig.

Tastevin, G.E., 1914. *Futurizm: Na puti k novomu simvolizmu* [Futurism: On the Path Toward a New Symbolism]. Moscow.

Thibaudet, A., 1913. *La poésie de S. Mallarmé.* Paris.

Toman, J., 1987. "A Marvellous Chemical Laboratory and its Deeper Meaning: Notes on Roman Jakobson and the Czech Avant-Garde Between the Two Wars," in Pomorska *et al.*, eds., 1987, 313- 346.

Tomashevskij, B., 1921. "Teorija poèticheskogo jazyka" [The Theory of Poetic Language], *Kniga i revoljucija*, 12 [under the pseudonym Borskij: a review of Jakobson, *The Newest Russian Poetry*].

——, 1990. "Pis'ma B.V. Tomashevskij k S.P. Bobrov" [B.V. Tomashevskij's Letters to S.P. Bobrov], a publication of K. Ju. Postoutenko, *Pjatye Tynjanovskie Chtenija. Tezisy dokladov i materialy dlja obsuzhdenija.* Riga.

Triolet, E., 1925. *Na Taiti* [On Tahiti]. Leningrad.

——, 1926. *Zemljanichka* [Wild Strawberry]. Moscow.

——, 1969. *La mise en mots.* Geneva.

——, 1975. "Voinstvujushchij poet" [A Warring Poet], in Jangfeldt and Nilsson, eds., 1975, 25-69.

Tynjanov, Ju., 1977. *Poètika. Istorija literatury. Kino.* [Poetics. History of Literature. Cinema.]. Moscow.

Umansky, K., 1920. *Neue Kunst in Russland 1914-1919.* Berlin.

Umov, N., 1914. *Xarakternye cherty i zadachi sovremennoj estestvo-nauchnoj mysli* [The Characteristic Features and Tasks of Contemporary Natural Scientific Thought]. Saint Petersburg.

Valjuzhenich, A., 1993. *O. M. Brik. Materialy k biografii* [O.M. Brik. Materials Toward a Biography]. Akmola.

Vallier, D., 1987. "Intimations of a Linguist: Jakobson as a Poet," in K. Pomorska *et al.*, eds., 1987, 291-304.

Vertinskij, A., 1990. *Dorogoj dlinnoju. . . .* [Along a Long Road]. Moscow.

Vesennee kontragenstvo muz [A Spring Contractorship of the Muses]. Moscow, 1915.

Vinogradov, V., 1922. [Review of] "R. Jakobson. Novejshaja russkaja poèzija. Nabrosok pervyj." [R. Jakobson. The Newest Russian Poetry. A First Sketch], *Bibliograficheskie listy Russkogo bibliograficheskogo obshchestva* 3.

Vinokur, G., 1921 [Review of] "R. Jakobson. Novejshaja russkaja poèzija" [R. Jakobson, *The Newest Russian Poetry*], *Novyj put'* (Riga) 6 [under the pseudonym L.K.].

——, 1990. *Filologicheskie issledovanija* [Philological Investigations]. Moscow.

Watts, H., 1988. "The Dada Event: From Transsubstantiation to Bones and Barking," in Foster, ed., 1988, 119-131.

Winner, T., 1977. "Roman Jakobson and Avant-garde Art," in Armstrong and van Schooneveld, eds., 1977, 503-14.

Xardzhiev, N., 1975. "'Veselyj god' Majakovskogo" [Majakovskij's "Jolly Year"], in Jangfeldt and Nillson, eds., 1975, 108- 151.

——, 1975a. "Novoe o Velimire Xlebnikov" [New Information about Velimir Xlebnikov], *Russian Literature, 9.*

——, 1976. "Poèzija i zhivopisi (Rannij Majakovskij)" [Poetry and Painting (Early Majakovskij)], in N. Xardzhiev, K. Malevich, M. Matjushin, *K istorii russkogo avangarda.* Stockholm.

——, 1981. "Iz materialov o Majakovskom" [From Materials on Majakovskij], *Richerche Slavistiche, 27-28* (1980–1981).

INDEX

Zinov´ev, G.E. 40, 82
Zola, É. 284 n. 94
Zubat˝, J. 198, 340 n. 25